AIRCRAFT CARRIERS
OF THE ROYAL AND COMMONWEALTH NAVIES

Cover: Ray Honisett, *HMAS Sydney in Korean Waters, 1951*. 1975, oil on canvas 121.9 x 182.9cm. Australian War Memorial (28077)

HMS *Implacable* in the Clyde area after her completion in August 1944. (FAA Museum)

AIRCRAFT CARRIERS
OF THE ROYAL AND COMMONWEALTH NAVIES
The Complete Illustrated Encyclopedia from World War I to the Present

Commander David Hobbs MBE RN

Greenhill Books, London
Stackpole Books, Pennsylvania

Aircraft Carriers of the Royal and Commonwealth Navies
First published 1996 by Greenhill Books
Lionel Leventhal Limited, Park House, 1 Russell Gardens,
London NW11 9NN
and
Stackpole Books, 5067 Ritter Road, Mechanicsburg, PA 17055, USA

British Library Cataloguing in Publication Data:
Hobbs, David, 1946–
Aircraft carriers of the Royal and Commonwealth Navies: the complete illustrated encyclopedia from World War I to the present
1. Aircraft carriers – Encyclopedias
I. Title
623.8'255'03

ISBN 1-85367-252-1

Library of Congress Cataloging-in-Publication Data available

To my wife Jandy and my son Andrew
for their typing, help and encouragement

Edited, designed and typeset by Roger Chesneau
Flight deck diagrams drawn by Ross Purcell
Printed and bound in Great Britain

Contents

Part 4: Merchant Aircraft Carriers

Appendices

Preface

Hundreds of Commonwealth warships have been designed to operate aircraft but could not be considered aircraft carriers. Pre-war battleships and cruisers, modern destroyers, frigates, amphibious ships and fleet auxiliaries are examples. For this book I have selected those ships whose primary function was the carriage, support and operation of aircraft. Most of them were equipped to sustain flying operations in the open oceans, far from land, over a protracted period. Ships that meet these criteria have gone through several stages of evolution and I have been liberal with my definition in order to illustrate the full scope of the developments for which the Royal Navy has largely been responsible.

There are four main reference sections in the book. The first deals with aircraft carriers capable of launching and recovering aircraft from a flight deck; the second deals with seaplane carriers which had to operate their aircraft from the water alongside; the third covers naval-manned helicopter support and training ships; and the fourth covers the variety of auxiliary carriers manned by the Merchant Navy.

The name 'aircraft carrier' is the most liberal applied to any type of warship. It applies to a modified tanker capable of operating three Swordfish in the local defence of a wartime convoy and also to HMS *Eagle*, capable of carrying one hundred aircraft in 1952. Unlike 'cruiser' or 'torpedo boat destroyer', the name does little to specify the role or roles in which an aircraft carrier could be operating. These might be as diverse as fleet air defence, shipping strike, sea control, amphibious assault or anti-submarine warfare—indeed, the same carrier could operate simultaneously in more than one role.

Aircraft carriers continue to be used in a number of secondary roles, including the movement of military forces to trouble spots, the movement of RAF and Commonwealth aircraft to operational theatres they are incapable of reaching on their own, the delivery of ammunition and equipment when needed, trooping, disaster relief and the traditional peacetime duty of showing the flag. Add to these the latent potential for search and rescue, and for command, control and communication on a global scale, and it can be seen that the aircraft carrier is not just a weapons system but a mobile base of strategic importance

The information in this book has been researched from original source documents in the custody of the Public Record Office, Kew; the Naval Historical Branch, Ministry of Defence; the Research Department of the Fleet Air Arm Museum, Yeovilton; the Department of National Defence, Canada; the Department of Defence, Australia; and the Imperial War Museum, London.

Acknowledgements

I wish to thank David Brown, Mike McAloon and Arnold Hague of the Naval Historical Branch; Graham Mottram and Dave Richardson of the Fleet Air Arm Museum; Paul Kemp of the Imperial War Museum; Roger Sarty of the Directorate of History, Canadian Department of National Defence; Commander Tim Mussared and Commander Bruce Haines of the Australian High Commission, London; the World Ship Society Photographic Library; and the many other individuals and organisations who have provided help whilst I have been compiling this book. **David Hobbs**

About the Author

David Hobbs was born in Plymouth in 1946 and was educated at Plymouth College before joining the Royal Navy in 1964. During his naval career he has served on the aircraft carriers *Victorious*, *Centaur*, *Hermes*, *Bulwark*, *Albion* and two *Ark Royals* (the 1955 and 1985 ships) and in 849, 845, 846 and 737 Naval Air Squadrons as well as in 360 RN/RAF Squadron. He has flown Gannets, Wessex 5s, Hunters and Canberras. Whilst serving in the Director General Aircraft (Naval)'s Department in the Ministry of Defence he was responsible for developing the visual and electronic recovery aids for the Sea Harrier to operate to the deck. He also organised the flying trials that cleared the *Invincible* class and *Hermes* to operate the modern generation of aircraft at sea.

He contributes regularly to various publications and has written four earlier books. He has also presented papers at two international naval historical symposia. He lives in Dorset with his wife (a former WRNS officer) and his son.

Abbreviations

AAM	air-to-air missile
AAR	air-to-air refuelling
ACG	Amphibious Combat Group
ACS	Aircraft Carrier Squadron
AEW	airborne early earning
AF	Atlantic Fleet
AFWR	Atlantic Fleet Weapons Range
AHU	Aircraft Holding Unit
AMRAAM	Advanced Medium-Range Air-to-Air Missile
ANAS	Australian Naval Air Squadron
AOR	Auxiliary Oiler Replenishment (Ship)
AS	anti-submarine
ASM	air-to-surface missile
ASW	anti-submarine warfare
ASWEX	Anti-Submarine Warfare Exercise
ATG	air-to-ground missile
AVCAT	Aviation Catoline Spirit
AVGAS	Aviation Gasoline Spirit
AVG	Auxiliary Aircraft Carrier
A&WIS	America and West Indies Station
BAMP	Base Assisted Maintenance Period
BAVG	British Auxiliary Aircraft Carrier
B Bomb	Buoyant Bomb
BCF	Battlecruiser Fleet
bhp	brake horsepower
BPF	British Pacific Fleet
CAF	Canadian Armed Forces
CAG	Carrier Air Group
CAP	combat air patrol
CAS	close air support
CASEX	Canned Anti-Submarine Exercise
CDO	Commando
CENTO	Central Treaty Organisation
CINC	Commander-in-Chief
CIWS	Close-In Weapon System
CNAS	Canadian Naval Air Squadron
CNSA	Commodore Naval Ship Acceptance
CO	Commanding Officer
COMAT	Commodore Air Train
COMAW	Commodore Amphibious Warfare
COST	Continuation Operational Sea Training
CS	Cruiser Squadron
CS	China Station
CTF	Commander Task Force
CTG	Commander Task Group
CTU	Commander Task Unit
CV	aircraft carrier
CVA	attack aircraft carrier
CVE	escort aircraft carrier
CVS	support aircraft carrier
DAMP	Docking and Assisted Maintenance Period
DED	Docking and Essential Defect Repair
DFC	Designated Flying Course
DLCO	Deck Landing Control Officer
DLT	Deck Landing Training
DNC	Director of Naval Construction
DTS	Dartmouth Training Squadron
EF	Eastern Fleet
EIF	East Indies Fleet
FAA	Fleet Air Arm
FAW	All Weather Fighter
FEF	Far East Fleet
FFO	Furnace Fuel Oil
FNS	French Naval Ship
FO	Flag Officer
FO2	Flag Officer Second-in-Command
FOAC	Flag Officer Aircraft Carriers
FOCAS	Flag Officer Carriers and Amphibious Ships
FOCFT	First of Class Flying Trials
FOF	Flag Officer Flotillas
FOF1	Flag Officer Flotilla 1
FOF2	Flag Officer Flotilla 2
FOF3	Flag Officer Flotilla 3
FOST	Flag Officer Sea Training
FOTEX	Fleet Operational Training Exercise
GF	Grand Fleet
GP	general-purpose
GPMG	general-purpose machine gun
GS	General Service
GWS	Guided Weapon System
HA	high-angle
HAS	Helicopter Anti-Submarine
HAT	Harbour Acceptance Trial
HDS	Helicopter Delivery Service
HF	Home Fleet
HFTS	Home Fleet Training Squadron
hp	horsepower
HMS	His/Her Majesty's Ship
HMAS	His/Her Majesty's Australian Ship
HMCS	His/Her Majesty's Canadian Ship

HMNZS	His/Her Majesty's New Zealand Ship
HNLMS	Her Netherlands Majesty's Ship
HS	Canadian/RAN/USN Helicopter AS Squadron Designator
IAS	indicated air speed
IFTU	Intensive Flying Trials Unit
ihp	indicated horsepower
IJN	Imperial Japanese Navy
IN	Indian Navy
INAS	Indian Naval Air Squadron
INS	Indian Naval Ship
JAS	Joint Anti-Submarine School
JHDU	Joint Helicopter Development Unit
JMC	Joint Maritime Course
LA	low-angle
LGB	laser-guided bomb
LPH	Landing Platform Helicopter
LSO	Landing Signal Officer
LST	Landing Ship Tank
MC	medium capacity
MEF	Middle East Fleet
MF	Mediterranean Fleet
MG	machine gun
Mk	Mark
MN	Merchant Navy
MOGAS	Motor Vehicle Gasoline Spirit
MPA	maritime patrol aircraft
MT	motor transport
NAS	Naval Air Squadron/Station
NATO	North Atlantic Treaty Organisation
NDB	nuclear depth bomb
NF	Night Fighter
NL	Netherlands
ODMA	Operational Date Material Assessment
ORI	Operational Readiness Inspection
OST	Operational Sea Training
PASSEX	Passage Exercise
PCRS	Primary Casualty Receiving Ship
pdr	pounder
POW	prisoner-of-war
PR	Photographic Reconnaissance
PTA	Pilotless Target Aircraft
RAAF	Royal Australian Air Force
RAE	Royal Aircraft Establishment
RAF	Royal Air Force
RAN	Royal Australian Navy
RANAS	Royal Australian Naval Air Station
RCAF	Royal Canadian Air Force
RCN	Royal Canadian Navy
RCNAS	Royal Canadian Naval Air Station
RF	Reserve Fleet
RFA	Royal Fleet Auxiliary
RM	Royal Marines
RN	Royal Navy
RNAS	Royal Naval Air Service/Station
RNEE	Royal Naval Equipment Exhibition
RNethN	Royal Netherlands Navy
RNethMC	Royal Netherlands Marine Corps
RP	rocket projectile
SAC	South Atlantic Command
SAM	surface-to-air missile
SAP	semi-armour piercing
SAR	search and rescue
SAT	Sea Acceptance Trial
SEATO	South-East Asia Treaty Organisation
shp	shaft horsepower
SO	Staff Officer
SMP	Self-Maintenance Period
SNS	Spanish Naval Ship
SP	Senior Pilot
STOVL	short take-off /vertical landing
SWAPPS	South-West Approaches (to UK)
TBR	Torpedo Bomber Reconnaissance
TE	Task Element
TF	Task Force
TG	Task Group
TU	Task Unit
UK	United Kingdom
UN	United Nations
u/s	unserviceable
USA	United States of America
USMC	United States Marine Corps
USN	United States Navy
USPF	United States Pacific Fleet
USS	United States Ship
Va	Virginia (USA)
VE-Day	Victory in Europe Day
VF	Canadian/RAN/USN Fighter Squadron Designator
VJ-Day	Victory over Japan Day
VS	Canadian/RAN/USN Fixed Wing AS Squadron Designator
WAC	Western Approaches Command
WASEX	War At Sea Exercise
WF	Western Fleet
WW1	World War One
WW2	World War Two

Introduction

Roles

The role of an aircraft carrier is dictated by the air group embarked for a particular operation and by its ability to carry fuel, weapons and spares for the aircraft types in question. The light fleet carrier *Bulwark*, for example, operated air groups comprising fighters, commando helicopters and large anti-submarine helicopters. Her outside appearance changed little, but her internal space—stores, workshops and messdecks—were modified to carry appropriate support facilities.

From time to time, major changes in aircraft design have influenced the ability to carry out some roles: thus the introduction of large, transonic jets in the late 1950s reduced the usefulness of the remaining 1942 light fleet carriers. Their larger cousins proved remarkably resilient. Both *Victorious*, laid down to operate Swordfish, and *Hermes*, laid down to operate Seafires, proved, with modifications, able to operate the Buccaneer strike aircraft in the 1960s. The following pages abound with examples of flexibility: *Warrior*, which ferried evacuees from North Vietnam; *Centaur*, which ferried troops to quell a mutiny by local forces in East Africa; and *Bulwark*, whose aircraft at various times carried out strike missions against Egyptian positions during the Suez crisis, supported military operations during the Borneo confrontation with helicopters and carried out 'Cold War' ASW patrols in the Atlantic.

The primary role of the aircraft carrier is to provide the Fleet with whatever air power it needs, wherever it needs it. This is best achieved by a balanced air group, trained to work together, but this does not mean that changes in aircraft numbers or even in squadrons embarked are not quickly achievable. The move towards modular workshops in future ships will help this, since workshop support can be changed as rapidly as the air group.

In the pages that follow, the reader will notice that carriers have been classified either by size (fleet carrier, light fleet carrier) or by function (escort carrier, ferry carrier, trials carrier, training carrier, etc.). The latter classification is intended to give a historical perspective of what the ships did do, not what they could theoretically have done.

Carrier Design

Like any warship, an aircraft carrier design has to balance a number of priorities; minor considerations, if given too much emphasis, can have a very great influence on the subsequent operational ship. With the exception of the Lend/Lease escort or 'Woolworth' carriers, all Commonwealth carriers to date have been designed and built in the United Kingdom. It is, therefore, the Royal Navy that has had the greatest influence on their design and subsequent capability.

The design of British carriers has evolved as the method of employing the ships within a balanced fleet has changed. The original seaplane carriers were conversions from merchant ships, intended to work as auxiliaries in support of the Fleet, not necessarily as an integral part of it. They provided a measure of air support but were limited in speed and needed to stop in order to lower their aircraft into the sea and recover them. The need to operate high-performance fighters for fleet air defence led to a number being carried on platforms on board battleships and cruisers of the Grand Fleet and to the conversion of hybrids, such as *Campania* and *Furious*, which had the speed to operate with the Fleet and launch (but not recover) fighters.

Argus was the logical next step, with an unobstructed flight deck built over a substantial hangar with lifts to move aircraft between the two. Original plans to have a 'goal post' style island amidships were dropped when trials with an after landing deck in *Furious* showed the difficulty of landing into the air currents caused by the structure and funnels amidships. After *Argus*'s completion she mounted a mock-up wood and canvas island which was moved about to find the ideal position. The result, amidships on the starboard side, was adopted by all subsequent British and the great majority of foreign carriers.

The inter-war carrier conversions made the best use of available hulls and introduced the concept of having two hangars mounted one over the other in an attempt to achieve the maximum on the tonnage allowed by the Washington Naval Treaty. Whilst this increased the number of aircraft that could be carried, it did little to increase the number of aircraft that could be operated.

However, the US Navy provided a lead here with the invention of arrester wires and barriers and the use of catapults. During this period progress was hampered by the fact that the Air Ministry, not the Admiralty, controlled the specification of naval aircraft and thus their integration into the ship was a complicated bureaucratic process. This situation improved after Lord Inskip passed control of naval aviation back to the Admiralty.

During rearmament in the late 1930s, it would have been simple to construct repeat *Ark Royal*s but this did not suit the Controller, Admiral Sir Reginald Henderson, who demanded armoured carriers. The most experienced carrier admiral in the Royal Navy, Henderson had commanded *Furious* and has been the first Rear-Admiral Aircraft Carriers in 1931. He wanted ships capable of withstanding attacks by shore-based bombers in the North Sea and Mediterranean. In the *Illustrious* class fleet carriers he got them. Previous carriers had incorporated hull armour; *Illustrious* had a hangar built as an armoured box, with an armoured flight deck above it.

None of the *Illustrious* group were sunk by enemy action in World War 2, although all suffered from attacks with bombs, torpedoes and Kamikazes. Whilst this was to their credit, it has to be said, on the other hand, that they were complicated and expensive ships to build with their medium-range guns, fire-control systems and high-performance machinery. After the war only one of the six was modernised as the cost of alteration was prohibitive.

Wartime design was pragmatic. The recommendation of the Future Building Committee, that aircraft should form the backbone of the Fleet, led to the 1942 light fleet carrier programme, arguably the most successful British carrier design. Sixteen of these ships and eight of the later 1943 design were laid down and fifteen of the former and four of the latter completed. Armour, medium-calibre guns and their fire-control equipment were eliminated to save time and cost, although an extensive radar outfit was retained. Machinery was similar to that fitted in the War Emergency destroyers, giving adequate speed. Mercantile construction techniques were used to save time and cost and to use shipyards that were not normally employed building warships.

Work also continued on fleet carriers during the war and four modified *Implacable*s were laid down, two of which emerged post-war as *Eagle* and *Ark Royal*. Considerable effort went into the projected *Malta* class, which were to be large fleet carriers relying heavily on American influence. Whilst the hull was to be armoured, the hangar was open to allow aircraft engines to be run in it, and the flight deck above was a thinly armoured structure with two centreline and two deck-edge lifts. The *Malta*s would have carried one hundred aircraft, about eighty of which could have been launched in a single strike. Three were ordered, only *Malta* herself was laid down and she was not completed.

The wartime shortage of flight decks was overcome by the commissioning of escort carriers. Some of these were converted in the United Kingdom and Lend/Lease arrangements enabled others to be loaned to the Royal Navy by the US Navy. The British ships started with the austere *Audacity* and ended with sophisticated vessels such as *Pretoria Castle* and *Campania*. The US-supplied ships included conversions such as *Avenger* and progressed to ships of the *Ruler* class, built as carriers but based on a mercantile hull design. All of these had hangar decks that curved following the original hull lines and this made aircraft difficult to move. Later US classes cured this shortcoming. The shortage of fleet carriers in the Royal Navy led to a number of these ships fulfilling fleet tasks throughout the world—to the detriment of their intended escort role.

In the post-war economic climate, the Royal Navy was unable to complete most of the carriers still under construction and was forced to make the best use of those it had. The 1942 light fleet carriers proved ideal for peacetime operations, being capable of operating a sizeable air group whilst being relatively cheap to run. Australia, Canada and India took advantage of this and bought incomplete *Majestic* class hulls to create carrier task groups of their own.

Faced with the need to operate larger and more sophisticated jet aircraft in the 1950s, the Royal Navy developed the angled deck, steam catapult and mirror/projector landing aids, concepts subsequently adopted by the world's navies. The light fleet carriers, with the exception of *Warrior*, were not modernised by the RN and were broken up from the late 1950s. The CVA-01 fleet carrier design was the culmination of ten years' work and had much in it that was good. Its cancellation in 1966 and the withdrawal by 1978 of the remaining conventional carriers left a gap in the Royal Navy's capability that is still unfilled. The present *Invincible* class grew out of a command cruiser design, intended to complement CVA-01. The design suffers from a lack of focus, trying as it does to fulfil the roles of a cruiser, a destroyer and an aircraft carrier. This means that too much equipment encroaches on to the flight deck. However, the use of the ski-jump makes the operation of STOVL fighters from a confined deck possible.

Aircraft Fuel

Two sorts of fuel have been commonly used from the early days of flying to the present day. Aviation Gasoline Spirit (AVGAS) was used for all piston-engine aircraft.

HMS *Ocean* in an Admiralty Floating Dock. (FAA Museum)

It had a low flash point and gave off a vapour which was even more dangerous when mixed with air since it could be detonated by a simple spark. The measures necessary to protect against this are described later. Aircraft with gas turbine engines use a much safer fuel, known as Aviation Catoline Spirit (AVCAT) which is basically a type of diesel. It has a high flash point and usually only burns when pressurized. It is alleged that lighted matches can be thrown into a bucket of the liquid without danger (although the author has seen no evidence to prove this assertion). The general change from 1950 towards aircraft that used AVCAT led to a relaxation of the stringent requirement for protecting fuel storage. With the gradual change from steam to gas turbine propulsion some carriers run on a type of diesel fuel enabling both ship and aircraft to use the same bulk fuel supply in an emergency.

The Flight Deck

The flight deck of a carrier is the area from which aircraft are launched and on to which they are recovered. It is also the area where aircraft are parked, ranged for take-off, armed, maintained and ground-run. It cannot be too big.

All flight decks are basically a flat space, clear of obstructions, but the design has gone through five phases. The first decks comprised a rectangular area, following the dimensions of the hull beneath them. They were pierced by openings for lifts, and wires ran fore and aft to engage with hooks on the aircraft undercarriages in order to hold them on deck after landing. A pronounced 'hump' aft provided an anchorage for the wires, keeping them above deck level, and provided an aerodynamic shape to smooth the airflow astern of the ship. After the failure of the early landing experiments in *Furious*, British designers went to considerable lengths to provide the optimum airflow characteristics. They continued to do so after more powerful aircraft made the requirement less necessary.

The fore and aft wires were not a success as it was felt that they caused more damage than they prevented and were thus removed from all carriers in the early 1920s. In the second phase, decks were clear and aircraft relied on their brakes in order to land safely. Recovery rates were slow, and deck parks were impractical due to the amount of space needed for launch and recovery.

In the third phase the deck was divided, by barriers amidships, into operating and parking areas. Aircraft that missed all the wires would be stopped by the barrier, allowing a considerable deck park to be maintained, thus increasing the size of the air group. The deck park would have constantly had to be moved: forward for recovery operations aft of the barrier, aft for launch operations using the whole deck with the barriers down. The ability to park on deck increased *Illustrious*'s air group from the designed thirty-six to fifty-four in 1945. This positive gain was partially offset by the fact that aircraft on deck were more vulnerable to salt-water corrosion and weather damage.

The adoption of jets invalidated the barrier concept since with no engine in front of the pilot to absorb the impact a 'barrier prang' could prove fatal. Furthermore, sophisticated post-war aircraft were too expensive to risk in this way. The RN was continually faced with the problem of trying to get ever larger aircraft into existing carriers—'quarts into pint pots'. The rubber deck experiment in HMS *Warrior* attempted to obtain the maximum performance from smaller aircraft that did not need undercarriages to land. It was completely impractical and could never have worked at sea, but it did lead indirectly to the fourth phase of flight deck development, the angled deck.

Carrier aviation was revolutionised by the Royal Navy in the early 1950s by the angled deck, invented by Captain D. R. F. Campbell RN. The landing area (and associated arrester wires) were offset up to eight degrees to port of the ship's centreline, thus doing away with the need for barriers. An aircraft that missed all the wires with its hook (i.e., 'bolted') could simply open the throttle and fly another circuit to land; aircraft in the deck park forward would be to starboard of the flight path and therefore protected. The concept was adopted by all carrier navies and is still in use today by the USN, French Navy and other smaller navies. The angled deck had the additional benefit of increasing the deck area with a large sponson overhanging the side of the hull to port. Launches were possible from bow catapults whilst recoveries to the angled deck were taking place (an arrangement known to the US Navy as 'the battle flexideck').

The Royal Navy retired its last conventional frontline fixed-wing aircraft in the late 1970s and adopted all-STOVL air groups comprising Sea Harriers and helicopters. This removed not only the need for catapults and arrester wires, but the divided deck as well, since all aircraft land vertically on a spot. The need for a deck park remains, but it does not have to be protected by angle or barrier. A 'ski-jump' forward gives Sea Harriers an optimum performance off a short deck run. Therefore, the deck in this fifth and current phase has reverted to a simple rectangular structure, with a painted fore and aft runway and landing spots. There is no machinery to go wrong, and rapid launch and recovery times are possible.

One hazard that has affected all flight decks through the decades is a crash which could block the deck and make it difficult, or impossible, to recover aircraft. The solution was to have excellent fire-fighting facilities that could cut down any fire in seconds and 'Jumbo' the crane which could lift any aircraft clear of the runway and put it in a parking area or over the side as necessary. The V/STOL deck has the further advantage that it is not blocked by a crash on deck: if there is a 'dead' aircraft on 2 spot, the rest can land on 5 spot and taxi clear. There is, however, still the need for 'Jumbo' to clear the runway for launches.

The Island Structure

The conflict between the requirements of the ship and flying operations is shown most clearly by the early discussion on the merits of an 'island structure'. Early drafts of the *Argus* (1918) design envisaged a completely clear deck but the lack of a bridge, funnel uptakes and siting for W/T aerials would have made her a difficult ship to command. The design to which she was laid down included a 'goalpost' arrangement amidships with a bridge athwartships connecting islands at either side of the deck amidships. It was not intended that aircraft would fly through the gap but would rather taxi forward from a landing area aft to the launching strip forward.

Tests at the National Physical Laboratory at Teddington showed that air turbulence from this arrangement would make flying impossible even before the centreline island flying trials in *Furious* failed in 1917. *Argus* was, therefore, completed to a flush-deck design with the bridge and charthouse functions condemned to a box-like structure raised above the flight deck for cruising and lowered hydraulically for flying operations.

The ideal solution had been proposed in 1915 by Flight Commander H. A. Williamson, a pilot serving in the Air Department after being wounded whilst serving in the seaplane carrier *Ark Royal* (1914) at the Dardanelles. He made a wooden model of a carrier with the island structure displaced to starboard, a concept adopted by virtually every aircraft carrier since then throughout the world. J. H. Narbeth, the Assistant DNC, saw the merit of the design but was aware of the problems of weight distribution. *Argus* was completed to the flush-deck design, but so much importance was placed on the resolution of the best island design for the other carriers under construction that she carried out trials with a canvas 'dummy' island in October 1918 before working up for operational service. The starboard side amidships was confirmed as the optimum position for the island and pilots found that they liked having the structure there as it gave visual clues and depth which helped their landing (as a pilot gets near a flush deck, he tends to lose sight of it under the wings).

Many theories have been put forward to explain the choice of the starboard side and there may be merit in all of them. First, it is what Williamson modelled. Secondly, it is a fact that some contemporary aircraft turned more easily to port than to starboard because of the gyroscopic effect of their rotary engines; left-handed circuits were, therefore, common ashore. A flying control position on a starboard island would command a view of both the deck and the left-handed circuit pattern whilst pilots turning left after a missed approach were turning safely away from the structure. Lastly, it has been argued that British cars had the driving position on the right hand side and it therefore followed that the 'driving' position of a ship should be on the starboard side. Foreign carriers followed the same idea because British designers helped with the design of the American *Lexington*/*Saratoga*, the Japanese *Hosho* and the French *Béarn*.

With the exception of the fully converted *Furious*, all subsequent Commonwealth carriers have had starboard-side islands. These have grown in size as the need to incorporate briefing, radar, fighter direction and operations rooms, VHF/UHF radio and improved flying control have reflected advances in technology. Growth reached a point during World War 2 where the projected *Malta* class was designed with two separate islands to take the amount of radar and communication equipment specified in the design.

It is alleged that the long, low island with its two large funnels in the *Invincible* class was designed to make the ships look like cruisers in silhouette. It may or may not have succeeded in this but it is certainly the weakest design feature since it takes up an inordinate amount of flight-deck area whilst making very little use of the available space. The light fleet carriers, *Victorious* after 1958 and *Hermes* had the ideal ratio of island size to flight deck.

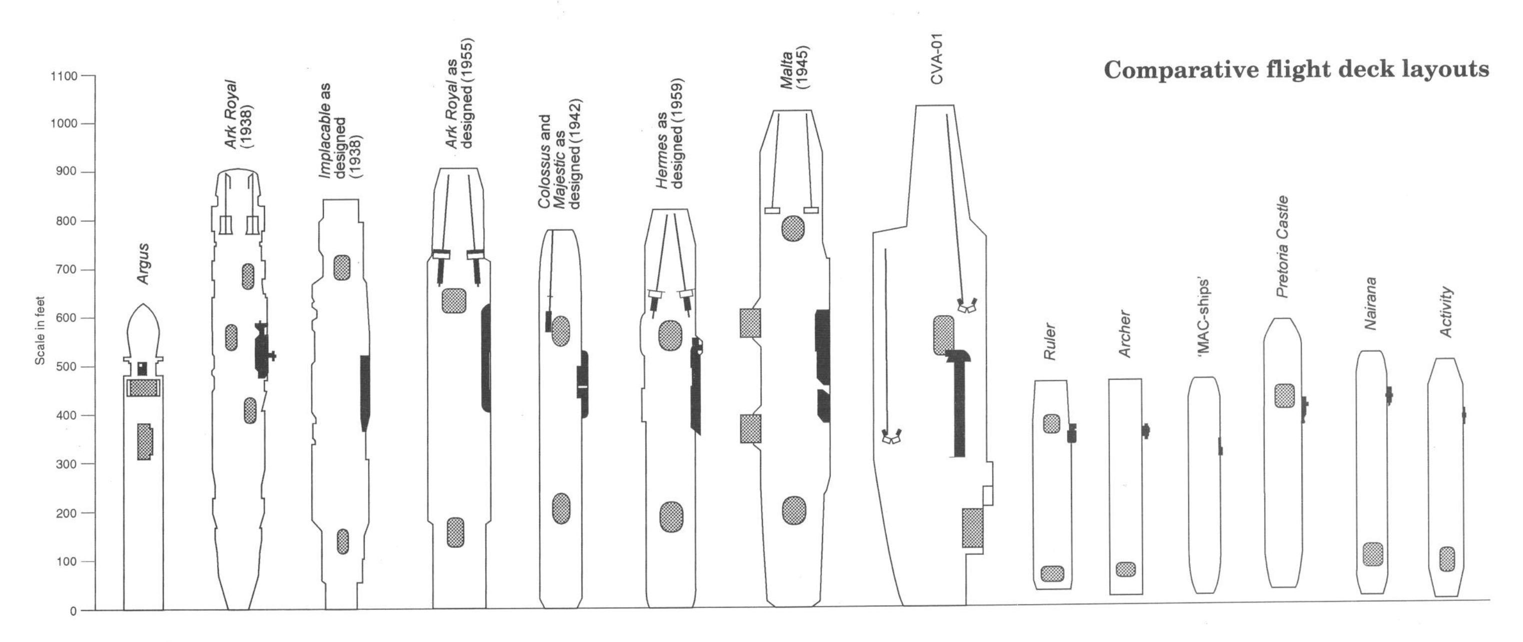

The Hangar

There has been a tendency in the Royal Navy to regard the number of aircraft which a carrier can embark as being the number that will fit in the hangar. This is not so and the reality of war has shown that a deck park is not only possible but desirable. The US Navy has always tended to keep large numbers of serviceable aircraft on deck for flying operations, leaving the hangar for maintenance. This may stem from the fact that the first US carrier, *Langley*, was a converted collier, and it was not easy to get aircraft from the holds up to the flight deck.

The hangar is a rectangular space beneath the flight deck in which folded aircraft can be densely parked, lashed to ring bolts set in the deck. Because of the risk from fuel vapour, British designers have tended to make the hangar an enclosed space entered, from the remainder of the hull, through air locks. Aircraft are moved up to the flight deck on lift platforms, which normally lie at flight deck level and leave an open well beneath them in the hangar which is 'wasted' space because aircraft cannot be parked there. It is difficult to see why more extensive use has not been made of sidelifts, like those in *Hermes* and all current US and French carriers. In these, the platform is suspended from a sponson outboard of the hull and the aircraft pushed sideways into the hangar at the bottom of travel. The sponson and the lift, in the 'up' position, increase the size of the flight deck, and strengthen it by obviating the need for apertures to contain centreline lifts. The whole hangar deck area is then available for parking.

Hangars are the technical home of the embarked squadrons and have changed little over the years. Early hangars opened aft to enable floatplanes to be launched. All, until the advent of *Implacable*, were high enough to accept such aircraft on trolleys. *Furious*, *Courageous* and *Glorious* had 'slip' flight decks, forward of the upper hangar, to enable light fighters such as the Flycatcher to take off almost out of the hangar. Increasing aircraft requirements for take-off runs, and the likely wind blast damage when the hangar door was open, brought the usefulness of this idea to an end in the 1930s.

The sides of all hangars contain the workshops, technical stores and offices. It is possible to arm and fuel aircraft in the hangar, but care has to be taken that weights do not exceed the capacity of the lifts. Every inch of space has to be used and spares such as propellers, mainplanes and wheels are lashed to the bulkheads. Crates are fitted into the gaps between the deep beams that support the flight deck overhead.

Aircraft carriers are unusual warships in that they support weapons systems more technically complex than themselves. The workshop support has, therefore, to be extensive. In earlier carriers this included facilities for carpenters, riggers (who worked on the fabric and structure) and fitters (who worked on the engines).

Sopwith Cuckoo aircraft in the hangar of HMS *Argus* shortly after the ship's completion in 1918. (FAA Museum)

The movement of aircraft in the hangar and up to the flight deck resembles a game of complicated, three-dimensional chess. It is coordinated by the Aircraft Control Room Officer (ACRO) in the island, aided by the Hangar Control Officer (HCO), who has a position amidships, high on the starboard bulkhead of the hangar. Aircraft are, commonly, lashed in rows fore and aft, and it is not unknown for those furthest from the lifts to be serviceable and needed to fly, and those nearest the lifts to be otherwise. It might, therefore, be necessary to move a number of aircraft on to the deck in order to get the required ones into a position where they can fly, and then return the others.

Serviceability constantly changes, and there is usually a need to move aircraft between the deck (known to handlers in the hangar as the 'roof') and the hangar. The process of moving aircraft from the hangar to the deck is known as 'ranging' and from the deck to the hangar as 'striking down'. Although air engineers would never admit it, most squadrons have one airframe that goes deeply unserviceable and ends up in a corner of the hangar being 'cannibalised' for spare parts. This is known as the 'hangar queen' or 'Christmas tree', and getting it serviceable in time to disembark is usually a major achievement requiring considerable effort.

Each squadron has an Aircrew Duty Officer every day who spends much of his time in the hangar. His tasks include making sure that both aircraft and portable equipment are securely lashed to prevent them causing damage by hitting something as the ship moves.

Catapults

The first generation of aircraft carriers had no flight deck machinery and relied on aircraft making a free take-off from a clear deck. Hydraulic catapults were incorporated during refits to the larger ships in the 1930s and were installed in *Ark Royal* (1938) during construction. These were intended to launch floatplanes, and were fitted with a cumbersome trolley arrangement that mated with spigots fitted to strongpoints on the fuselage. It took about five minutes to fit an aircraft on to the trolley and launch it. Surprisingly, no alternative was provided for conventional, wheeled aircraft and these had to be fitted to the same trolley arrangement.

It is worth digressing here to say that early carriers were intended to be operated in a secondary role as mobile bases for floatplanes, as the World War 1 seaplane carriers had done. All were equipped with cranes to lift seaplanes to and from the water, and carried floats to convert aircraft such as the Flycatcher, Osprey, Swordfish and Roc into floatplanes. Hangars were high enough to accommodate aircraft, plus floats, on trolleys. These aircraft suffered a double performance loss: first, the spigots stood proud from the airframe and caused drag; and secondly, both floats and airframe were strengthened to permit catapult launches, with a resultant weight penalty. Not surprisingly, floatplanes played no part in World War 2 British carrier operations.

By contrast, the hydraulic catapults fitted to the US-supplied escort carriers were neat affairs intended to launch wheeled aircraft by means of a strop or bridle attached to hooks on the aircraft. These were invariably positioned in the wheel wells and caused no drag once the undercarriage was raised. During World War 2, fleet carriers' catapults were modified with a sled, to which a strop could be attached, so that US aircraft such as the Martlet, Corsair and Avenger could be launched. British aircraft such as the Swordfish were never modified in production and could not, therefore, use the American catapult.

Throughout the war there was the anomaly that escort carriers could only catapult American aircraft by the tail-down method with a strop, and British aircraft could only carry out a free take-off from them. This was to prove a problem for Swordfish operating in the anti-submarine role, since light winds in the Indian Ocean and even in the North Atlantic in summer reduced the number of depth charges or rockets that could be carried.

By the end of World War 2 the use of catapults had become the normal way of launching at least the first aircraft from a large deck-load strike. As higher-performance aircraft entered service, free take-off became the exception and catapulting the norm. With heavy jet aircraft on the drawing boards it was apparent that hydraulic catapults—with a hydraulic piston driving a pulley which magnified the power to the strop which launched the aircraft—were approaching the point of their maximum development

British designers were faced with a problem which had to be resolved if the Royal Navy was to remain in the carrier business. The solution was the steam catapult, which has seen service with all the world's carriers and is still in use in the US, French and other navies. A better name might be 'slotted cylinder catapult', since steam is merely a convenient gas; the high-pressure gas from slow-burning cordite performs as well. The catapult consisted of a shuttle, to which the strop towing the aircraft was attached. The hook on the shuttle was the only part visible on the flight deck. Two parallel cylinders ran under the deck, which housed pistons fixed to the shuttle and 'sliders' which opened and shut slots in the cylinders as the shuttle moved, keeping in the steam pressure. Steam from the boilers was fed to an accumulator and the actual launch pressure could be varied to take account of different aircraft weights. At launch the aircraft would select full power but be restrained by a hold-back fixed near the tail. When the catapult was fired the combined force of engines and steam pressure broke a weak link in the hold-back, allowing the aircraft to accelerate rapidly forward, to reach a speed of the order of 135 knots in as little as 150 feet. The pistons would be stopped by water rams and the shuttle motored back for the next launch. A good crew would launch an aircraft every two minutes.

The steam catapult was the invention of a naval officer, Commander C. C. Mitchell RN. It first went to sea for trials in HMS *Perseus* in 1949. However, the number of ships in Commonwealth navies fitted with steam catapults steadily reduced from the 1970s with carriers being withdrawn from service or modified to operate STOVL fighters and helicopters. There are now none in service.

Arrester Gear

The first arrester gear was designed to hold aircraft on deck after landing. In *Furious*, *Hermes* (1924) and *Eagle* (1924) there was a well about eighteen inches deep stretching from an aerodynamic 'hump' aft to a ramp a little forward of amidships. Fore and aft wires anchored on the raised deck at either end stretched across the well and were intended to engage hooks on the aircraft undercarriages upon landing, thus holding them on deck. This system made movement difficult and did not make for fast recovery times. It was removed from all carriers by 1927, after which aircraft landed without any form of arresting system.

In that year the Air Attaché in Washington wrote to say that the US Navy were experimenting with transverse arrester wires which engaged a trailing hook lowered by aircraft before landing. The USN found the system so successful that the USS *Saratoga* was fitted with it and carried out 2,000 accident-free landings within the year. Her captain was impressed and stated that the gear materially reduced the landing interval, thus shortening the carriers' vulnerable time into wind during recovery.

Work was put in hand to design an equivalent British system at the Royal Aircraft Establishment and several designs were tested ashore. These included electric and hydraulic retardation systems with winch or piston operation. Early problems included 'hook bounce', showing the need for a damper to stop the hook from bouncing over the wires once it hit the deck, and the eccentric retardation effects of an off-centre landing. Eventually in 1933 the Mk III hydraulic arrester gear was accepted for service and it or its derivatives were fitted to all carriers capable of operating conventional, 'hooked', fixed-wing aircraft. *Courageous* was the first ship to be fitted and her gear was originally capable of arresting an 8,000lb aircraft at an entry speed of 61 knots. Later marks of gear were rigged so that two wires were attached to the same hydraulic piston.

Barriers were installed forward of the arresting gear from the late 1930s onwards, consisting of heavy, steel wire cables rigged between steel stanchions, one on either side of the flight deck. These stanchions held the barrier in the upright position or lay it flat on the deck to enable aircraft to taxi over it. The barrier was rigged to withstand an impact by an aircraft at the same weight and speed as for the arrester wires but with a pull-out of forty feet or less.

Once the angled deck removed the need for barriers the possibility that damage might prevent a returning aircraft from lowering its hook led to the introduction of emergency nylon barrier packs. These were kept in lockers at the deck edge and rigged across the deck if required. It took about five minutes to rig them and practice evolutions were commonplace to see which of the two watches of aircraft handlers were quicker at doing so.

Ark Royal (1955) was fitted, after her 1970 refit, with water spray arrester gear which substituted a piston being forced into a water ram for the hydraulic cylinders of the earlier equipment. The new gear offered a smoother retardation and was capable of stopping heavier, faster aircraft.

With the change from conventional aircraft to STOVL fighters and helicopters, there are now no carriers left in the Commonwealth navies with arrester gear.

Visual Landing Aids

At first pilots judged their approach to the carrier by eye and had the whole of the deck to land on. With the adoption of wires and barriers in the late 1930s, it became obvious that this was no longer good enough and pilots would need to be guided off a standardised approach into a target position in the wires. The US Navy had developed a system using experienced pilots as Landing Signal Officers and the RN adopted the idea in 1939. The LSO or 'batsman' stood on a sponson on the port side of the flight deck aft and gave instructions to approaching pilots by means of brightly coloured, hand-held bats. His instructions were mandatory and told the pilots that they were high or low, left or right. The 'cut' told them when to close their throttles and the 'wave off' told them to break off their approach and go round for another circuit. Lighted wands could be used for night approaches.

The LSO was viewed with suspicion at first by pilots unused to such tight control but by 1940 he was widely employed and was essential to the operation of the higher powered aircraft that came into service as the war progressed. LSOs were trained ashore at the Deck Landing Training School and 'passed out' using real aircraft as 'clockwork mice' on a training carrier.

With the gradual introduction of jet aircraft after 1945, batsmen reached the limit of their ability to control the landing because approach speeds increased dramatically. This meant that by the time the LSO spotted an error, signalled it to the pilot and the latter moved the controls it might well be too late for a safe arrival. Future operations were put in doubt and again it was a naval officer, Commander H. C. N. Goodhart RN, who came up with an imaginative solution that was adopted by the world's navies.

It is rumoured that the music hall phrase 'all done by mirrors' formed the genesis of the idea, but, whatever the truth of that is, the mirror landing sight proved the ideal recovery aid for carrier aircraft. A curved mirror was mounted on a stable platform on the port side amidships where the effects of ship pitch would be minimal. A set of green lights was constructed in a line on either side of the mirror to give a datum and the platform kept the whole assembly stable. A bank of source lights, each with a different power supply in case of emergency, was mounted to port, aft, so that the reflected spot of light shone astern along the centre of a three-degree glideslope. The height of the mirror could be adjusted for the 'hook-eye' distances of different aircraft so that, with the pilot's eye on the optimum approach path, the hook underneath him would catch the target wire. The hook-eye distance of a Gannet was seventeen feet, that of a Sea Hawk much less.

In operation, all the pilot had to do was keep the spot of reflected light, known as the 'meatball', in line with the green datum arms. If the 'meatball' appeared to go low, he was low; if it went high, then he was high. A Mirror Control Officer (MCO) sat by the sight looking at the approach through a telescope bore-sighted to the ideal glideslope. He was able to talk to the approaching pilot and, if necessary, wave him off with flashing red lights. A spare sight was mounted on the starboard side of the flight deck aft but pilots hated using it.

From 1960 a projector sight was introduced which substituted a vertical bank of lights for the mirror. The appearance of the 'meatball' to the pilot was slightly better since he was looking at radiated, rather than reflected, light. Optically, the lights shine through a shutter, which corrects for pitch and makes only the required lights visible. The projector sight is still in service today, but for Sea Harrier operations in the Royal and Indian Navies it is mounted on the island in order to show a glideslope that brings aircraft to a forty-foot hover to port of the deck rather than a point on the deck aft.

Protection

The standards of hull protection for aircraft carriers have varied greatly. The earlier carrier conversions inherited the armour and sub-division of their original battleship and battlecruiser hulls. Fleet carriers have been armoured and partitioned to contemporary cruiser standards. Light fleet carriers had their machinery arranged *en echelon* in order to minimize the effect of torpedo damage. The escort carriers were given such splinter protection as was possible around the vulnerable parts of their hulls. Beyond this, British designers went to great lengths to protect ships from the effects of damage to aircraft and their supporting systems. However, AVGAS and the volatile vapour it gave off remained a serious threat, even in peacetime operations. As a result it was stowed behind coffer dams surrounded by sea water which provided the pressure to force fuel into the main piping. Whilst this risked water contamination on occasion, it removed the danger of a vapour trap between any pump and the tank. The coffer dams were not part of the hull structure and were thus unlikely to crack due to the 'whiplash' effect that followed a hit. No British designed or converted carrier was lost to a fuel vapour explosion but many foreign carriers, such as the Japanese *Kaga* and *Akagi*, were literally and spectacularly blown apart. The cost in terms of the amount of AVGAS that could be stowed in the safer British designs is shown by the changes worked into *Indomitable* compared with her half-sister *Illustrious* to support the extra aircraft her second hangar made possible: the space that had contained 350 tons of FFO was converted into AVGAS stowage that contained 25,000 gallons (or 89 tons) of aircraft fuel.

Notwithstanding the measures taken to prevent fire, further measures were incorporated to fight it rapidly and effectively should it happen to break out. Fire curtains were built into hangar deckheads which could be dropped to divide them into three distinct sections, in each of which a fire could be contained. From the 1930s overhead sprays were incorporated in hangars which could drench any blaze with salt water. To prevent the resultant water forming a free surface, effective scuppers had to be fitted throughout the hangar. There was the risk that any aircraft could be written off by salt water corrosion but this was considered acceptable when compared to the possible loss of the ship if fire went unchecked.

Most carriers were not armoured but still incorporated precautions to limit damage. Magazines were sited below the waterline and were placed as far apart as possible if there was more than one. The conversion to RN standards undergone by US-built escort carriers included a number of protective measures including a change to British AVGAS stowage arrangements and, after the loss of *Avenger*, modification to the bomb room to build in splinter protection and reduce it in size so that it did not reach to the ship's side. In some ships void compartments were filled with sealed drums to give a measure of buoyancy in the event of flooding after action damage.

Most British carriers have incorporated enclosed hangars to date, with the exception of the unbuilt *Malta* class. Access from the remainder of the hull was through air locks. In the fleet carriers of the *Illustrious* and *Eagle* groups the hangar was, as already noted, a completely armoured box intended to protect the aircraft within from bombs and from cruiser or destroyer gunfire. On the advice of the RAF, the flight deck was designed to defeat a 500lb bomb dropped on it from any height. In fact no bomb that small was dropped on a fleet carrier, but the deck did prove effective against hits by Kamikazes. *Illustrious*'s deck was penetrated by a 1,100lb bomb off Malta in January 1941 which exploded in the hangar with devastating effect. An open hangar like that in the USN carriers would have allowed the blast to vent.

The need to minimise openings in the armoured flight deck led to the design of small lifts in the first three ships of the *Illustrious* group, which proved a disadvantage when larger aircraft came into service. It is also of interest that the single catapult in that class was mounted above the armour and had to be faired in so that it did not become an obstruction for aircraft taking off over it.

Examples of Aircraft Weapon Loads

***Hermes* (1924)**
8 x 18in torpedoes
120 x 100lb bombs
102 x 65lb bombs
200 rockets
500 explosive darts
.303in gun ammunition
Flares and pyrotechnics

***Eagle* (1924; load as 1942)**
31 x 18in torpedoes
48 x 500lb SAP bombs
342 x 250lb SAP and B bombs
130 x 100lb AS bombs
360 x 20lb anti-personnel bombs
54 depth charges
24 mines
.303in gun ammunition
Flares and pyrotechnics

Courageous
54 x 18in torpedoes
120 x 500lb SAP bombs
72 x 250lb SAP/GP bombs
144 x 100lb GP bombs
422 x 20lb bombs
.303in gun ammunition
Flares and pyrotechnics

***Ark Royal* (1938)**
72 x 18in torpedoes
360 x 500lb SAP bombs
300 x 250lb SAP/GP bombs
576 x 100lb GP bombs
800 x 20lb bombs
6,000 x 8½lb bombs
.303in gun ammunition
Flares and pyrotechnics

Activity
10 x 18in torpedoes
36 x 500lb SAP bombs
96 x 250lb SAP bombs
144 x Mk XI depth charges
.303in gun ammunition
Flares and pyrotechnics

***Illustrious* (1940)**
45 x 18in torpedoes
250 x 500lb SAP bombs
650 x 250lb SAP/GP bombs
100 x 100lb GP bombs
600 x 20lb bombs
.303in gun ammunition
Flares and pyrotechnics

Indomitable
54 x 18in torpedoes
120 x 500lb SAP bombs
650 x 250lb SAP/GP bombs
240 x 250lb B bombs
500 x 100lb GP bombs
600 x 20lb bombs
3,000 x 11½lb bombs
.303in gun ammunition
Flares and pyrotechnics

***Colossus* (load as 1945)**
36 x 2,000lb bombs
216 x 500lb bombs
72 x 500lb MC bombs
108 x 250lb B bombs
32 x 18in torpedoes
108 x Mk XI depth charges
24 mines
360 x 40lb bombs
.5in gun ammunition
.303in gun ammunition
Flares and pyrotechnics

***Ocean* (1945; load as 1952)**
52 x 1,000lb bombs
450 x 500lb bombs
1,900 x 3in RP
20mm cannon ammunition
Flares and pyrotechnics

Aircraft Weapons Stowage

Aircraft weapons are stowed in magazines known as bomb rooms. Various publications have set out to illustrate the number of weapons that could be carried by weight, number or volume. Some examples of designed weapon loads are shown above.

Different weapons have differing requirements for space in bomb rooms. For example, 1,000lb bombs can be laid on wooden spreaders and stacked like barrels in a brewery to fill a given space. On the other hand, guided weapons need protective boxes, and need to be carefully stowed to avoid damage. Fins and wings can be stored separately outside the magazine, but in such a case space must be available for weapon assembly prior to their being taken to the flight deck.

Torpedoes and other large, complicated weapons are stowed in special bins that protect them from ship movement and, in some cases, from splinters in the event of action damage. When taken for use, such weapons are usually fitted to specially designed trolleys and taken in these from the bomb room, which is usually deep in the ship below the waterline, to the flight deck by means of a bomb lift. The lift trunking would be fitted with flash-tight doors.

Air weapons are usually fused or made ready on the flight deck in an area clear of aircraft where they can be pushed over the side in the event of an emergency. In a period of sustained strike operations such as the Korean War, the weapon supply team or 'bombheads' can be hard put to deliver the number of bombs required. This is even more apparent now that 'smart' bombs and missiles have replaced 'dumb' bombs.

The number of weapons carried in a given ship can vary according to such factors as the strength of the air group carried or the ship's role for that particular cruise, both of which could change in a matter of hours. (Hence, in this book, individual ships show only the types of weapon stowed, not weights or numbers.) As a rule of thumb, carriers carry a 'load out' that enables each aircraft embarked to fly four sorties in each of its primary missions and, for fighter aircraft, sufficient gun ammunition for sixteen sorties. Wartime gun ammunition was belted and mixed to give 45 per cent ball, 30 per cent armour-piercing and 25 per cent tracer, although this could of course be varied for specific missions. Flares for night illumination, smoke and flame floats for wind-finding and other pyrotechnics all had to be carried in large numbers.

Since World War 2 carriers have relied on armament store ships to re-supply ammunition during replenishment periods at sea. The quantities of ammunition available in the carrier could therefore be considered as a 'ready use' supply capable of being replaced quickly. Some idea of the air weapons usage during sustained operations may be gained from looking at the data for individual light fleet carriers that fought in the Korean War.

Carrier Operating Methods

The number of aircraft that can be operated from a given carrier is not necessarily the same as the number that could be embarked in it. For example, a ferry carrier could have 90 aircraft on board but there would be insufficient flight-deck space to launch or recover any of them. Furthermore, even if a slight reduction in numbers were made to clear space for some launches and recoveries, there would not be enough fuel or air weapons to sustain viable operations. A balance, therefore, has to be struck between the number of aircraft embarked and the ability to man, fuel, arm and maintain them.

Given an appropriate balance, there are two classic operating methods: predictive and reactive. In the former, groups of aircraft are launched and recovered according to a prearranged flying programme to keep a specified number of aircraft airborne over a prolonged period. In the latter, aircraft are held at readiness on deck alert and only launched to deal with a specific threat or mission. Predictive operations are in fact very much more flexible, with the ship turning into wind to launch and recover at intervals and the flight deck clear for moves and ground runs in between them. Aircraft airborne with a minor unserviceability would be kept up until the next recovery; those with a major problem would have to be brought on early. This caused problems in the era of conventional recoveries, but today, with air groups that are all capable of vertical landings, it is relatively easy to clear a single spot for an unscheduled recovery.

Reactive flying works well in small ships with a single helicopter embarked but it does not work in carriers. To give an example, two Sea Harriers at Alert 5 (i.e., airborne within five minutes of being ordered to launch) in an *Invincible* class carrier must be manned, armed and parked in position for their 300-foot deck run. Sufficient maintainers and handlers must stay with the aircraft for an immediate start-up when it is called for. This is a waste of manpower since in a predictive programme they could have seen to the launch and then got on with other important tasks. The runway in front of the alert aircraft must be kept clear, limiting the amount of aircraft movement that can take place. It is unusual for flight deck tractors to break down, but if they do it is often in a position where they block an aircraft on alert! Tactically, reactive flying is unlikely to produce decisive results as interceptions cannot be made at ranges that would give defence in depth. The same criticism applies equally to strike and anti-submarine warfare.

Before launch all aircrew are briefed with a 'Charlie' Time, which is the moment when their wheels must hit the deck on landing. It is vital that this is achieved since it is the basis for all the split-second timing that governs carrier operations. Most pilots achieve 'Charlie' plus or minus 15 seconds; any that cannot may expect to have an interview with 'Little F' to explain their shortcomings.

Aircraft Maintenance

The need for maintenance influences a carrier's ability to generate aircraft sorties. Methods have changed over the years, but, essentially, maintenance falls into one of two categories, planned and unplanned.

Planned maintenance includes major servicing (formerly known as 'mainchecks') at set numbers of flying hours, 'before and after' flight inspections and daily checks. Engineers try to even out the major servicings so that they do not all fall due at once, ground the squadron and make excessive demands on manpower. Most aircraft engines and components are 'lifed' by the number of hours they have flown and need to be replaced by new or refurbished items at major servicings. It would be a matter of judgement whether or not to replace items that were not yet life-expired in an airframe that was already stripped down for other work in order to save time and effort later, assuming sufficient spares to cover the 'lost' hours were available.

Unplanned maintenance includes the repair of failed or battle-damaged components and structure. Before a period of sustained operations, engineers would try to clear as much major servicing as possible in order to have resources available for repair. This would also have the benefit of giving the squadron the maximum number of airframes to fill the flying programme.

Aircraft each have their own log book, the Form A700. All maintainers would sign for their work on the appropriate page and pilots would sign out and back in again after flight. Sections of the '700' show Acceptable Deferred Defects, Weight and Balance Data and Hours Flown by various lifed items. There is also a section for the pilot to enter any unserviceabilities that might have occurred in flight. An entry here might ground the aircraft as 'u/s' or it might be a minor snag that could be put down as an Acceptable Deferred Defect for repair later.

During the British Pacific Fleet operations in 1945, the difficulties involved in maintaining the large numbers of aircraft embarked aboard the fleet carriers came close to limiting operations. Had the war continued, it is likely that support escort carriers would have been kept near the operating area in order to carry out major servicing and component replacement operations. This would have left the squadron maintainers free to carry out daily checks and implement the flying programme.

The need to reduce maintenance man-hours is specified in the staff requirements of modern aircraft. This will have the effect of easing the burden on future carrier maintenance crews. Computerisation of the A700 is the next logical step forward and it is slowly being introduced. Future carriers are likely to have 'containerised' workshops that can be disembarked with the aircraft and changed to reflect the different aircraft types embarked for different operations. The inherent flexibility of the carrier will be enhanced by such a logical step.

Sensors

Prior to World War 2 aircraft carriers, in common with other warships, had no sensors other than the human eyeball, aided by binoculars, to detect other ships and aircraft. By the 1930s the threat posed to the Fleet by fast shore-based monoplanes could not be countered by standing patrols of carrier-borne fighters without any form of direction. Part of the rationale behind the armoured carriers was the tacit acceptance that enemy aircraft would get through and score hits.

From 1940 onwards radar changed this perception completely. Radar-equipped carriers were able to locate and track targets and to vector fighters from the combat air patrol on to them. Operations in the Mediterranean were the crucible for developing and improving aircraft direction techniques and from 1942 the Royal Navy led the world in theory and practice, forming a specialist Aircraft Direction Branch to carry the work forward. A series of radars capable of detection, tracking and height-finding were developed during and after the war, culminating with the massive Type 984 fitted to *Victorious*, *Hermes* and *Eagle* which combined all three functions.

From the 1950s flights of AEW Skyraiders, Gannets and more recently Sea Kings have been embarked in RN carriers. Their radar picture could be data-linked to the parent ship or a picket destroyer and in addition the AEW observer could detect a destroyer-size target out to 200 miles and control interceptions with CAP aircraft. Modern carriers and AEW helicopters have active and passive electronic warfare capabilities.

Camouflage

Most British and Commonwealth warship types have been painted in various shades of grey since 1904. Numerous forms of camouflage were recommended by an American artist named Thayer in the first years of World War 1 but they were not adopted by the Admiralty. Later in the war a marine artist named Norman Wilkinson proposed a form of dazzle painting which attempted to confuse enemy range-takers relying on optical equipment who would thus find it difficult to assess range, course and speed. *Argus* (1918) was completed in such a scheme together with several other warships for trial purposes. The Admiralty did not proceed further with this scheme because it was felt to make ships more obvious to the observer in the first place.

In 1919 the Commonwealth Fleets reverted to a peacetime scheme comprising dark grey for ships in the Atlantic, light grey in the Mediterranean, white with 'primrose yellow' funnels and masts in the East Indies and white with light grey upperworks in the Far East.

On the outbreak of World War 2 the Admiralty established a Directorate of Camouflage at Leamington Spa. Individual disruptive schemes were produced for all aircraft carriers which often differed on port and starboard sides and were painted in up to five different tones and colours. By 1943, however, it was accepted that disruptive paint schemes were difficult and time-

HMS *Indomitable* in a typical mid-World War 2 camouflage scheme. (FAA Museum)

consuming to apply and gave such marginal benefits that they were not worth continuing. Instead, an Admiralty scheme was adopted which was designed to conceal a ship at dawn, dusk and night. This was optimised for the sea and sky tones found in the Pacific. The whole ship was painted light grey with a blue/green panel on the hull over two-thirds of its length to give a shortening effect and confuse the apparent inclination. Areas usually in shadow, such as the undersides of sponsons, were painted in gloss white to effect a contrast. The BPF carriers were painted in this scheme in 1945–46.

After the war the Royal Navy adopted a light grey scheme worldwide. For a number of years the Royal Canadian Navy used a dark hull/light upperworks combination before reverting to light grey overall and the Royal Australian Navy has experimented with various shades of grey. The Indian Navy has lately adopted a dark grey scheme in line with the theory that dark objects do not reflect sunlight and are therefore more difficult to see when there is little or no cloud cover.

A return to less orthodox camouflage or deception was not considered in the Korean War nor has been since, but there may be a renewal of interest now that a generation of ships is being designed to incorporate 'stealth' technology. It seems logical that if efforts are being made to reduce the radar, thermal, noise and electronic signatures of warships, then something must be done to reduce their visual signature as well.

HMS *Argus* as completed in 1918 in an experimental, disruptive paint scheme. (FAA Museum)

Carrier Survivability

During World War 2 the Royal Navy lost five aircraft carriers to submarine-launched torpedoes, one to gunfire, one to aircraft bombs and one to accidental explosion. A total of sixty-six carriers, excluding MAC-ships and seaplane tenders, were deployed and it has been calculated from all the available statistics that a smaller percentage of carriers was lost than any other type of warship. In the same war the US Navy lost eleven carriers and the Japanese twenty-one. No British-built carrier was lost to fire whereas 55 per cent of American and Japanese carriers were lost to AVGAS vapour explosions. Since 1945 no enemy has located a Commonwealth carrier in actions ranging from Korea and the Falklands to Palestine, Suez and the Borneo Confrontation, let alone demonstrated an ability to attack it.

Whatever platform an attacker might use, hits on a carrier are notoriously difficult to obtain. It should be borne in mind that a 25-knot carrier can move to any one of 17,600 square miles in the three hours that might elapse between a sighting and the arrival of any land-based attack aircraft. These latter must expect to have to penetrate a layered defence, coordinated by AEW helicopters using 'gapless' radar cover, comprising fighters, medium-range missiles, electronic 'soft kill' options, short-range missiles and CIWS. Motion should not be discounted as a defence against the sort of manned fighter-bomber that caused the most damage in the Falklands conflict. A 25-knot, 700ft carrier moves its own length every sixteen seconds, which equals the time taken by the pilot of a 500-knot aircraft to cover the last 4,000 yards to his weapon release point, continually having to adjust his point of aim whilst under heavy and accurate fire. Air-launched stand-off weapons suffer the drawbacks that the target must be located before they can be launched and that they too have to 'run the gauntlet' of the layered defence. Land-based missiles, targeted against fixed points on the earth's surface, pose no threat to carrier battle groups.

Returning to those wartime losses, it is interesting to note that six of the eight were employed away from a balanced task force and that air attacks damaged a number of carriers but only succeeded in sinking *Hermes* (1924), which had no air group embarked and relied on shore-based RAF fighters for protection. Some of the lost carriers were engaged in tasks of questionable value and it is clear from any study that it took senior officers a number of years before they appreciated how best to employ carriers.

Contemporary navies, especially the RN, have a capability to combat submarines that is light years away from World War 2. This, together with the inherent survivability demonstrated by carriers of all generations, means that they continue to be more likely to survive conflict than any other type of warship.

Machinery

The early carrier conversions retained the machinery designed for their previous role. The 1924 *Hermes* was the first to be designed and built as a carrier and she was given machinery essentially similar to that fitted in contemporary large destroyers. This precedent has been followed by several light carrier designs.

The 1938 *Ark Royal* can be said to represent the end of an experimental period with aircraft carriers and her design reflected the latest thoughts on how a carrier would operate. She was expected to serve as an auxiliary unit in support of the battle line and flying operations would constantly take her away from the 'main' fleet. High speed and an endurance greater than that of capital ships were therefore specified so that she could resume station in between flying operations. It was this requirement, rather than aircraft operations, that dictated the type of machinery fitted. The required power could not be provided by two shafts but four would have made too great an inroad into a hull which was to be limited by the various pre-war naval treaties and so, unusually for the Royal Navy, the 1938 'Ark' adopted a three-shaft arrangement. A similar layout was built into the first four units of the *Illustrious* group. Three shafts had the advantage that the units could be worked into the hull abreast of each other, saving weight and space, but the disadvantage that the machinery was more vulnerable to action damage than that displaced to be less compact. The last two ships of the *Illustrious* group adopted a four-shaft layout to maintain their high speed despite their increased size and weight. The change was not entirely successful, however, since the extra machinery and the personnel to man it absorbed much of the extra space achieved in the re-cast design. For example, part of the expanded lower hangar had to be used as messdeck accommodation.

The wartime carrier designs adopted a more austere approach and were forced to use machinery that was already available. The escort carriers retained their mercantile engines, diesel in the British and early American conversions and low-pressure steam units in the majority of the USN-supplied Lend/Lease ships. The latter gave excellent range and endurance characteristics but a low top speed. They were manned in large part by Merchant Navy personnel serving with the Royal Navy under T124X articles.

The 1942 light fleet carriers absorbed many of the lessons learnt by carriers in the early war years. They were intended to be austere ships and made use of the standard Admiralty boilers and turbines that were being produced in large numbers. In this they followed the design of the maintenance carrier *Unicorn*, which can, in many ways, be seen as a prototype of the light fleet design. The decision to accept the low top speed that this machinery offered was reinforced by a study into carrier operations to date which revealed that high-speed capability had seldom been used. The units were arranged *en echelon* to lessen vulnerability to a single torpedo hit and the hull was divided by transverse rather than fore and aft bulkheads so that it would settle on an even keel rather than list after underwater damage.

The 1951 *Eagle* and the 1955 *Ark Royal* followed the same design philosophy as that for *Indefatigable*, with four shafts but with more hull volume to absorb both the machinery and the men required to run it. The 1943 light fleet carriers responded to the concern that their predecessors' 24 knots was inadequate for modern fleet operations and had nearly double the power to give an extra 4 knots. By the late war years, operating philosophy had changed and the carriers formed the centre of battle groups rather than adjuncts to it, with the result that the remainder of the fleet conformed to the carriers' movements.

In post-war carrier designs nuclear power was considered and rejected for CVA-01 since it was regarded as a development risk and the initial cost (as opposed to the 'through-life' cost) would have been prohibitive. As designed this ship would have been built with an advanced high-pressure steam system.

Steam was important to the jet carriers since it provided the gas pressure for the slotted cylinder catapults. The use of steam led to some interesting situations in the Far East, where small carriers such as *Hermes* (1959) operated large aircraft like the Buccaneer and Sea Vixen. In low wind conditions it was a question whether to use the available steam pressure to re-charge the catapult accumulators quickly or to strive for maximum revolutions from the steam turbines in order to gain another knot of wind over the deck from ship speed through the water. Such was the noise in steam machinery spaces that it was not always obvious to those on watch that flying operations were in progress. A red light was sited in the machinery control room which was illuminated whenever launches or recoveries were in progress. When lit the specified revolutions were maintained, even if some problem developed, in order to maintain safe wind conditions on the flight deck.

The most revolutionary change in carrier machinery came with the adoption of gas turbine propulsion for the *Invincible* class. By eliminating boilers, which were slow to light and inflexible to operate, gas turbines proved very much more adaptable. They could be started and shut down almost at will to provide more or less power and could even be changed whilst a ship was under way at sea. The *Invincible* installation impedes aircraft operations, however. The volume of air that needs to be fed to the intake and removed from the exhaust of a gas turbine is large and the trunking requires a significant amount of space and cannot be taken around tight corners. This is especially so when the turbines are sited low in the hull. *Invincible*'s two funnels are a manifestation of this requirement to move exhaust gas out of the hull. To make matters worse, each Olympus gas turbine in *Invincible* has its own lift shaft to allow its removal up to the hangar deck. These four lift wells take up a considerable percentage of the hull's interior volume and, apart from stowing the ship's Land Rover on one of the lift platforms, they have no other function. They cause a severe 'dumb-belling' of the hangar and it is difficult to believe that some more space-efficient system could not have been devised to have allowed larger workshops, stores and hangarage.

For the future, the new *Ocean* is to have diesel engines and it will be interesting to see if supercharged diesels will be considered for fleet carrier designs. They have the advantage of giving good range and endurance with an adequate speed without the requirement for the amount of air trunking that gas turbines would call for.

Communications

The Commonwealth Navies developed and shared a sophisticated system of ship-to-shore wireless communication in the early years of this century. It was based on radio transmitters in each station or command area which sent messages to specific ships and general 'broadcasts' which gave information to all ships in the area. Most used both the medium- and high-frequency bands and messages were transmitted on more than one frequency to ensure adequate reception throughout the station. Large warships such as carriers were able to maintain a 24-hour watch on many frequencies and were able to re-broadcast information for smaller ships that could only set watch at certain times because of lack of manpower. Within a task force specific ships would be delegated to 'guard' certain frequencies so that the available receivers in the force could be put to the maximum use.

High-frequency transmissions have the advantage that they can be heard world-wide since the radio waves bounce off the ionosphere, the exact height at which they do so varying with the frequency in use. The distances between the 'rings' where the waves return to the earth's surface are known as skip distances. By transmitting the same signal on different frequencies, good coverage can be maintained throughout the station. This world-wide reception can be a disadvantage in wartime since ships give away their position by using it. Most therefore read broadcasts but did not transmit unless in contact with the enemy.

Before 1945 broadcasts were transmitted in morse and read by a communicator wearing earphones. The resulting signal had to be manually de-coded using a cryptographic machine like a typewriter. In this way a high-priority 'flash' signal could be transmitted and received in minutes, whereas a low priority 'routine' might take many hours or even days. Decryption was usually the slowest part of the process. In 1945 the BPF adopted US Navy procedures and typed rather than wrote morse, thus speeding the process.

From the 1960s, 'on line' cryptographic systems began to remove the need for manual encryption and decryption, thus speeding the process still further. From the 1970s satellite communications came into general use and messages from fleet headquarters could be 'bounced off' satellites to the ship concerned. This method represents today's state of the art. Transmissions are line-of-sight between ship and satellite and are therefore not easy to detect, and so satellite communications can be used from the ship in wartime.

Until World War 2 tactical communication between ships relied on visual signals using flags, semaphore or flashing lights transmitting morse. These were supplemented by VHF radio, known as 'Talk Between Ships' or TBS, from 1944 onwards. Different navies used very different procedures, which often made combined operations difficult. The BPF solved this problem in 1945 by adopting USN communication procedures. Since 1948 the adoption of common NATO doctrine by the Allied navies has helped further in this respect.

Communication with aircraft developed rapidly in World War 2. Before that, bulky WT sets were carried by reconnaissance aircraft, which needed specialist telegraphist/air gunners (TAGs) to operate the equipment. Fighters had no radio between the wars but the adoption of four-channel VHF sets in 1940 allowed them to make use of the developing radar direction techniques that made fleet air defence with CAP fighters viable. By 1943 even the lumbering Swordfish embarked in MAC-ships had VHF sets to pass tactical ASW information on voice nets.

Since 1945 aircraft communications have improved rapidly and it is possible to pass radar information by secure data-link and to use secure speech on VHF and UHF communication systems.

Guns and Missile Systems

In March 1920 the Post War Questions Committee, established to examine the ideal characteristics of future warships, stated that the armament of carriers should be a defensive one. New ships were expected to outrun light cruisers and so 4.7in guns, to give a margin of superiority over destroyers, were recommended. *Courageous* and *Glorious* were so fitted but the other conversions had a heterogeneous collection of medium guns intended for surface or AA fire.

The 1938 *Ark Royal* had batteries of 4.5in guns in open mountings, two of which were sited on sponsons at each quarter. These were seen as the main anti-aircraft armament and the ship's original orders called for aircraft to be de-fuelled and struck down into the hangar in the event of air attack in order to clear the arcs for the guns which could then fire across the flight deck. Close-range pompoms completed the armament. This reflected the pre-war philosophy that the aircraft were there to spot for the battleship's guns and such fighters as were embarked were to protect them, not the ship. The guns were to ward off enemy aircraft that might try to inhibit flying operations.

The *Illustrious* group mounted a similar number of weapons but the 4.5in guns were in sophisticated, semi-automatic turrets and the sponsons had to be deep enough to carry the gunhouses under the turrets in which ammunition was handled. These weapons were also designed to fire across the flight deck at low elevation but seldom did so due to the damage caused by blast to flight deck fittings and equipment. With the increasing scale of air attack, numerous close-range weapons were added throughout the war. The 20mm Oerlikon was the most common at first but when this proved incapable of destroying a Kamikaze aircraft committed to its dive, 40mm Bofors were fitted in large numbers from 1945.

The wartime escort carriers reflected a desire to get flight decks to sea with the minimum build time. Their armament was simple, mainly aimed by eye and not complicated to install. Sophisticated medium-calibre weapons were rejected by the designers of the light fleet carriers who accepted that aircraft constituted the ships' primary weapons. Guns were only required to counter aircraft that broke through the CAP. This was a sensible approach that contributed to the remarkably short build time achieved by the type

Post-war carriers were mostly completed with some of the original armament suppressed in order to provide flight deck extensions to operate the new large jets. As the ships were refitted, more and more guns were removed to allow space for structure such as angled decks and to free messdeck space for the larger number of maintainers required to support the complex second-generation jet aircraft. Most retained a minimal outfit of close-range weapons but *Ark Royal* (1955) spent her last ten years with no hull-mounted weapons at all.

As it became apparent that the Bofors was becoming limited in use against modern aircraft it was replaced in some ships with more effective weapons. The USN 3in/50-calibre gun was fitted in *Victorious* and *Bonaventure* and Seacat close-range missile systems were fitted in *Eagle* and *Hermes*. The CVA-01 design included a Sea Dart medium-range missile system because it was felt that the optimum place to put such a weapon was on the potential target rather than an escort which might have been out of position.

The *Invincible* class retained Sea Dart from the original design as an ASW cruiser. When the Falklands conflict showed that defences against the threat of sea-skimming missiles (and even tactical aircraft such as the A-4 dropping iron bombs at close range) were inadequate, 20mm Phalanx CIWS and other close-range weapons were added to the whole class as soon as practicable.

Future carriers are likely to be 'designed to cost' and will therefore probably be built with CIWS for 'last ditch' defence rather than medium-range missiles. This is to the good since firing arcs for missiles and the need to operate aircraft are seldom compatible. Experience has shown that the carrier is best left to provide the force with aircraft whilst escorts make the best use of missiles to defend it. The Aegis cruisers and destroyers in the US Navy reflect this philosophy.

Stores Support

Unlike other warships, aircraft carriers support and operate other weapon systems more complex than they are themselves. This requires not only flying facilities and workshops but also an extensive outfit of spare parts in a stores organisation that can access them readily. The first carriers were able to store or make any item they might need, but as aircraft and their weapons grew in complexity in the 1930s more support became necessary. After the deployment of carriers to the Eastern Mediterranean during the Abyssinian Crisis, the Admiralty accepted the need for a maintenance carrier to support fleet carriers operating at a distance from a major naval base. It was to be able to carry spare aircraft, engines, instruments and a much larger outfit of stores than operational carriers could carry. The result was HMS *Unicorn*.

The BPF eventually included three aircraft maintenance ships together with engine and instrument repair ships and several air stores-issuing ships, all under the command of Commodore Air Train. The supply chain to support the carrier squadron included not only these forward units but depots and ferries carrying aircraft and their supporting stores from the United Kingdom to the Pacific via India and Ceylon. The complex stores system was fundamental to the fighting operations of the carriers and had to work if they were to succeed.

After 1945, such a comprehensive system of forward support proved too expensive to maintain and the RN gradually moved to a system where 'high-hit' stores items were held in a task force but equipment had to be returned to the UK for repair. Extra stores had to be flown out to meet the relevant carrier at suitable maintenance or replenishment periods. For many years a specialist air stores Royal Fleet Auxiliary supported Commonwealth carrier operations in the Far East, but since the 1970s air stores have been embarked with other stores and fuel loads in general-purpose RFAs. Today, carrier operations are supported by tankers and 'one-stop' auxiliaries able to deliver fuel, ammunition and a whole range of stores both by jackstay transfer and helicopter replenishment ('vertrep').

Within the carrier, air stores are run by an air stores utilisation control office in which both maintainers and stores accountants work. They translate squadron requirements into stores reference numbers and either provide them or order them from the UK using a priority code system. Urgently required items can be moved to much of the world within hours, either by military aircraft or national airlines.

Although air stores are of critical importance to the air groups, carriers are complex ships, with ships' companies measured in thousands. Their stores complexes need to take into account naval and engineering stores together with victualling stores to provide food and clothing over protracted periods at sea. All can be replenished at sea by rendezvousing with auxiliaries which have been loaded with the necessary items and equipment.

A Buccaneer S.2 of 801 NAS seconds after leaving the starboard catapult of HMS *Victorious* in 1966. The wire strop by which the steam catapult has towed the aircraft up to its 'end speed' can be seen falling away into the sea. (Author)

Flying From a Carrier

An aircraft flies relative to the air that surrounds it; thus, when taking off and landing on a runway ashore, in still air, it will become airborne at a speed governed by its weight and the distance covered over the ground will be constant. Taking off into wind will not alter the Indicated Air Speed (IAS) at which an aircraft will become airborne but will lessen the ground roll required to achieve it. For example, an aircraft that becomes airborne at 100 knots would only cover the distance over the ground needed to reach 85 knots when taking off into a 15-knot wind. Conversely, an aircraft taking off downwind would cover a greater distance over the ground (but this unlikely instance will not be developed here further).

When aircraft launch from a carrier, the speed of the ship contributes to the motion of the aircraft relative to the air about them (a fact that has made the design of modern aircraft inertial navigation platforms difficult since they are always in motion). Carriers turn into wind to launch their aircraft and, by increasing their own speed through the water, they lessen still further the deck run that aircraft need to achieve the IAS necessary to become airborne at a given weight. To enlarge upon the previous example, were the aircraft to take off from a carrier steaming into wind at 25 knots, it would still become airborne at 100 knots IAS but would be moving at 15 plus 25 knots—wind speed plus ship speed—relative to free air before even releasing its brakes and would only require the deck run relative to 60 knots to become airborne.

Landing is similarly affected by wind and ship speed. An aircraft in the landing pattern flies relative to free air but its landing roll or arrested landing is relative to the ship. Thus an aircraft with an approach speed of 90 knots IAS will hit the deck of a carrier steaming at 25 knots into a 15 knot wind at a relative speed of 50 knots and it is this energy that has to be absorbed by arrester gear. The fact that the 'target' is constantly moving away from the aircraft makes for tight landing circuits at sea and a period of mental adjustment for pilots disembarking to stationary runways ashore!

In the Royal Navy, pre-war carriers operated small air groups which carried out rolling take-offs down the flight deck. Aircraft would be parked in a 'range' aft, herring-boned so that each could taxi onto the centreline in turn, come to full power and roll down the deck. A worked-up carrier could launch with an interval of as little as 10 seconds between aircraft. This was important since, with the threat of torpedo attack by submarines in wartime operations, time spent on a steady heading into wind was (and still is) dangerous. Time spent recovering aircraft was just as potentially difficult and the RAF, who controlled naval aviation in the 1920s, did not help by insisting that aircraft land on to a clear flight deck so that they could go round again if a pilot was not happy with his arrival. The forward lift in most carriers was T-shaped so that aircraft could taxi on to it and be struck down with wings spread prior to being folded in the hangar where all aircraft were stowed when not flying. Even so, two minutes could elapse before the lift was back at flight deck level for the next aircraft and a carrier could thus spend 25 minutes into wind recovering twelve aircraft possibly steaming in the opposite direction to the rest of the fleet. The potential size of air groups was also limited by the practical number that could be recovered if the carrier was not to steam permanently into wind.

The introduction of transverse arrester wires and naval aircraft fitted with hooks in the 1930s cut down this interval slightly but the biggest advance came with the resumption of naval control of carrier aviation and the adoption of the USN safety barrier forward of the arrester wires. This simple device, and the adoption of Landing Signal Officers (LSOs; also known as batsmen), to control aircraft approaches revolutionised carrier operations by reducing the landing interval to between 30 and 40 seconds. A wire barrier was raised forward of the foremost arrester wire; this was lowered when an aircraft was successfully arrested, allowing it to taxi into a deck park forward. The barrier was then raised to protect the park by stopping any subsequent aircraft that failed to take a wire. By the end of World War 2 most carriers had two barriers and new designs for fleet carriers had four to allow for damage and to encourage the shortest possible landing interval.

Catapults (known originally as accelerators) were fitted in carriers built from the 1930s onwards intended to launch floatplanes. Until the later war years there was little need to use catapults on fleet carriers which, with high ship speed available to augment the vagaries of natural wind, continued to use free take-offs. However, the size of air groups grew and led to the use of permanent deck parks of aircraft that could not be struck down into the hangar. In 1944 the limit was reached where the range aft before a launch was so large that the ability of the foremost aircraft to get airborne was questionable. Rather than inhibit the number of aircraft that could be operated, the Royal Navy again followed a USN lead and used the catapult to launch at least the first aircraft from the range, thus allowing the maximum number of aircraft to launch from a single ship for a given operation. The cradle arrangement was abandoned during the war and the USN concept of a shuttle pulling a wire strop (which fell away after launch), looped over hooks on the aircraft was adopted.

Throughout this book, the speed quoted for a given catapult is an 'end' speed, that is, the speed which the shuttle (and the aircraft pulled by it) can achieve relative to the deck. To draw on our earlier example, an aircraft that would get airborne at 100 knots IAS, when launching from a carrier steaming at 25 knots into a 15 knot wind needs a deck run equivalent to the accelera-

A Sea Vixen FAW.1 of 892 NAS with wheels, flaps and hook down, seen from the planeguard helicopter seconds before crossing the round-down of HMS *Hermes*. (Author)

A Sea Venom FAW .21 of 894 NAS about to catch an arrester wire on HMS *Albion*. (FAA Museum)

tion from 0 to 60 knots for a free take off. If a catapult such as the BH III (14,000lb at 66 knots) were used, the aircraft would leave the deck at 106 knots having only needed the 100-foot length of the catapult to achieve it. Most catapults were flexible, and the figures in the data sections that follow are typical examples of weight and end speed. If the carrier in our example had a maximum speed of 30 knots, it will be noted that a minimum of 4 knots of natural wind would be needed to launch our aircraft at the given weight: 66 knots catapult end speed plus 30 knots ship speed equals 96 knots, 4 knots short of flying speed and thus with that amount of wind needed. An alternative, if there were no natural wind, would be to lighten the aircraft by removing fuel or weapons to the point where the achievable flying speed/ weight combination would be acceptable. Searching for a wind is common to this day where a ship seeks to launch aircraft at their maximum weight.

By the end of World War 2 the catapult had become the normal method of launching aircraft from the range and the increasing size and weight of post-war aircraft emphasized this policy. The barrier continued in use but with the advent of jet aircraft, where the pilot sat in the nosc, thcrc was considcrably more risk to him and the cost and complexity of the new aircraft also militated against its continued use. The rubber deck experiment proved totally impractical, in that it took five minutes to remove the undercarriageless Sea Vampire fighter from it and on to a trolley, it but led directly to the invention of the angled deck. This ingenious concept led to the second revolution in carrier operating technique. By offsetting the landing area 4 to 8 degrees to port, the parking area forward was safe and a pilot who missed all the wires had a free deck in front of him to select full power and carry out another circuit. An aircraft that missed the wires was known as a 'bolter'; where the pilot compounded his error by failing to apply power it was known as a 'whispering bolter' The latter often had wet consequences. It is interesting to note that all the improvements to carriers that have been made to enable them to keep pace with operations by heavier, faster and more complex aircraft have been made by naval officers, both in the US Navy and the Royal Navy. Scientists seem to have lacked the practical experience necessary to lead the way.

In the post-war era, carrier operations can be divided into two phases: first, the operation of fixed-wing aircraft from angled deck carriers, and latterly, the operation of STOVL fighters and helicopters from light carriers fitted with ski-jumps. The ski-jump is the latest modification to revolutionise the operation of aircraft from carriers and was also invented by a naval officer, Lieutenant-Commander D. R. Taylor RN. He calculated that by giving an upward velocity to a Sea Harrier as it left the flight deck from its take-off roll, the actual deck run could be shortened or extra weight could be carried.

On leaving the deck on a part-ballistic trajectory, the aircraft will sink but continue to accelerate with the result that flying speed and full wing-borne flight will be reached before it has sunk back to the level of the flight deck. The requirement for a deck run is thereby greatly reduced.

The majority of the ships in this book did not operate helicopters. They are not easy to assimilate into a mixed carrier air group and present several major problems on a flight deck that fixed-wing aircraft do not. That said, their tactical flexibility, especially in AS warfare and amphibious operations, has made it imperative that these be overcome, and helicopters have become an important part of integrated air groups since 1960.

Helicopters cannot be densely parked since they need space to engage and run their rotors. For safety, a clear area has to be left between the rotor tips of running helicopters and thus a carrier will operate fewer helicopters than fixed-wing aircraft. Furthermore, helicopters use less power to take off when they have air flowing past the rotor disc and so the ship is obliged to turn into wind to launch them at typical operating weights loaded with fuel and weapons. They cannot easily taxi and so have to be recovered facing fore and aft with the ship into wind. Carriers that operate both large helicopters such as the Sea King and fighters are best designed so that they operate from different parts of the deck well clear of each other, using a flying programme that is balanced to achieve the best compromise between the differing needs.

Advances in aircraft performance have, over the years, seemed to make carrier flying more difficult but the improvements described made just the right difference in timely fashion. However, some things do not change: the aviator who returns to his airfield ashore can land on it immediately, providing that the runway is clear, but his naval colleague does not enjoy this luxury. Moreover, as noted, carriers that remain steady into wind are vulnerable in wartime and so no carrier will take on aircraft as they return; instead, the pilots are given a time when their wheels are to hit the deck ('Charlie' time), and woe betide the hapless individual who misses it. In order to set themselves up for their 'C', pilots will recover into a 'wait' position near the carrier and hold with similar aircraft in formation. There is a helicopter 'wait' low down to starboard together with high and low jet 'waits' to port of the Designated Flying Course (DFC). All patterns are flown relative to this no matter in which direction the carrier is pointed prior to her turn into wind.

At night, pilots 'stack' on a range and bearing with a height separation of 1,000 feet between aircraft. They are then fed, at one-minute intervals, into a Carrier Controlled Approach (CCA) pattern from which they land. If the first crime is to miss the allotted 'C' time, the second is to 'bolt' off a night approach and have to be fed around the pattern for a second time while the ship stays into wind.

Throughout the history of carrier flying, one fear has been constant for those airborne with nowhere else to go but the deck, namely a crash that prevents other aircraft from landing. It is less of a factor now in the days of vertical landing than it was in the days of wires and barriers, but it is still important nonetheless. Only those who have circled the carrier flying for endurance in the 'wait', anxiously looking at the state of the deck on every pass, can know how it feels.

There is most definitely a difference between flying from a carrier and flying from ashore. It is best summed up by the second verse of 'The A25 Song':

They say in the Air Force a landing's okay,
If the pilot gets out and can still walk away,
But in the Fleet Air Arm your prospects are dim,
If the landing's pisspoor and the pilot can't swim.

Written by Wright and Stevenson in HMS *Formidable* in 1942–43, this is Naval Aviation's theme song and chorus, with many verses, sung in wardrooms in every carrier and air station. The Form A25 referred to is the Accident Form, filled in after every accident or incident.

Part 1: Aircraft Carriers

Activity (D94) *Escort Carrier*

Laid down: 1 February 1940
Launched: 30 May 1942
Completed: 14 October 1942

Builder: Caledon Shipbuilding & Engineering Co., Dundee
Machinery: 2-shaft Burmeister & Wain diesels, 12,000bhp = 18 knots
Displacement: 11,800 tons standard; 14,250 tons deep load
Dimensions: 512ft overall x 66ft 6in max beam x 25ft 1in max draught
Gun armament: 1 twin 4in Mk XVI HA (2); 6 twin 20mm Oerlikon (12); 8 single 20mm Oerlikon (8)
Fuel: 2,000 tons diesel
Endurance: 4,500 miles @ 18 knots
Complement: 700

Protection: Splinter protection around bomb room
Flight deck: 498ft x 66ft steel
Arrester wires: 2 x 15,500lb @ 60 knots; 2 x 15,500lb @ 55 knots; 1 x 15,500lb @ 55 knots 'safety wire'; 1 barrier
Hangar: 87ft x 59ft x 21ft
Catapults: None fitted
Lifts: *Aft* 42ft long x 20ft wide
Aircraft: Up to 15 (usually fewer owing to small hangar)
Aircraft fuel: 20,000 gallons AVGAS
Air weapons: 18in torpedoes; 500lb SAP bombs; 250lb SAP bombs; 3in RP; Mk 11 depth charges; .303in gun ammunition; flares and pyrotechnics

Notes: The small hangar and minimal aviation fuel stowage limited her usefulness as an operational car-

HMS *Activity* in 1944 with Swordfish and Wildcat aircraft on deck. (FAA Museum)

rier. She was laid down as a fast refrigerated merchant ship to have been named *Telemachus* for the Ocean Steam Ship Line. After her acquisition by the Admiralty she was converted by her builder into an austere carrier, incorporating improvements suggested by the operation of *Audacity*. Five similar conversions were planned but did not materialise, perhaps because of the poor aircraft support features compared with later escort carrier construction. She was preferred for use on the Russian convoy run in 1944 because, unlike US-built escort carriers, her hull was riveted, not welded, and thus less prone to cracking in sub-zero temperatures.

Summary of service

29.09.42 Commissioned in Dundee
09.10.42 Taken to Rosyth for fitting of Admiralty Supplied Items
18.10.42 Sailed for Clyde
03.11.42 Work-up at Lamlash
20.12.42 To Clyde for post work-up defect repair
01.01.43 Assigned to WAC as DLT Carrier based on Clyde
04.10.43 Refitted in Liverpool for operational service
12.01.44 Returned to WAC; work-up in Clyde area with 819 NAS (Swordfish, Wildcat) embarked
29.01.44 Covered OS.66/KMS.40
02.02.44 Covered ON.222/NS.28
07.02.44 Covered SL.147/MKS.38
11.02.44 Covered HX.277
24.02.44 Covered KMS.43/OS.69
06.03.44 Arrived in Gibraltar
09.03.44 Sailed with MKF.29 for Clyde
27.03.44 Joined JW.58 in Scapa Flow with 833 NAS (Swordfish, Wildcat) embarked
28.03.44 Sailed for North Russia
03.04.44 Aircraft from 833 NAS sank *U288*
07.04.44 Escorted RA.58 back to Scapa Flow
19.04.44 Sailed with RA.59 for North Russia
06.05.44 Defect rectification in Clyde
23.05.44 Covered OS.78/KMS.52
28.05.44 Covered SL.158/MKS 49
02.06.44 Covered OS.78/KMS.52
03.06.44 Covered SL.159/MKS.50
10.06.44 Arrived in Clyde
20.06.44 Covered SL.162/MK.53
11.07.44 Arrived in Clyde
19.07.44 Escorted KMF.33 to Gibraltar
04.08.44 Escorted MKF.33 to Clyde
11.08.44 Covered OS.86/KMS.60
21.08.44 Covered SL.167/MKS.58
27.08.44 Redesignated as ferry carrier; sailed from Clyde for Far East with cargo of replacement aircraft
23.10.44 Arrived in Trincomalee to unload aircraft and cargo; on completion, returned to UK, joining MKF.36 at Gibraltar
05.12.44 Defect rectification in Clyde
21.12.44 Docking in Portsmouth Dockyard
17.01.45 To Belfast with replacement aircraft
28.01.45 Allocated to EIF as ferry carrier; sailed from Clyde with convoy KM.39 loaded with aircraft
20.02.45 Arrived in Colombo
21.02.45 Loaned to BPF for ferry duties; sailed for Australia
24.03.45 Sailed from Sydney for Colombo; returned to EIF, which used her to ferry aircraft between Cochin and Colombo
01.09.45 Sailed from Colombo
06.09.45 Arrived in Singapore
15.09.45 Sailed for Trincomalee
22.09.45 Sailed for UK
20.10.45 Arrived in Clyde; de-stored into reserve
30.01.46 Category B reserve in the Clyde
25.04.46 Sold for mercantile conversion; renamed *Breconshire*
24.04.67 Broken up in Mihara, Japan

Albion (R07) Centaur *Class Light Fleet Carrier*

Laid down: 23 March 1944
Launched: 6 May 1947
Completed: 26 May 1954

Builder: Swan Hunter & Wigham Richardson, Wallsend-on-Tyne; machinery by Wallsend Slipway & Engineering Co.

Machinery: 2-shaft Parsons geared turbines; 4 Admiralty 3-drum boilers; 78,000shp = 28 knots
Displacement: 22,000 tons standard; 27,800 tons deep load
Dimensions: 737ft 9in overall x 123ft max beam x 27ft 10in max draught
Gun armament: 2 sextuple 40mm Bofors (12); 8 twin

HMS *Albion* sailing from Portsmouth for the Middle East with 42 RM Commando and its equipment embarked in 1958. Over 1,000 extra eyebolts had to be welded on to the flight deck so that the transport could be securely lashed down. (Author)

40mm Bofors (16); 4 single 40mm Bofors (4); 4 single 3pdr saluting (4)
Fuel: 4,083 tons FFO
Endurance: 6,000 miles @ 20 knots
Complement: 1,596
Protection: 1in–2in flight deck; 1in uptakes; 1in magazine crowns
Flight deck: 732ft x 84ft steel; 5.75-degree angled deck
Arrester wires: 6 x 30,000lb @ 75 knots; emergency nylon barriers
Hangar: 274ft (plus 55ft extension fwd of fwd lift) x 62ft x 17ft 6in
Catapults: 2 x BH5 hydraulic; 30,000lb @ 75 knots
Lifts: *Fwd* 54ft long x 44ft wide; *aft* 54ft long x 44ft wide; both 35,000lb
Aircraft: 42
Aircraft fuel: 309,750 gallons AVCAT
Air weapons: Mk 30 homing torpedoes; 2,000lb MC bombs; 1,000lb MC bombs; 500lb GP bombs; 3in RP with 28lb or 60lb warheads; Mk 11 depth charges; 20mm cannon ammunition; flares and pyrotechnics

Notes: HMS *Albion* was the first British carrier to be completed with the angled deck and mirror landing aid installed during construction. Details are for 1959 as a fixed-wing carrier. She was converted to a commando carrier during 1961–62 with details similar to those shown for *Bulwark*.

Summary of service

00.05.47	Hull laid up immediately after launch
18.10.49	Collided with collier *Maystone* whilst under tow off Farne Islands (*Maystone* sank with loss of all but 4 hands)
00.05.54	On completion, worked up with air group

comprising 813 (Wyvern), 815 (Avenger), 898 (Sea Hawk), 890 (Sea Venom) and 849C (Skyraider) NAS (Wyverns proved difficult to operate and Sea Venoms encountered teething troubles)

00.09.54	Joined MF
27.10.54	Hoisted Flag of FOAC
00.01.55	Carried out exercises with US Sixth Fleet in Mediterranean
23.03.55	Joined HF
10.01.56	Sailed for FEF flying Flag of FOAC in company with *Centaur*; carried out training exercises with Commonwealth navies
15.05.56	Returned to Portsmouth for refit
15.09.56	Sailed hurriedly for MF with 800 (Sea Hawk), 809 (Sea Venom), 802 (Sea Hawk) and 849C (Skyraider) NAS embarked for operations connected with Suez Crisis.
01.11.56	Operation 'Musketeer': aircraft struck at Al Naza airfield 6 miles from Cairo and 130 miles from fleet; strikes continued that day and next in regular cycle
05.11.56	Aircraft gave cover to parachute drops; when Gamil airfield near Port Said was taken, helicopters and Skyraiders landed with water, medical supplies and beer and helped evacuate seriously wounded; helicopters also delivered operation orders around Fleet on dark, moonless night (first time this had been done)
29.11.56	Returned to Malta
05.03.57	Visited by HRH the Duke of Gloucester on return to UK
00.01.57	824 (Gannet AS) NAS joined air group and ship allocated to HF
00.01.58	Refit until May 1958
20.07.58	Diverted to Portsmouth from Rosyth to load 42 RM Cdo and military equipment
22.07.58	Sailed for Mediterranean as part of force intended for defence of Jordan following revolt in Iraq
00.10.58	Sailed for Far East, where ship hoisted flag of FO2 FEF during visits to Australia and New Zealand
00.06.59	Visited Madagascar flying flag of CinC South Atlantic and South America; air group comprised 849C (Skyraider) 820 (Whirlwind), 804 (Sea Hawk) and 809 (Sea Venom) NAS
18.08.59	Returned to Portsmouth for refit
14.12.59	Recommissioned in Portsmouth and worked up with new air group comprising 806 (Sea Hawk), 894 (Sea Venom), 815 (Whirlwind) and 849D (Skyraider) NAS
26.03.60	Visited Athens and hoisted flag of HM King Paul of Greece, honorary Admiral in RN; afterwards sailed for Far East
00.10.60	CENTO exercise 'Midlink 3' with Middle East forces
17.12.60	Returned to Portsmouth to pay off
00.01.61	Taken in hand for conversion to commando carrier in Portsmouth Dockyard
00.08.62	Recommissioned by HRH the Duke of Edinburgh in Portsmouth; worked up in home and Mediterranean waters with 845 (Wessex) and 846 (Whirlwind) NAS and 40 RM Cdo before joining FEF
00.11.63	Brunei revolt occurred while ship was visiting Mombasa; diverted to area via Singapore and used to ferry Royal Marines, British and Commonwealth Army units as well as stores, vehicles and helicopters to advance bases in Borneo such as Labuon, Kuching and Taiwan; squadrons operated from ashore for much of this period; trooping duties took ship as far west as Tobruk to collect Army and RAF units for Far East
00.04.64	Returned to Portsmouth for refit and subsequent work-up
00.03.65	Sailed for FEF, embarking 848 (Wessex) NAS; on arrival in FEF, resumed ferrying operations to and from Singapore, Hong Kong and Borneo (helicopters operating largely ashore)
00.08.66	Left Singapore for UK
08.09.66	Refit in Portsmouth.
14.09.67	Sailed for FEF with 848 (Wessex) NAS embarked after exercises with WF
08.10.67	With *Eagle* and *Hermes*, formed part of RN task force covering withdrawal from Aden; helicopters lifted off 45 RM Cdo, last British unit to leave
08.12.67	Left Aden area, proceeding to Singapore
00.00.68	Visits to Australia, Japan, Korea and Cambodia
14.07.69	Left FEF for refit in Portsmouth
20.03.70	Refit completed and spent 6 months working up in home waters with 848 (Wessex) NAS embarked
00.09.70	Deployed to Mediterranean for exercises based on Cyprus
25.03.71	Sailed from Portsmouth for FEF
00.10.71	Part of fleet that withdrew from Singapore for last time when FEF disbanded; returned to UK via Persian Gulf and Cape Town

HMS *Albion* entering Sydney Harbour in 1960. (Author)

24.01.72 Portsmouth for refit
00.05.72 Exercises in Mediterranean, then visits to Brest and Rotterdam, after which 845 (Wessex) replaced 848 NAS
10.10.72 Sailed from Portsmouth with 845 NAS (Wessex) and 42 RM Cdo for amphibious exercises in Canada and visits to Halifax, Quebec and Montreal
24.11.72 Arrived in Portsmouth for last time to de-store and prepare for disposal
02.03.73 Decommissioned.
22.10.73 Sold to Wilson Walker Engineering (who intended to convert ship to heavy lift vessel for North Sea oilfield exploration); towed from Portsmouth to Tail o' the Bank for handover
00.11.73 Conversion scheme fell through
16.11.73 Towed to Faslane and broken up for scrap

Ameer (D01) Ruler *Class Assault Escort Carrier*

Laid down: 18 July 1942
Launched: 18 October 1942
Completed: 20 July 1943

Builder: Seattle-Tacoma Shipbuilding Corp., Seattle
Machinery: 1-shaft General Electric geared turbine; 2 Foster Wheeler boilers; 8,500shp = 18.5 knots
Displacement: 11,200 tons standard; 15,400 tons deep load
Dimensions: 492ft overall x 108ft 6in max beam x 25ft 5in max draught
Gun armament: 2 single 5in US Mk 12 (2); 8 twin 40mm Bofors (16); 4 twin 20mm Oerlikon (8); 25 single 20mm Oerlikon (25)
Fuel: 3,290 tons FFO
Endurance: 27,500 miles @ 11 knots
Complement: 646
Protection: Splinter protection for bomb room
Flight deck: 450ft x 80ft wood-covered steel
Arrester wires: 9 x 19,800lb @ 55 knots; 3 barriers
Hangar: 260ft x 62ft x 18ft
Catapults: 1 x H4C; 16,000lb @ 74 knots (tail-down method only)
Lifts: *Fwd* 42ft long x 34ft wide; *aft* 34ft long x 42ft wide; both 14,000lb
Aircraft: Up to 30 could be operated; up to 90 could be ferried
Aircraft fuel: 36,000 gallons AVGAS
Air weapons: 22.4in torpedoes; 18in torpedoes; 500lb SAP bombs; 250lb SAP bombs; 250lb GP bombs; Mk 11 depth charges; .5in gun ammunition; flares and pyrotechnics

Notes: Built from the start as an aircraft carrier but based on the US C3 merchant hull design. The hangar deck retained the curvature of the mercantile upper deck and this could make aircraft movement difficult. Launched as USS *Baffins* (CVE-35). Transferred to the RN under Lend/Lease arrangements. Originally to have been named *Upraider*.

Summary of service

28.06.43 Commissioned as USS *Baffins*
19.07.43 Decommissioned and transferred to RN at Vancouver
20.07.43 Commissioned in Vancouver; some months of defect rectification followed
02.01.44 Sailed from New York to Clyde for conversion to assault carrier.
06.05.44 Sailed to join I ACS EF
27.06.44 Arrived in Trincomalee; used initially to ferry aircraft
00.08.44 Employed on trade protection duties in Indian Ocean with 845 NAS (Avenger/ Wildcat) embarked
00.12.44 845 NAS disembarked
18.01.45 804 NAS (Hellcat) embarked to provide cover for shore bombardments by battleship *Queen Elizabeth* and cruiser *Phoebe* in support of landings on Ramree Island (Operation 'Matador')
26.01.45 804 NAS provided cover for Royal Marines landing on Cheduba Island (Operation 'Sankey')
26.02.45 804 NAS provided CAP and escort for PR Hellcats of 888 NAS from *Empress* which carried out photographic reconnaissance of Kra Isthmus, Penang and Northern Sumatra (Operation 'Stacey')
01.03.45 804 NAS shot down three Japanese aircraft
18.06.45 888 NAS (PR Hellcat) added to air group; photographic reconnaissance carried out of southern Malaya together with strikes

HMS *Ameer* in 1945. (Fred Smallwood)

against Sumatran airfields (Operation 'Balsam')

05.07.45 896 NAS (Hellcat) embarked for strikes on Nicobar Islands and to provide cover for minesweeping forces (Operation 'Collie')

24.07.45 804 NAS re-embarked with one SAR Walrus of 1700 NAS for strikes on northern Malaya and cover for minesweeping forces off Phuket Island (Operation 'Livery); in three days Hellcats from *Ameer* and *Emperor* flew over 150 sorties and destroyed more than 30 enemy aircraft on the ground together with trains and road transport

26.07.45 Attacked by only Kamikaze raid to be encountered in Bay of Bengal; one 'Sonia' hit and deflected by AA fire and crashed only 500 yards from *Ameer*

08.09.45 808 NAS (Hellcat) together with Walrus of 1700 NAS embarked for operations to re-occupy Malaya and Singapore (Operation 'Zipper')

30.10.45 Sailed for UK

18.11.45 Arrived in Clyde; de-stored ready for return to USN

22.12.45 Sailed for Norfolk, Va

17.01.46 Returned to USN at Norfolk, Va

17.09.46 Sold by USN for mercantile conversion

00.00.48 Renamed *Robin Kirk*

00.00.69 Broken up in Taiwan

Arbiter (D31) Ruler *Class Ferry Carrier*

Laid down: 26 April 1943
Launched: 9 September 1943
Completed: 31 December 1943

Builder: Seattle-Tacoma Shipbuilding Corp., Seattle; completed by Commercial Ironworks; machinery by Allis-Chalmers
Machinery: 1-shaft geared turbine; 2 Foster Wheeler boilers; 8,500shp = 18.5 knots
Displacement: 11,200 tons standard; 15,390 tons deep load
Dimensions: 492ft overall x 108ft 6in max beam x 25ft 5in max draught
Gun armament: 2 single 5in US Mk 12 (2); 8 twin 40mm Bofors (16); 14 twin 20mm Oerlikon (28); 7 single 20mm Oerlikon (7)
Fuel: 3,160 tons FFO
Endurance: 27,500 miles @ 11 knots
Complement: 646
Protection: Splinter protection for bomb room
Flight deck: 450ft x 80ft wood-covered steel
Arrester wires: 9 x 19,800lb @ 55 knots; 3 barriers
Hangar: 260ft x 62ft x 18ft
Catapults: 1 x H4C; 16,000lb @ 74 knots (tail-down method only)
Lifts: *Fwd* 42ft long x 34ft wide; *aft* 34ft long x 42ft wide; both 14,000lb
Aircraft: Up to 90 could be ferried; up to 30 could be operated
Aircraft fuel: 36,000 gallons AVGAS
Air weapons: None carried

Notes: Built from the outset as a warship but based on the US C3 merchant hull design. Launched as USS *St Simon* (CVE-51). Transferred to the RN under Lend/Lease arrangements. In July 1945 a plan was put forward to convert her to a fleet oiler due to the shortage of tankers available to the BPF but this was never implemented.

Summary of service

31.12.43 Commissioned in Portland, Oregon

09.01.44 Arrived in Vancouver for alterations and additions

25.04.44 Passed through Panama Canal

02.06.44 Allocated to WAC as ferry carrier; used to carry aircraft from USA to UK including 853 (Avenger), 1820 (Helldiver) and 1843 (Corsair) NAS

12.09.44 Belfast for refit

30.01.45 Allocated to BPF as ferry carrier

01.03.45 Sailed from Clyde with 1843 NAS (Corsair) embarked for passage

00.05.45 Aircraft delivery ferry trip from Australia to Manus Island to support forward operations (standard load for ferry carriers: 9 Seafires, 7 Avengers, 6 Corsairs, 1 Hellcat, 1 Firefly)

00.07.45 Ferry trip from Manus to Leyte Gulf to support 1 ACS.

00.08.45 Replenishment operations off Honshu; after Japanese surrender, returned to Australia and used briefly as DLT carrier by 899 NAS

HMS *Arbiter* whilst serving as a ferry carrier with the BPF in 1945. (Author)

	(Seafire) training ex-RAAF pilots who had volunteered to serve in FAA
11.10.45	Arrived in Hong Kong; used to repatriate POWs to Australia
03.12.45	Returned to Hong Kong to repatriate 300 POWs to UK
10.01.46	Arrived in Clyde; allocated to Rosyth Command
06.02.46	Sailed for Portsmouth
12.02.46	Sailed from Portsmouth for Norfolk, Va, via Halifax
03.03.46	Returned to USN at Norfolk
00.00.46	Sold by USN as mercantile *Coracero*
00.00.65	Renamed *President Macapagal*
00.00.72	Renamed *Lucky Two*
00.05.72	Broken up in Taiwan.

Archer (D78) Archer *Class Escort Carrier*

Laid down: 7 June 1939
Launched: 14 December 1939
Completed: 24 April 1940 (as carrier: 17 November 1941)

Builder: Sun Shipbuilding & Drydock Corp., Chester; converted to carrier by Newport News Shipbuilding & Dry Dock Co., Newport News
Machinery: 1-shaft through clutches; 4 Busche Sulzer diesel engines; 8,500shp = 17 knots
Displacement: 10,220 tons standard; 12,860 tons deep load
Dimensions: 492ft overall x 111ft 3in max beam x 26ft 3in max draught
Gun armament: 3 single 4in US Mk 9 (3); 6 twin 20mm Oerlikon (12); 7 single 20mm Oerlikon (7)
Fuel: 1,430 tons FFO
Endurance: 7,000 miles @ 10 knots
Complement: 555

Protection: Splinter protection around bomb room
Flight deck: 438ft x 70ft wood-covered steel
Arrester wires: 9 x 10,000lb @ 60 knots; 3 barriers
Hangar: 260ft x 62ft x 18ft 9in
Catapults: 1 x H2; 7,000lb @ 60 knots (tail-down method only)
Lifts: *Aft* 38ft long x 34ft wide; 12,000lb
Aircraft: 12 (May 1943); up to 15 could be operated
Aircraft fuel: 36,000 gallons AVGAS
Air weapons: 18in torpedoes; 500lb SAP bombs; 250lb SAP bombs; 250lb GP bombs; 3in RP; Mk 7 depth charges; .5in gun ammunition; .303in gun ammunition; flares and pyrotechnics

Notes: Built as US mercantile *Mormacland*. Purchased by Admiralty prior to Lend/Lease arrangements. The original bridge was retained under the flight deck with wings either side to give visibility. The small hangar deck retained the curvature of the original upper deck.

Summary of service

17.11.41 Commissioned in Newport News
23.12.41 Sailed for trials
24.12.41 Philadelphia Navy Yard for repairs
10.01.42 Norfolk, Va, to embark ferry aircraft for transit to UK
12.01.42 Collided with USS *Brazos*; towed to Charleston, SC, for repairs
19.03.42 Allocated to WAC; sailed with 834 NAS (Swordfish) plus 12 reserve Martlet fighters embarked for transit; joined cruiser *Devonshire* and 2 destroyers to act as support group to work in vicinity of Sierra Leone convoys
04.04.42 Entered Freetown following machinery breakdown
13.05.42 Sailed for operations which included carrying bullion from Cape Town to Freetown
26.06.42 Sailed from Freetown to New York via Bermuda
15.07.42 Repairs to machinery in New York and modifications to allow ship to ferry aircraft
02.11.42 Completed refit; sailed with UGS.2 ferrying US aircraft and personnel to Morocco
18.11.42 Arrived in Gibraltar from Casablanca
27.11.42 Sailed for UK with MKF.3
04.12.42 Refit in Liverpool, during which flight deck was lengthened; on completion, allocated to WAC
17.02.43 Commenced work-up in Clyde and Scapa Flow areas
20.03.43 Inspected by HM King George VI
21.03.43 Defect rectification in Clyde and Belfast
02.05.43 Sailed from Clyde; joined 4th Escort Group off Hvalfjord; employed on convoy support duty in North Atlantic; air group comprised 819 (Swordfish) and 892 (Martlet) NAS; covered ON.182 and HX.239
23.05.43 Swordfish 'B' sank *U752* with rocket projectiles—second successful escort carrier aircraft attack (by 24 hours) and first to use RP
27.06.43 Exercises in Irish Sea.
19.07.43 Allocated to CinC Plymouth for anti U-boat patrol in Bay of Biscay
26.07.43 Patrol unsuccessful and ship withdrawn
28.07.43 Devonport for machinery defect rectification
03.08.43 Arrived in Clyde for major engine repairs
06.11.43 Defects proved to be so major that ship paid off into care and maintenance; used as stores hulk in Gareloch
16.03.44 Transferred to Loch Alsh and used as accommodation ship.
03.08.44 Arrived in Belfast for work to replace main gearing and fit ship out as aircraft ferry
15.03.45 Transferred to Ministry of War Transport for use as aircraft ferry; renamed *Empire Lagan*
08.01.46 Returned to USN at Norfolk, Va
00.00.46 Sold as mercantile *Anna Saelen*, registered in Sweden
00.00.55 Sold and renamed *Tasmania*, registered in Greece
00.00.61 Sold and renamed *Union Reliance*, registered in Taiwan
00.03.62 Broken up in New Orleans

HMS *Archer* shortly after her conversion, with Swordfish and Martlet aircraft on deck. Note the open structure supporting the flight deck forward of the small boxed-in hangar aft and the lack of an island structure. (FAA Museum)

Argus (1918) (I49) *Fleet Carrier*

Laid down: June 1914
Launched: 2 December 1917
Completed: 16 September 1918

Builder: William Beardmore & Co., Dalmuir
Machinery: 4-shaft Parsons geared turbines; 12 cylindrical boilers with Howdens forced draught; 20,000shp = 20.2 knots
Displacement: 14,000 tons standard; 16,500 tons deep load
Dimensions: 560ft overall x 79ft 6in max beam x 22ft 6in max draught
Gun armament: 6 single 4in (6); 4 single 3pdr (4); 4 single MG as built (4); 13 single 20mm Oerlikon added in 1943 (13)
Fuel: 2,000 tons FFO
Endurance: 5,200 miles @ 12 knots
Complement: 760
Protection: 2in magazine crowns; 2in sides on after magazine; external bulges fitted in 1920s
Flight deck: 470ft x 85ft steel (extended to 548ft x 85ft in 1943)
Arrester wires: Experimental fore and aft as built; 4 x 11,000lb @ 53 knots fitted during 1936–38 refit
Hangar: 350ft x 68ft (48ft min clear width) x 20ft
Catapults: None as built; 1 hydraulic, 12,000lb @ 66 knots, fitted during 1936–38 refit
Lifts: *Fwd* 30ft long x 36ft wide; *aft* 60ft long x 18ft wide (removed 1936–38); both 13,440lb
Aircraft: Designed for 20; 15 operated in November 1941
Aircraft fuel: 14,000 gallons AVGAS
Air weapons: 18in torpedoes; 500lb SAP bombs; 250lb SAP bombs; 250lb GP bombs; Mk 7 depth charges; .303in gun ammunition; flares and pyrotechnics

Notes: The first flush-deck aircraft carrier capable of operating wheeled aircraft to complete in any navy, *Argus* had in her design most of the essentials to be found in modern carriers. When the forward lift was at hangar deck level, two roller platforms could cover the hole in the flight deck to allow flying to continue. An overhead crane in the hangar could lift aircraft and carry them over others to extricate them; the problem of getting serviceable aircraft out of the middle of the hangar has never been solved more elegantly. Funnel smoke was trunked into tunnels built into the space between the roof of the hangar and the base of the flight deck. It was then cooled by fans and vented aft. Never really successful, this complicated system was not repeated.

Summary of service

14.09.18	Commissioned in Dalmuir
24.09.18	Flying trials in Firth of Forth
00.10.18	Trials with a wood and canvas 'island' to provide data for *Eagle*'s final design carried out with considerable success
10.10.18	Embarked No185 Squadron RAF with Cuckoo T.1 torpedo bombers which, after work-up, were intended to attack German High Seas Fleet at Wilhelmshaven (armistice came before plan could materialise)
23.12.18	Fitted with prototype fore and aft system of arrester wires
21.03.19	Carried out series of flying trials aimed at perfecting operation of aircraft
00.04.19	Allocated to AF on dispersal of GF; intended for use in harbour
23.06.19	Ferried Fairey IIIC floatplanes to *Pegasus* in Archangel
31.01.20	AF spring cruise to Gibraltar and Western Mediterranean with 8 1½-Strutters, 4 Camels, 2 D.H.9As and 2 Fairey floatplanes embarked; most flying was slow and experimental (it could take 40 minutes to launch two aircraft at worst because their rotary engines could not be kept idling and ship had to be faced into wind before start-up)
26.07.20	Devonport Dockyard to fit improved arrester gear
21.01.21	Re-joined AF for trials in UK and Mediterranean waters; aircrew training carried out at Spithead with *ab initio* pilots flying out to ship from Gosport
26.11.21	Refit and boiler clean in Portsmouth
00.09.22	Stationed near Dardanelles during Chanak crisis
11.10.22	Landed 12 Bristol F.2B fighters to operate with Anglo-French forces ashore
04.01.23	Refit in Portsmouth
23.06.23	Re-joined AF at Portland, again operating around UK and in Western Mediterranean
01.11.25	Paid off for major refit at Chatham
19.01.27	Recommissioned

HMS *Argus* whilst serving with the Atlantic Fleet in 1920. Note the charthouse, just visible above the flight deck, the raised W/T masts and the amount of structure cut away to give clear arcs of fire for the 4in gun on the port side forward. (Author)

01.02.27	Sailed to join China Station, embarking 441 Flight (Fairey IIID) at Malta
27.07.27	Arrived in Hong Kong
26.03.28	Sailed for UK
01.08.28	Reverted to AF
06.12.29	Repairs in Portsmouth
24.04.30	Sailed for Devonport with small steaming party and reduced to reserve
00.00.32	Refitted in Chatham; on completion, towed to Rosyth
20.12.32	At Rosyth in reserve at extended notice
23.05.36	Approval given for ship to be modernised to act as a training carrier and Queen Bee pilotless target aircraft tender
30.07.38	Recommissioned in Devonport; carried out piloting trials on new catapult and arrester gear; on completion, allocated to HF
00.11.39	Sailed for Mediterranean to act as DLT carrier based at Toulon with 767 NAS (Swordfish) embarked
00.01.40	DLT off Hyères with 770 NAS (Swordfish) embarked
00.06.40	Returned to Clyde after collapse of France and entry of Italy into war; 767 NAS disembarked to Malta for front-line operations
27.06.40	Ferried 701 NAS (Walrus) to Iceland
02.08.40	Operation 'Hurry': ferried 12 RAF Hurricanes from UK to point 300 miles west of Malta, where they flew off in two groups of 6, guided to island by RN Skua (RAF groundcrew ferried in submarines *Proteus* and *Pandora*)
05.09.40	Operation 'White', a further Hurricane

reinforcement for Malta (launch range was greater than that in 'Hurry' and changes to Hurricanes that reduced range had not been explained to aircrew so 9 out of the 14 aircraft failed to reach destination)

17.11.40 Disembarked 30 Hurricanes at Takoradi, from where they flew across Africa to reinforce Egypt

00.12.40 Sailed from Clyde with *Furious* in WS.5A, both loaded with more RAF Hurricanes for Takoradi (*Argus* carried in addition 3 Swordfish of 821 NAS for AS defence); convoy attacked by cruiser *Hipper*, but she achieved little before breaking off, having engaged in gun duel with cruiser *Berwick*

00.01.41 Returned to Clyde

00.03.41 Ferried RAF fighters from UK to Gibraltar, from where *Ark Royal* took them into Mediterranean to within flying range of Malta; 812 NAS (Swordfish) embarked for AS defence

00.05.41 Assisted in escort of WS.8B to Middle East; afterwards acted as DLT carrier in Clyde area

30.08.41 Sailed from Scapa Flow with 24 partially dismantled Hurricanes for delivery to Russia (Operation 'Strength'); 2 Martlets of 802 NAS embarked for self-defence but transferred to *Victorious* on 06.09.41; Hurricanes assembled whilst on passage; Force M, including *Victorious*, provided heavy cover for both *Argus* and Operation 'Dervish' (first convoy to North Russia)

07.09.41 Hurricanes flown off to Vaenga, where all arrived safely

16.09.41 Returned to Scapa Flow

00.10.41 Further ferry trips to Gibraltar with 807 NAS (Fulmar/Sea Hurricane) embarked to provide air defence (to 00.11.41)

14.11.41 Joined Force H after loss of *Ark Royal*; detachments of 807 and 812 NAS embarked as required for sorties into Western Mediterranean

00.06.42 Operation 'Harpoon' (resupply convoy for Malta), supported by Force H which comprised *Eagle* as well as *Argus*; latter had 807 (Fulmar) and 824 (Swordfish) NAS embarked

00.09.42 Refit on Tyne; used as DLT carrier in Clyde on completion

03.11.42 Operation 'Torch' (Allied invasion of North Africa); ship operated as part of Eastern Naval Task Force off Algiers with 880 NAS (Seafire) embarked

10.11.42 Damaged by 500lb bomb aft and near-missed by 2,000lb and 500lb bombs; ability to operate aircraft not affected

00.11.42 Repairs in Clyde

11.12.42 SO Escort's ship, KMF.5 to North Africa

22.01.43 KMF.8 to North Africa

04.02.43 MKF.8 from North Africa to Clyde

09.02.43 Repairs in Clyde

00.04.43 Resumed duties as DLT carrier, based in Clyde

00.08.44 Paid off into reserve and used as accommodation ship at Chatham

00.03.47 Arrived at Inverkeithing to be broken up by T. W. Ward

HMS *Argus* in 1938 after her conversion to a training carrier. Note the more substantial support for the flight deck forward, needed to sustain the weight of the catapult. The prominent palisades amidships were intended to stop aircraft going over the side after a bad recovery. The raised charthouse is more easily seen in this view. (Author)

HMS *Ark Royal* anchored off Spithead on 16 June 1939. The two port side pompom mountings have not yet been fitted. (Author)

Ark Royal (1938) (91) *Fleet Carrier*

Laid down: 16 September 1935
Launched: 13 April 1937
Completed: 16 November 1938

Builder: Cammell Laird & Co., Birkenhead
Machinery: 3-shaft Parsons geared turbines; 6 Admiralty 3-drum boilers; 102,000shp = 31 knots
Displacement: 22,000 tons standard; 7,720 tons deep load
Dimensions: 800ft overall x 112ft max beam x 27ft 9in max draught
Gun armament: 8 twin 4.5in QF Mk 1 HA (16); 4 octuple 2pdr pompom (32) ; 4 single 3pdr saluting (4); 8 single .5in MG (8)
Fuel: 4,620 tons FFO
Endurance: 11,200 miles @ 10 knots
Complement: 1,580
Protection: 4.5in side belt; 2.5in–3in bulkheads
Flight deck: 720ft x 95ft steel
Arrester wires: 8 wires: *1 to 6* 11,000lb @ 55 knots, *7* 11,000lb @ 50 knots, *8* 11,000lb @ 45 knots; max pull-out *1 to 3* 155ft, *4 to 6* 137ft, *7* 114ft; *8* 90ft; 1 barrier capable of stopping 11,000lb @ 45 knots in 40ft
Hangars: *Upper* 568ft x 60ft x 16ft, *lower* 452ft x 60ft x 16ft
Catapults: 2 x BH3 hydraulic; 12,000lb @ 56 knots
Lifts: *Fwd* 45ft long x 25ft wide; *centre* 45ft long x 22ft wide; *aft* 45ft long x 22ft wide; all 14,000lb

Aircraft: 60 as designed (54 operated in 1941)
Aircraft fuel: 100,000 gallons AVGAS
Air weapons: 18in torpedoes; 500lb SAP bombs; 250lb SAP bombs; 100lb GP bombs; Mk 7 depth charges; .303in gun ammunition; flares and pyrotechnics

Notes: Each lift had two platforms so that it took two moves to get an aircraft from the flight deck to the lower hangar since each platform only went down one deck. The narrowness of the lifts also limited the type of aircraft that could be embarked but made for a stronger flight deck.

Summary of service

16.11.38	Commissioned, replacing *Courageous* as Flagship Rear-Admiral Aircraft Carriers HF
03.09.39	At sea with HF with 800 and 803 (Skua) and 810 and 820 (Swordfish) NAS embarked (820 included 1 Walrus).
14.09.39	Attacked by *U39*, which launched 2 torpedoes which missed (*U39* was sunk by escorting destroyers, the first U boat to be lost in WW2)
26.09.39	Attacked by German aircraft (pilot of one of which, Lt Adolf Francke, was awarded Iron Cross and promoted for his claim to have

sunk the ship; for some time German radio continued to ask 'Where is the *Ark Royal*?', earning her international fame)

00.10.39 Operated in South Atlantic searching for enemy commerce raiders

00.03.40 Deployed to MF

00.04.40 Recalled to HF after German invasion of Norway

23.04.40 Sailed from Scapa Flow with 800 and 801 (Skua/Roc) and 810 and 820 (Swordfish) NAS embarked to give fighter protection for British forces in Norway; continued to operate off Norway until after final withdrawal in June 1940

18.06.40 Sailed from Scapa Flow to join Force H in Gibraltar

03.07.40 Part of the force that attacked French Fleet in Oran

02.08.40 Struck at Cagliari airfield to provide cover whilst *Argus* ferried RAF Hurricanes to Malta

01.09.40 Struck at Elmas airfield as a diversion to allow *Illustrious* through the narrows en route for MF

23.09.40 Operation 'Menace' (strikes against Vichy French naval units in Dakar); envoys, flown ashore in 2 Caudron Luciolles embarked for purpose, failed; air group consisted of 800 and 803 (Skua) and 810, 818 and 820 (Swordfish) NAS

26.09.40 Strikes and 15in shellfire from remainder of force proved unsuccessful and operations broken off after loss of 9 of *Ark Royal*'s aircraft; returned to UK for short refit

00.11.40 Re-joined Force H in Gibraltar; 808 NAS (Fulmar) having replaced 803 NAS (Skua)

09.11.40 Struck at Sicilian airfields to divert enemy attention from *Illustrious*'s attack on Taranto two days later

17.11.40 Covered further ferry operations to Malta by *Argus*

27.11.40 Three strikes launched against Italian force south-west of Sardinia (some damage achieved and Italians withdrew at high speed but ship's NAS were insufficiently worked up to achieve decisive results)

02.02.41 Swordfish attacked Tirso Dam in northern Sicily with torpedoes

08.02.41 Swordfish spotted for *Renown* and *Malaya* bombarding Genoa; other Swordfish struck at La Spezia and Pisa

22.03.41 Slightly damaged when Swordfish with depth charge crashed ahead of ship (depth charge exploded but, although hull was shaken, there was no immediate need for repairs)

00.04.41 Ferried RAF Hurricanes to Malta

24.05.41 Ordered into Atlantic immediately after further ferry trip to Malta, to cover troop convoy against German battleship *Bismarck*

26.05.41 Swordfish strike wrecked *Bismarck*'s steering gear, enabling her to be brought to action and sunk by the HF (earlier strike had mistaken cruiser *Sheffield* for *Bismarck* but new magnetic-fuzed torpedoes had missed target; contact fuzes substituted for successful attack) ;at about this time 807 NAS (Fulmar) replaced 800 NAS (Skua); 807 and 808 NAS shot down 30 enemy aircraft between them May–November 1941.

00.06.41 825 NAS (Swordfish) replaced 820 NAS (Swordfish)

00.07.41 816 NAS (Swordfish) replaced 818 NAS (Swordfish)

00.09.41 812 NAS (Swordfish) replaced 810 NAS (Swordfish)

13.11.41 When returning from Operation 'Perpetual', ferrying RAF fighters to Malta, ship was hit by one contact-pistol torpedo from salvo of four fired by *U81* 30 miles east of Gibraltar

14.11.41 Sank after 14 hours in approx. 36° 03' N 4° 45' W; only one man lost

HMS *Ark Royal* (1938) flying off a range of Swordfish. The lack of natural wind, shown by the funnel smoke, and the low ship speed show how simple the launch was for the relatively lightweight biplanes of the day. The lighter rectangles on deck show the unusual arrangement of the lifts. (Author)

HMS *Ark Royal* (1955) in the Cromarty Firth in May 1957 with hands fallen in for an 'Alpha' Range with Sea Hawk, Gannet, Wyvern and Skyraider aircraft parked neatly on deck. Note the side lift on the port side abeam the funnel, and that the two 4.5in mountings forward of it have already been removed and plated over to allow an extension of the angled deck. (FAA Museum)

Ark Royal (1955) (R09) *Fleet Carrier*

Laid down: 3 May 1943
Launched: 3 May 1950
Completed: 25 February 1955

Builder: Cammell Laird & Co., Birkenhead
Machinery: 4-shaft Parsons geared turbines; 8 Admiralty 3-drum boilers; 152,000shp = 30.5 knots
Displacement: 43,060 tons standard; 49,950 tons deep load
Dimensions: 808ft 3in overall x 158ft 5in max beam x 35ft 7in max draught
Gun armament: 8 twin 4.5in Mk 6 DP (6); 5 sextuple 40mm Bofors Mk 6 (30); 2 twin 40mm Bofors (4); 6 single 40mm Bofors (6); 4 single 3pdr saluting (4)
Fuel: 5,500 tons FFO
Endurance: 7,000 miles @ 14 knots
Complement: 2,756
Protection: 4.5in waterline belt; 4in flight deck over hangar; 1.5in rest of flight deck; 1.5in hangar sides; 2.5in hangar deck; 1.5in longitudinal bulkheads
Flight deck: 790ft x 120ft armoured steel; 5-degree angled deck
Arrester wires: 6 x 35,000lb @ 103 knots; emergency nylon barriers
Hangars: *Upper* 364ft (plus extension fwd of fwd lift) x 67ft x 17ft 6in; *lower* 364ft x 53ft 6in x 17ft 6in
Catapults: 2 x BS4 steam (151ft stroke); 50,000lb @ 94 knots
Lifts: *Fwd* 54ft long x 44ft wide; *aft* 54ft long x 33ft wide; *deck-edge* 54ft long x 35ft wide; all 40,000lb, 35-second cycle
Aircraft: 80
Aircraft fuel: 522,000 gallons AVCAT; 15,700 gallons AVGAS
Air weapons: Tactical nuclear weapons; Firestreak AAM; Sidewinder AAM; Bullpup ASM; 18in torpedoes; Mk 30/44/46 homing torpedoes; 2,000lb bombs; 1,000lb MC bombs; 500lb SAP bombs; 500lb MC bombs; 3in RP; 2in RP; Glowworm rocket flares; Mk 11 depth charges; 20mm cannon ammunition; flares and pyrotechnics.

Notes: *Ark Royal* was the first British carrier to be fitted with a side lift. In her 1966–70 modernisation she recieved a full 8-degree angled deck, improved steam catapults and facilities to support Phantom aircraft. All gun armament was removed (although she was fitted for, but not with, GWS.22 Seacat). Details are for *Ark Royal* as completed. Flight deck details after modernisation resembled those of *Eagle*. After the refit, air weapons carried were: tactical nuclear bombs; nuclear depth bombs; Sparrow AAM; Sidewinder AAM; Martel ASM; Mk 44/46 homing torpedoes; 1,000 lb MC bombs; 540lb MC bombs; 500lb MC bombs; 28lb practice bombs; 2in RP; Mk 11 depth charges; Lepus flares; and flares and pyrotechnics.

Summary of service

00.00.42 Adopted by Leeds during that city's war week
26.02.55 Accepted and commissioned by RN in Devonport; allocated to Plymouth Command for trials
31.05.55 Visited Gibraltar prior to carrying out flying trials
21.07.55 Completed flying trials and embarked 800 and 898 (Sea Hawk) and 824 (Gannet AS) NAS and sailed to join MF
08.12.55 849B NAS (Skyraider) joined air group
11.02.56 891 NAS (Sea Venom) joined air group
00.03.56 Exercise 'Dawn Breeze' with other NATO forces in Western Mediterranean
27.03.56 Allocated to HF
00.04.56 Visited in Portsmouth by HM Queen Elizabeth the Queen Mother
30.04.56 To Devonport for refit (completed 00.11.56)
00.01.57 Re-joined MF with 802, 804 and 898 (Sea Hawk), 815 (Gannet AS), 831 (Wyvern) and 849B (Skyraider) NAS embarked
00.02.57 Returned to Devonport for turbine repairs (completed May)
27.05.57 Visited by HM Queen Elizabeth II with other ships of HF in Cromarty
29.05.57 HM Queen Elizabeth II witnessed flying operations at sea
30.05.57 Sailed for International Naval Review, Hampton Roads, Va, with destroyers *Duchess* and *Diamond*; continued with HF on return
28.08.57 893 NAS (Sea Venom) joined air group
27.01.58 800 NAS (Sea Hawk) joined air group
28.01.58 Re-joined MF; completed heavy flying programme and took part in 3 major exercises
26.06.58 Returned to Portsmouth
05.07.58 Entered Devonport
07.07.58 Visited by HM Queen Elizabeth the Queen Mother
21.07.58 Devonport Dockyard for refit
00.04.59 Damaged by fire which delayed completion of refit
28.12.59 Recommissioned at Devonport
04.03.60 After trials, embarked 800 and 807 (Scimitar), 820 and 824 (Whirlwind), 892 (Sea Vixen) and 849A (Gannet AEW) NAS and proceeded to Mediterranean; operations followed in Norwegian Sea and west of Greenland, where ship carried out cold-weather flying trials
28.02.61 Visited New York
00.03.61 DED in Devonport
00.09.61 Recommissioned for GS commission in HF/ MF
13.11.61 Embarked 800 (Scimitar), 815 (Wessex), 849C (Gannet AEW) and 890 (Sea Vixen) NAS
00.01.62 Returned to Devonport for leave and SMP
16.02.62 Sailed for FEF, re-embarking same air group; as well as visits to Fremantle and Okinawa, ship participated in RN/ USN Exercise 'Rawfish' and SEATO Exercise 'Sea Devil'
16.12.62 Disembarked air group and entered Devonport for leave and SMP
28.02.63 Embarked same air group for work-up plus 801 NAS (Buccaneer)
16.03.63 Disembarked 801 NAS after NATO Exercise 'Dawn Breeze'
19.03.63 Sailed for FEF
00.07.63 Visited Mombasa
16.09.63 Exercise 'Dovetail'
12.10.63 Exercise 'Biltong' with MEF
10.11.63 Exercise 'Midlink 6'
30.12.63 Returned to UK
04.01.64 Commenced refit in Devonport
13.11.64 Refit completed; post-refit trials commenced
14.01.65 Embarked 803 (Scimitar), 819 (Wessex), 849C (Gannet AEW) and 890 (Sea Vixen) NAS and joined HF
00.03.65 Exercise 'Pilot Light'
00.07.65 Re-joined FEF; participated in Beira patrol
00.06.66 Re-joined HF
21.08.66 Exercise 'Straight Lace'
24.09.66 Exercise 'Link West'
04.10.66 Entered Devonport Dockyard for major refit and reconstuction
24.02.70 Recommissioned at Devonport (ceremony attended by HM Queen Elizabeth the Queen Mother); allocated to WF with air group now comprising 892 (Phantom), 809 (Buccaneer), 849B (Gannet AEW) and 824 (Sea King) NAS
14.09.70 Exercise 'Northern Wedding'
09.11.70 Collided with Russian 'Kotlin' class destroyer during Exercise 'Lime Jug' in Mediterranean
29.11.70 Launched hot air balloon *Bristol Belle*, flown by Lt Adams RN to Malta with delivery of mail (only known instance when balloon has been used for this purpose)
18.12.70 Returned to Devonport
04.05.71 Trials with RAF Harrier aircraft

HMS *Ark Royal* after extensive modernisation. Note the larger angled deck and the relocation of the two catapults to the port bow and waist. The aircraft on deck are Buccaneers and Phantoms, with an AEW Gannet forward and a Sea King helicopter landing on aft. The white rectangles painted along the edges of the angled deck were intended to improve visual line-up cues for night landings. (FAA Museum)

27.09.71 Exercise 'Royal Knight'
20.01.72 Deployed to Norfolk, Va, for WESTLANT training, returning 00.03.72
10.07.72 Exercise 'Westward Ho!'
00.09.72 Exercise 'Strong Express'
23.11.72 Exercise 'Corsica' in Mediterranean
28.01.73 Fire party carried by helicopter to rescue Belgian trawler off Start Point
04.02.73 Exercise 'Sunny Seas'
09.02.73 Exercise 'Med Train 73' in Gibraltar area
00.03.73 Exercise 'Ruler'
26.07.73 Refit in Devonport Dockyard
10.04.74 Refit completed
16.09.74 Exercise 'Northern Merger'
08.01.75 Sailed for WESTLANT deployment
07.05.75 Visited Rio de Janeiro, meeting other ships returning from FEF via Cape
17.05.75 Exercise with ships of Brazilian Navy; embarked Brazilian Sea King squadron for several days
12.06.75 Returned to Devonport
00.11.75 Exercise 'Ocean Safari'
30.01.76 Exercises in SWAPPS; then WESTLANT deployment with film crew on board to make 'Sailor' series for BBC Television
23.02.76 2 Sea Kings winched sick sailor from US submarine *Bergall* and flew him to USAF base at Lages in Azores
16.07.76 Returned to Devonport
28.09.76 Visited Lisbon, followed by Exercise 'Display Determination' in Mediterranean
11.10.76 Visited Toulon
21.10.76 Returned to Devonport for refit
00.05.77 Last refit completed
28.06.77 Spithead for Silver Jubilee Review of Fleet by HM Queen Elizabeth II
17.09.77 Exercise 'Ocean Safari'
17.11.77 Exercise 'Iles d'Or' after visit to Toulon
28.11.77 Visited Naples
14.12.77 In Devonport
05.04.78 Sailed for last WESTLANT deployment
04.12.78 Returned to Devonport to pay off
22.09.80 Towed to breaker's yard in Cairnryan, Wigtownshire

Ark Royal (1985) (R07) Invincible *class Light Fleet Carrier*

Laid down: 14 December 1978
Launched: 2 June 1981
Completed: 1 July 1985

Builder: Swan Hunter, Wallsend-on-Tyne
Machinery: 2 shafts (each with reversible gearbox); 4 Rolls-Royce TBM3 Olympus gas turbines; 112,000shp = 28 knots (94,000 max continuous shp)
Displacement: 16,000 tons standard; 20,000 tons deep load
Dimensions: 677ft 9in overall x 104ft 6in max beam x 29ft max draught
Missile/gun armament: Single GWS.30 Sea Dart SAM (2); 3 x 20mm Vulcan Phalanx CIWS (3); 2 single 20mm GAM BO1 (2)
Fuel: 3,000 tons diesel
Endurance: 5,000 miles @ 18 knots
Complement: 1,318
Protection: None
Flight deck: 600ft x 65ft steel
Arrester wires: None
Hangar: 500ft (including lift wells) x 74ft (max)/40ft (min) x 20ft
Catapults: None
Ski-jump: 12-degree
Lifts: *Fwd* 54ft 8in long x 31ft 8in wide; *aft* 54ft 8in long x 31ft 8in wide; both 35,000lb
Aircraft: Up to 22
Aircraft fuel: 250,000 gallons AVCAT
Air weapons: Tactical nuclear weapons; nuclear depth bombs; Sidewinder AAM; Sea Eagle ASM; Stingray homing torpedoes; Mk 46 homing torpedoes; 1,000lb MC bombs; BL.755 cluster bombs; Mk 11 depth charges; 30mm cannon ammunition; 7.62mm GPMG ammunition; flares and pyrotechnics

Notes: The last of the *Invincible* class to complete, *Ark Royal* incorporated some of the improvements suggested by her two sister-ships in service. A larger ski-jump with a 12-degree angle similar to that fitted in *Hermes* was built on with a leading edge 40ft forward of the smaller ski-jump fitted to the earlier ships during building. The improvement in operational capability for the Sea Harriers was marked and called into question the logic behind the earlier conservative design. Some strengthening of the hull aft cured the vibration to which *Invincible* was prone and a new bow was fitted to carry a Vulcan Phalanx Close-In Weapon System in the eyes of the ship. Two further mountings were installed, one on a sponson on the port quarter and one outboard of the island to starboard. All were actually fitted some months after *Ark Royal*'s completion. Internal modifications provided for more accommodation and improved Flag command and control facilities. Although ship and aircraft fuel are shown as separate figures, both could be used as fuel for either.

Summary of service

00.06.82	Key members of ship's company began to join at Wallsend Yard
00.09.82	Docked for installation of propellers, rudders and stabilisers
00.11.82	Moved to Walker Yard for completion (Wallsend Yard needed for *Atlantic Conveyor*)
03.05.84	Main engines turned for first time
19.10.84	Contractor's sea trials
12.04.85	Sailed for final machinery trials with a Wessex 5 of 707 NAS embarked for HDS duties
14.04.85	Returned to Walker Yard
24.06.85	Final inspection by CNSA
26.06.85	Ship's company moved on board
28.06.85	Sailed from Tyne with Swordfish from RNAS Lee-on-Solent embarked
01.07.85	Arrived in Portsmouth; Sea Harrier of 899 NAS landed-on for ceremonial entry
15.07.85	Sailed for shakedown cruise with Wessex 5 of 845 NAS embarked
22.07.85	SAT 'Air'
29.07.85	Portland work-up
01.11.85	Commissioned by HM Queen Elizabeth the Queen Mother in Portsmouth
04.11.85	Sailed for flying trials in Mediterranean
09.11.85	In Gibraltar
11.11.85	Flying trials in Gibraltar area
14.11.85	Laid wreath over spot where *Ark Royal* (1938) sank in 1941
25.11.85	Visited Marseilles
02.12.85	In Suda Bay
03.12.85	FORACS Range in Cretan waters
06.12.85	PASSEX with FNS *Jeanne d'Arc* and Italian MPAs
09.12.85	In Gibraltar
16.12.85	Arrived in Portsmouth
19.12.85	801 (Sea Harrier) and 820 (Sea King AS) NAS transferred to ship from *Invincible*
06.01.86	Harbour trials

27.01.86	Sea trials
06.02.86	Visited Amsterdam
10.02.86	Sea trials
13.02.86	Arrived in Portsmouth
20.02.86	ODMA
24.02.86	Sailed from Portsmouth for Portland work-up
10.04.86	Air group work up off Western Scotland with 801 and 820 NAS embarked
23.04.86	ORI
17.06.86	849 B (Sea King AEW) Flight added to air group; sailed from Portsmouth for WESTLANT deployment
19.06.86	Exercise 'Liberty Train' in North Atlantic
28.06.86	Arrived in New York with FOF3 (Vice-Admiral Sir Julian Oswald) embarked
03.07.86	International Naval Review for re-dedication of Statue of Liberty
08.07.86	Sailed from New York for 'ASWEX 1/ 86'
23.07.86	Visited Fort Lauderdale, Florida
31.07.86	Trial 'Baste 86' on Autec Range in Bahamas
09.08.86	Visited Norfolk, Va
15.08.86	Exercise 'Northern Engagement'
29.08.86	Exercise 'Northern Wedding'
22.09.86	Visited Amsterdam for NATO 'Wash-Up'
27.09.86	Arrived in Portsmouth for SMP
13.10.86	Sailed for Exercise 'Autumn Train'
23.10.86	Visited Gibraltar; BBC televised pop concert on flight deck
29.10.86	Visited Lisbon
05.11.86	Disembarked 820 NAS and embarked 845 NAS (Sea King Commando) and COMAW
07.11.86	Embarked 1 ACG, RNethMC, for amphibious exercises off Garelochhead
13.11.86	1 ACG disembarked to RNeth NAS Valkenburg
14.11.86	Visited Hamburg.
20.11.86	Arrived in Portsmouth for BAMP
12.01.87	Sailed for West Indies and WESTLANT
18.01.87	Exercise 'Caribtrain'
02.02.87	Visited Barbados
10.02.87	'ASWEX 1/87', Phase 1
19.02.87	Anchored off Tortola.
21.02.87	Fleetex with USN
23.02.87	Visited San Juan, Puerto Rico
27.02.87	'ASWEX 1/87' Phase 2
04.03.87	Visited Mayport, Florida
16.03.87	Trial 'Punish' in Autec Range, Bahamas
23.03.87	Visited Charleston, SC
09.04.87	Arrived in Portsmouth for docking
07.05.87	'ASWEX 2/87' in North-West Approaches
08.06.87	Moored to buoys off Greenwich for visit to London (largest warship to pass Thames Barrier)
13.06.87	In Rosyth for participation in Navy Days
15.06.87	JMC 872.
27.06.87	Exercise 'Hadrian's Wall'
03.07.87	Arrived in Portsmouth for BAMP
29.08.87	Portsmouth Navy Days
07.09.87	RNEE in Portsmouth.

HMS *Ark Royal* launching a Sea Harrier. (FAA Museum)

22.09.87 COST at Portland
14.10.87 Air group work-up
23.10.87 ORI
03.11.87 Sailed from Portsmouth for UK national exercise 'Purple Warrior' with 800 and 801 (Sea Harrier), 849B (Sea King AEW) and part of 826 (Sea King AS) NAS plus No 1 Squadron RAF (Harrier) embarked
08.11.87 Port inner gas turbine failed
12.11.87 No 1 Squadron RAF disembarked to West Freugh
19.11.87 Air group disembarked to parent air stations
20.11.87 Visited Cherbourg
24.11.87 Returned to Portsmouth
26.01.88 Sailed for shakedown with 801, 820 and 849B NAS embarked
29.01.88 Visited Newcastle
11.02.88 Visited Rosyth
16.02.88 JMC 881
01.03.88 Exercises with *Illustrious* in North Sea
04.03.88 Visited Hamburg
14.03.88 Exercise 'Mallet Blow' (achieved 104 interceptions in 25 Sea Harrier sorties and 8 hours' AEW flying)
18.03.88 Visited Rotterdam
23.03.88 Returned to Portsmouth for docking and BAMP
06.06.88 Sailed for shakedown with air group embarked
13.06.88 Sailed for Far East on deployment 'Outback 88' in company with *Edinburgh*, *Sirius*, *Fort Grange* and *Olwen*
17.06.88 Exercise 'Jolly Roger'
25.06.88 Visited Malta
29.06.88 Sailed for Singapore
02.07.88 Entered Suez Canal
23.07.88 Arrived in Singapore
08.08.88 Sailed to give Defence Export Day at Sea for 100 VIPs
13.08.88 Visited Subic Bay
17.08.88 Exercises in the Subic Bay area with USS *New Jersey*
23.08.88 Visited Hong Kong
28.08.88 Sailed from Hong Kong
29.08.88 Sea King of 849B NAS detected small boat full of Vietnamese refugees (rescued by *Edinburgh*)
01.09.88 Exercise 'Setia Kewan' off Brunei
06.09.88 Exercise 'Lima Bersatu'
11.09.88 Sea Day for Indonesian naval staff
17.09.88 Anchored off Possession Island, Australia; landed guard for re-dedication ceremony at Captain Cook memorial
19.09.88 PASSEX with RAN and RAAF
21.09.88 Visited Brisbane
27.09.88 Entered Sydney Harbour with Sir James Rowland, Governor of New South Wales, on board
01.10.88 Bicentennial International Fleet Review in Sydney Harbour, inspected by HRH the Duke of York; ships's air group participated in fly-past
07.10.88 Sailed for exercises with RAN in Jervis Bay
14.10.88 Visit to Melbourne cancelled because tug strike and high winds prevented berthing
23.10.88 Visited Fremantle
02.11.88 Sailed for Bombay
15.11.88 Visited Bombay
19.11.88 Sailed for Defence Export Sea Day
22.11.88 PASSEX with USS *Nimitz*
01.12.88 Commenced passage through Suez Canal
05.12.88 WASEX with FNS *Clemenceau* in Eastern Mediterranean
09.12.88 Visited Gibraltar
15.12.88 Returned to Portsmouth for BAMP
07.02.89 Sailed for shakedown
17.02.89 Alongside in Portsmouth; prepared for operation in LPH role
26.02.89 Embarked 845 and 846 (Sea King Commando) NAS and 45 RM Cdo and sailed for Exercise 'Cold Winter' off northern Norway
17.03.89 Returned to Portsmouth, having disembarked Commando units
01.04.89 Sailed for Exercise 'Springtrain' with 801, 820 and 849B NAS embarked
21.04.89 Visited Gibraltar
05.05.89 In Portsmouth
11.05.89 Exercise 'Square Nut' with Dutch naval task group
12.05.89 Visited Hamburg.
19.05.89 DLT by No 4 Squadron RAF (Harrier)
22.05.89 Exercise 'Vendetta'
04.06.89 Returned to Portsmouth
13.06.89 Sailed for Rosyth Navy Days and JMC 892
04.07.89 Joint Sea Harrier/Spanish Navy AV-8B operations in North Sea
07.07.89 Arrived in Portsmouth for SMP
21.08.89 Sailed for shakedown with air group embarked
04.09.89 Exercise 'Sharp Shear'
22.09.89 In Portsmouth; acted as host ship for SNS *Príncipe de Asturias*
05.10.89 Visited Brest
11.10.89 Visited Lisbon

14.10.89 In Portsmouth for DAMP

00.02.90 COST at Portland followed by visit to Copenhagen

00.03.90 Aviation work-up and ORI

18.04.90 Sailed for WESTLANT deployment with *Cumberland*, *Brave*, *Glasgow* and *Fort Grange*

19.04.90 Exercise 'Jolly Roger'

09.05.90 Visited New York

30.05.90 Exercise 'Marcot'

15.06.90 Visited Halifax, Nova Scotia

21.06.90 Visited Boston

26.06.90 Sailed for UK

04.07.90 Arrived in Portsmouth for BAMP

21.08.90 Sailed for shakedown with air group embarked

03.09.90 Exercise 'Teamwork 90'

20.09.90 Visited Oslo

26.09.90 Returned to Portsmouth

15.10.90 Sailed to Gibraltar

19.10.90 In Gibraltar

00.12.90 Returned to Portsmouth

10.01.91 Deployed to Eastern Mediterranean to join Allied forces securing area against threat of attack by Iraq; ship's group (including *Sheffield*, *Charybdis*, *Olmeda* and *Regent* and working closely with USS *Virginia*, *Philippine Sea* and *Spruance*) spent 51 days at sea off Cyprus standing by, but hostilities were confined to Gulf and Iraq itself

01.03.91 Visited Naples

00.03.91 Visited Athens

28.03.91 Visted Palma

00.04.91 Returned to Portsmouth for SMP

00.05.91 JMC 912

00.05.91 Exercise 'Ocean Safari 91'

00.08.91 Plymouth Navy Days and RNEE, Portsmouth

10.09.91 Sailed for WESTLANT deployment in company with *Gloucester*, *London*, *Talent*, *Olna* and *Regent*; Sea King HAS.5 replaced by Sea King HAS.6 in 820 NAS

20.09.91 Visited Bermuda

23.09.91 Visited Fort Lauderdale, Fl

28.09.91 Trial 'Woking' in Autec Range, Bahamas (test of Sea King HAS.6 sonics against nuclear submarine *Talent*)

11.10.91 Visited Mayport

22.10.91 Sailed for Gibraltar

04.11.91 Visited Gibraltar

08.11.91 Flying trials with RAF Chinook helicopters

18.11.91 Returned to Portsmouth

20.11.91 Ship visited by HM Queen Elizabeth the Queen Mother

21.11.91 Commenced DAMP

12.02.92 Sailed for trials in the English Channel

28.02.92 Ship visited by HRH the Princess Royal

04.03.92 Sailed for shakedown with air group

30.03.92 Arrived in Portland for COST

01.05.92 Visited Greenock

06.05.92 Returned to Portsmouth for SMP

05.06.92 Exercise 'Shop Window 92'

19.06.92 Visited Copenhagen

25.06.92 In Portsmouth

29.06.92 Exercise 'Purple Monarch'

01.07.92 Visited Gibraltar

12.07.92 Returned to Portsmouth for SMP

21.07.92 Ship visited by Russian Defence Minister

02.09.92 Sailed for Westlant deployment

11.09.92 'Fleetex 1/92' with USN

18.09.92 Visited Norfolk, Va

23.09.92 Sailed for weapon training in Jacksonville area

02.10.92 Visited Mayport

14.10.92 Trials in Autec Range, Bahamas

21.10.92 Visited Nassau

25.10.92 Sailed for UK

06.11.92 Arrived in Portsmouth for SMP

16.11.92 Royal Dinner on board (Admiralty Board entertained HM Queen Elizabeth II in honour of 40th anniversary of her accession to throne)

15.01.93 Sailed for shakedown with air group

00.02.93 COST at Portland

21.04.93 Visited Naples

23.04.93 Led TG.612.02 in Adriatic, supporting UN operations ashore in former Republic of Yugoslavia

24.04.93 Sea Harriers declared to NATO and UN as capable of using laser-guided bombs

18.05.93 Visited Bari

24.05.93 Visited Corfu

30.05.93 Alert 30 for Sea Harriers to support UN forces

08.06.93 Arrived in Malta for SMP

17.06.93 Sailed for Adriatic

20.06.93 Alert 30 for Sea Harriers to support UN forces

28.6.93 Cross-deck operations with Italian carrier *Garibaldi*

01.07.93 Visited Suda Bay in Crete

08.07.93 On station in Adriatic to support UN forces

00.11.94 Paid off into reserve at Portsmouth (planned refit and modernisation from 1997)

Atheling (D51) Ruler *Class Escort/Ferry Carrier*

Laid down: 9 June 1942
Launched: 7 September 1942
Completed: 1 August 1943

Builder: Seattle-Tacoma Shipbuilding Corp., Seattle; completed by Puget Sound Navy Yard
Machinery: 1-shaft Allis-Chalmers geared turbine; 2 Foster Wheeler boilers; 8,500shp = 18.5 knots
Displacement: 11,200 tons standard; 15,400 tons deep load
Dimensions: 492ft overall x 108ft 6in max beam x 25ft 5in max draught
Gun armament: 2 single 5in US Mk 12 (2); 8 twin 40mm Bofors (16); 14 twin 20mm Oerlikon (28); 7 single 20mm Oerlikon (7)
Fuel: 3,290 tons FFO
Endurance: 27,500 miles @ 11 knots
Complement: 646

Protection: Splinter protection for bomb room
Flight deck: 450ft x 80ft wood-covered steel
Arrester wires: 9 x 19,800lb @ 55 knots; 3 barriers
Hangar: 260ft x 62ft x 18ft
Catapults: 1 x H4C hydraulic; 16,000lb @ 74 knots (tail-down method only)
Lifts: *Fwd* 42ft long x 34ft wide; *aft* 34ft long x 42ft wide; both 14,000lb
Aircraft: Up to 30 could be operated; up to 90 could be ferried
Aircraft fuel: 36,000 gallons AVGAS
Air weapons: 18in torpedoes; 500lb SAP bombs; 250lb SAP bombs; 250lb GP bombs; Mk 11 depth charges; .5in gun ammunition; .303in gin ammunition; flares and pyrotechnics

Notes: Built from the outset as a warship but based on the US C3 merchant design. originally completed as

HMS *Atheling*. The derricks which are visible rigged on the starboard quarter were capable of lifting contemporary aircraft from a lighter or jetty on to the flight deck. (IWM A.21919)

USS *Glacier* (CVE-33). Provisionally named *Setter* by the RN before handover under Lend/Lease.

Summary of service

03.07.43	Commissioned as USS *Glacier* in Puget Sound
31.07.43	Handed over to RN at Vancouver
28.10.43	Commissioned as *Atheling* in Vancouver after modifications
06.12.43	Arrived in Balboa on passage
22.12.43	Arrived in New York on passage
01.01.44	Sailed for Belfast with 1836 NAS (Corsair) embarked for passage
10.01.44	To Clyde for modification into fighter carrier
26.02.44	Embarked 822 and 823 (Barracuda) and 1837 and 1838 (Corsair) NAS for passage to EF
03.03.44	Allocated to 1 ACS, EF; KMF.29A to Port Said
23.03.44	Passed through Suez Canal
28.03.44	AJ.2 Aden to Colombo
09.04.44	JC.34A Colombo to Madras
11.04.44	Aircraft offloaded
16.04.44	CJ.23B to Colombo
13.05.44	Embarked 889 (Seafire) and 890 (Wildcat) NAS and worked up as fighter carrier
10.06.44	Operation 'Councillor' (diversionary sweep in Indian Ocean with *Illustrious* designed to distract Japanese attention from US operations in Marianas)
21.07.44	Used as trade protection carrier with 818 NAS (Swordfish) embarked
25.08.44	Sailed from Trincomalee with 818 NAS embarked to ferry 1838 NAS (Corsair) to Wingfield
02.09.44	Arrived in Mauritius
12.09.44	Arrived in Cape Town
06.10.44	Disembarked 818 NAS to Cochin
10.10.44	Arrived in Trincomalee; used as a ferry carrier by EF
08.12.44	Loaned to USN as ferry carrier; sailed for Sydney
04.02.45	Arrived in Manus; operated by USN between San Diego and Pearl Harbor
15.02.45	Arrived in Pearl Harbor
23.08.45	Arrived in Norfolk, Va
03.09.45	Arrived in Trinidad
16.09.45	Arrived in Devonport; refitted for service on trooping duties
15.11.45	Sailed for Colombo
03.12.45	Arrived in Colombo
05.12.45	Sailed for Wellington
23.12.45	Arrived in Wellington
27.12.45	Sailed for Sydney, thence to UK via Fremantle and Aden
10.02.46	Arrived in Devonport; employed on general trooping duties
00.11.46	De-stored prior to return to USN
13.12.46	Returned to USN at Norfolk, Va
00.00.50	Sold as mercantile *Roma*
02.11.67	Broken up in Italy

Attacker (D02) Attacker *Class Assault Carrier*

Laid down: 17 April 1941
Launched: 27 September 1941
Completed: 10 October 1942

Builder: Western Pipe and Steel Corp., San Francisco
Machinery: 1-shaft General Electric geared turbine; 2 Foster Wheeler D type boilers; 8,500shp = 18 knots
Displacement: 10,200 tons standard; 14,400 tons deep load
Dimensions: 491ft 7in x 105ft 1in max beam x 21ft max draught
Gun armament: 2 single 4in US Mk 9 (2); 4 twin 40mm Bofors (8); 8 twin 20mm Oerlikon (16); 4 single 20mm Oerlikon (4)
Fuel: 3,123 tons FFO
Endurance: 27,300 miles @ 11 knots
Complement: 646
Protection: Splinter protection for bomb room
Flight deck: 442ft x 88ft wood-covered steel
Arrester wires: 9 x 19,800lb @ 55 knots; 3 barriers
Hangar: 262ft x 62ft x 18ft
Catapults: 1 x H2 hydraulic; 7,000lb @ 61 knots (tail-down method only)
Lifts: *Fwd* 42ft long x 34ft wide; *aft* 34ft long x 42ft wide; both 14,000lb
Aircraft: Up to 20 could be operated; up to 90 could be ferried
Aircraft fuel: 44,800 gallons AVGAS
Air weapons: 500lb SAP bombs; 250lb SAP bombs;

250lb GP bombs; 20mm gun ammunition; .303in gun ammunition; flares and pyrotechnics

Notes: Laid down as mercantile *Steel Artisan*. Acquired before launch for conversion to a carrier and built as USS *Barnes* (AVG-7) of the US *Bogue* class. Transferred to RN under Lend/Lease arrangements.

Summary of service

30.09.42 Commissioned in San Francisco
12.11.42 Began sea and flying trials off San Francisco
22.12.42 Passed through Panama Canal
01.04.43 Arrived in Clyde after stops at Norfolk (Va), Jamaica and Curacao
04.04.43 Arrived in Liverpool for modifications to RN standards
15.06.43 Sailed for Clyde area to work-up
03.08.43 Left Clyde for Mediterranean
08.09.43 Sailed for Malta for Operation 'Avalanche' (Salerno landings) with 879 and 886 (Seafire) NAS embarked as part of Force V
10.10.43 Arrived in Rosyth to refit as assault carrier
12.03.44 Work-up and training for new role
14.05.44 Sailed for Mediterranean
15.08.44 Operation 'Dragoon' (invasion of southern France) with 879 (Seafire) NAS embarked as part of Task Group 88.1
02.09.44 Arrived in Alexandria
15.09.44 Operations 'Outing', 'Cablegram' and 'Contempt' (strikes against German forces in Dodecanese islands and Aegean); NAS from *Attacker*, *Stalker*, *Hunter* and *Khedive* formed 4th Naval Fighter Wing, those from *Emperor*, *Pursuer* and *Searcher* 7th Naval Fighter Wing
13.10.44 Operation 'Manna' (reoccupation of Athens)
31.10.44 Sailed from Alexandria for UK
10.11.44 Devonport for repairs
07.12.44 Taranto for refit
01.04.45 Sailed to join 21 ACS, EIF, with 879 NAS (Seafire) embarked
07.08.45 Arrived in Trincomalee
17.08.45 Sailed for Operation 'Jurist' (reoccupation of Penang)
04.09.45 Part of force sent to reoccupy Singapore
14.09.45 Sailed from Singapore for return to UK
11.11.45 Arrived in Clyde to de-store into reserve
09.12.45 Sailed for return to USN, via Southampton
05.01.46 Returned to USN at Norfolk, Va; sold as mercantile *Castel Forte*; subsequently renamed *Fairsky*
23.06.77 Hit wreck and beached.
29.06.77 Refloated
18.12.77 Arrived in Hong Kong
23.03.78 Towed to Mariveles for conversion to floating hotel
28.03.78 Arrived in Mariveles and renamed *Philippine Tourist*
03.11.79 Gutted by major fire
24.05.80 Towed to Hong Kong; breaking up commenced

HMS *Attacker*. The flight deck in these ships was built on to the basic hull as superstructure. Expansion joints are clearly visible here as black lines against the wooden planking that covered the steel over the remainder of the deck. (Author)

HMS *Audacity* in 1941. The Martlets of 802 NAS are parked aft with windbreaks raised around the deck-edge to afford them some protection: with no hangar, they lived in a permanent deck park. The aircraft furthest forward is at readiness to launch. (IWM HU.54361)

Audacity (D10) *Escort Carrier*

Laid down: ?
Launched: 29 March 1939
Completed: 10 May 1939 as merchant ship; 20 June 1941 as carrier

Builder: Vulkan, Bremen
Machinery: 1-shaft Vulkan diesel; 5,200bhp = 14.5 knots
Displacement: 10,200 tons standard; 11,000 tons deep load
Dimensions: 467ft 3in overall x 56ft 3in max beam x 21ft 7in max draught
Gun armament: 1 single 4in QF Mk V HA (1); 1 single 6pdr (1); 4 single 2pdr (4); 4 single 20mm Oerlikon (4)
Fuel: 649 tons diesel
Endurance: 12,000 miles @ 14 knots
Complement: 210
Protection: None
Flight deck: 453ft x 60ft steel
Arrester wires: 2 x 9,000lb @ 55 knots; 1 similar safety wire; 1 barrier
Hangar: None
Catapults: None
Lifts: None
Aircraft: Up to 8 Martlet fighters plus 2 spares with wings removed
Aircraft fuel: 10,000 gallons AVGAS
Air weapons: .5in gun ammunition; flares and pyrotechnics

Notes: In her short but highly successful career *Audacity* proved the concept of the escort carrier, being the first to see action. Conversion was austere and little changed below the flight deck, with aircrew accommodated in the former cargo liner's passenger cabins. Most of the technical staff served with, but not in, the RN under T124X articles. So successful was her work with the Gibraltar convoys that Admiral Dönitz, in his War Diary for 23 December 1941, said, '... the worst feature was the presence of the aircraft carrier. Small, fast manoeuvrable aircraft circled the convoy, so that when sighted the boats were forced to submerge or withdraw. The presence of fighters also prevented shadowing or homing by German aircraft.' As a direct result of *Audacity*'s success, the Ministry of War Transport, which until then had seen such conversions as wasteful, released five British merchant ships under construction for conversion to escort carriers.

Summary of service

10.05.39	Completed as German cargo liner *Hannover*
07.03.40	Captured by HM Ships *Assiniboine* and *Dunedin*; renamed *Sinbad*
11.11.40	Converted to ocean boarding vessel and renamed *Empire Audacity*
00.01.41	Plans changed and ship converted to escort carrier (work started at Bootle and finished at Blyth)
20.06.41	Commissioned as HMS *Empire Audacity* at Blyth; trials in Clyde area
10.07.41	First deck landings by 802 NAS (Martlet)
31.07.41	Renamed HMS *Audacity*
13.09.41	Sailed with escort for OG.74 to Gibraltar; flying took place on 13 days (1 FW 200 shot down and 1 U-boat sighted)
02.10.41	Sailed from Gibraltar to UK with HG.74 (15-day passage almost entirely uneventful)
29.10.41	Sailed from Clyde as part of escort for OG.76 to Gibraltar (in 10 flying days, 802 NAS shot down 2 FW 200s and chased off a third)
14.12.41	Sailed for UK with HG.76 with only 4 serviceable fighters (subsequent action under Cdr F. J. Walker RN, SO Escort in HMS *Stork*, proved one of most famous and decisive of war: in 6 flying days, 802 NAS shot down 2 FW 200s, damaged 3 and chased off further 3 and also sighted or assisted in destruction of 8 U-boats)

21.12.41 Hit by 3 torpedoes from *U751*; first hit flooded engine room and caused ship to settle by stern but P1 and P2 guns were able to open fire on the U-boat which was clearly visible on the surface, close on port beam; ship sank at 2210, bows first, in position 43° 45' N 19° 54' W about 10 miles to starboard of HG.76 (no corvette could be spared to look after her and she was alone at time of attack)

Avenger (D14) Avenger *Class Escort Carrier*

Laid down: 28 November 1939
Launched: 17 November 1940
Completed: 1 March 1942

Builder: Sun Shipbuilding and Drydock Corp., Chester; completed by Bethlehem Steel Co.
Machinery: 1 shaft; 2 Doxford diesels; 8,500bhp = 17 knots
Displacement: 12,150 tons standard; 15,700 tons full load
Dimensions: 492ft overall x 70ft max beam x 26ft 4in max draught
Gun armament: 3 single 4in US Mk 9 (3); 10 single 20m Oerlikon (10); 6 single 0.5in Browning (6)
Fuel: 3,205 tons diesel
Endurance: 14,550 miles @ 10 knots
Complement: 545
Protection: None
Flight deck: 442ft x 70ft wood-covered steel
Arrester wires: 9 x 8,000lb @ 53 knots; 3 barriers
Hangar: 190ft x 47ft x 16ft
Catapults: 1 x H2; 7,000lb @ 60 knots (tail-down method only)
Lifts: *Aft* 34ft long x 42ft wide; 12,000lb
Aircraft: 15
Aircraft fuel: 29,000 gallons AVGAS

Air weapons: 18in torpedoes; 500lb SAP bombs; 250lb SAP bombs; 250lb GP bombs; Mk 7 depth charges; flares and pyrotechnics

Notes: Laid down as mercantile *Rio Hudson*. Taken up incomplete by USN for conversion to second American escort carrier for RN (BAVG-2) and transferred to RN under Lend/Lease arrangements. Her loss led to measures to improve protection in subsequent escort carriers, especially around the bomb room. In her short career Avenger proved mechanically unreliable. Her sister-ship *Charger* was retained by the USN for aircrew training.

Summary of service
02.03.42 Commissioned at Staten Island, NY
18.04.42 Broke down during trials, repaired at Staten Island
30.04.42 Sailed for Clyde with AT.15
11.05.42 Flight deck lengthened in Clyde shipyard
16.07.42 Allocated to HF
17.08.42 Work-up completed; 825 (Swordfish), 802 (Sea Hurricane) and 883 (Sea Hurricane) NAS embarked
08.09.42 Aircraft sank *U589*
12.09.42 Covered QP.14 to Sedisfjord

HMS *Avenger* shortly after delivery in 1942 with Swordfish aircraft on deck. (Author)

24.09.42 Arrived in Scapa Flow and disembarked NAS
22.10.42 Embarked 802 and 883 NAS plus 833B Flight (Swordfish) and sailed with KMS.1 to Algiers; 833B disembarked to Gibraltar; formed part of Eastern Naval Task Force during Operation 'Torch' (invasion of North Africa)
10.11.42 Transferred 4 fighters to *Argus* and entered Algiers for rectification of engine defects
12.11.42 Sailed for UK with MKF.1Y.
15.11.42 Sunk by a single torpedo from *U155* in Atlantic, west of Gibraltar (hit abreast bomb room, which exploded, causing ship to break up and sink in under 5 minutes with only 17 survivors)

Battler (D18) Attacker *Class Escort Carrier*

Laid down: 15 April 1941
Launched: 4 April 1942
Completed: 15 November 1942

Builder: Ingalls Shipbuilding Corp., Pascagoula; machinery by Westinghouse
Machinery: 1-shaft Westinghouse DR geared turbine; 2 Foster Wheeler boilers; 8,500shp = 18 knots
Displacement: 10,200 tons standard; 15,400 tons deep load
Dimensions: 495ft 9in x 111ft 6in max beam x 26ft max draught

HMS *Battler* with a Swordfish landing on. Even though the deck is clear, the barrier, abreast the island, is in the raised position. (FAA Museum)

Gun armament: 2 single 4in US Mk 9 (2); 4 twin 40mm Bofors (8); 8 twin 20mm Oerlikon (16); 2 single 20mm Oerlikon (2)
Fuel: 3,270 tons FFO
Endurance: 27,300 miles @ 11 knots
Complement: 646
Protection: Splinter protection for bomb room
Flight deck: 442ft x 88ft wood-covered steel
Arrester wires: 9 x 19,800lb @ 55 knots; 3 barriers
Hangar: 262ft x 62ft x 18ft
Catapults: 1 x H2 hydraulic; 7,000lb @ 61 knots (tail-down method only)
Lifts: *Fwd* 42ft long x 34ft wide; *aft* 34ft long x 42ft wide; both 14,000lb
Aircraft: Up to 20 could be operated; up to 90 could be ferried
Aircraft fuel: 44,800 gallons AVGAS
Air weapons: 18in torpedoes; 500lb SAP bombs; 250lb SAP bombs; 250lb GP bombs; .5in gun ammunition; .303in gun ammunition; flares and pyrotechnics

Notes: Laid down as the mercantile *Mormactern* and acquired before launch for conversion to a carrier (and consequently an improvement over the early conversions). Built as USS *Altamaha* (AVG-6) before transfer to the RN under Lend/Lease arrangements.

Summary of service
31.10.42 Commissioned in Pascagoula
09.11.42 Struck jetty during trials; repairs carried out in New Orleans
23.11.42 Defect rectification at Norfolk, Va
21.12.42 Embarked 890, 892 and 894 NAS (Martlet) in readiness for passage to Clyde with HX.220
12.01.43 In Liverpool for alterations; allocated to WAC

04.04.43	Work-up based on Greenock
04.06.43	Sailed with KMS.16 as ferry carrier
22.06.43	XK.9 to Clyde
01.09.43	Sailed for Mediterranean with 807 and 808 NAS (Seafire) embarked
09.09.43	Formed part of Force V during Operation 'Avalanche' (Salerno landings); force comprised carriers *Attacker*, *Battler*, *Hunter*, *Stalker* and *Unicorn*, all of which had Seafire air groups (between them they flew during 42 daylight hours for total of 713 sorties, more than half Allied tactical air effort over beach-head)
20.09.43	In Gibraltar
22.09.43	Allocated to 1 ACS, EIF, as trade protection carrier based on Bombay
04.11.43	Supported AB.18A with 834 NAS (Swordfish/Seafire/Martlet) embarked
11.11.43	Supported AB.20
12.12.43	Supported AB.24A
08.01.44	Supported AB.27
16.01.44	AS operations off East Africa and Madagascar
21.03.44	Refit in Durban
28.06.44	Escort for CM.53; fighters disembarked, 834 NAS (Swordfish) embarked
11.07.44	KR.11 to Colombo, followed by AS patrols in Colombo area
22.08.44	AS search based on Addu Atoll
08.11.44	Used as ferry carrier within EIF
09.12.44	Sailed for UK via Australia, South Pacific, Panama Canal and Norfolk, Va
05.03.45	Allocated to WAC; refitted on Clyde for DLT duties
24.05.45	Trials in Belfast area
04.06.45	Allocated to Rosyth Command; non-operational
10.09.45	DLT carrier in Rosyth area
06.01.46	In Clyde for de-storing
19.01.46	Sailed from Clyde for USA
12.02.46	Returned to USN at Norfolk, Va
12.06.46	Sold by USN for scrap

Begum (D38) Ruler *Class Escort Carrier*

Laid down: 3 August1942
Launched: 11 November 1942
Completed: 3 August 1943

Builder: Seattle-Tacoma Shipbuilding Corp., Seattle; engined by Allis-Chalmers
Machinery: 1-shaft Allis-Chalmers geared turbine; 2 Foster Wheeler boilers; 8,500shp = 18.5 knots
Displacement: 11,200 tons standard; 15,400 tons deep load
Dimensions: 495ft 9in overall x 111ft 6in max beam x 26ft max draught
Gun armament: 2 single 5in US Mk 12 (2); 8 twin 40mm Bofors (16); 27 single 20mm Oerlikon (27)
Fuel: 3,160 tons FFO
Endurance: 27,300 miles @ 11 knots
Complement: 646
Protection: Splinter protection for bomb room
Flight deck: 450ft x 88ft wood-covered steel
Arrester wires: 9 x 19,800lb @ 55 knots; 3 barriers
Hangar: 260ft x 62ft x 18ft
Catapults: 1 x H4C hydraulic; 16,000lb @ 74 knots (tail-down method only)
Lifts: *Fwd* 42ft long x 34ft wide; *aft* 34ft long x 42ft wide; both 14,000lb
Aircraft: Up to 30 could be operated; up to 90 could be ferried
Aircraft fuel: 34,860 gallons AVGAS
Air weapons: 22.4in torpedoes; 18in torpedoes; 500lb SAP bombs; 250lb SAP bombs; 250lb GP bombs; Mk 11 depth charges; .5in gun ammunition; flares and pyrotechnics

HMS *Begum* in the EIF during 1944 with Avenger and Wildcat aircraft embarked. (FAA Museum)

Notes: Built as escort carrier from the outset but based on US C3 merchant hull. Laid down as USS *Bolinas* (CVE-36), one of 24 units of the USN *Prince William* class. Provisionally allocated the name *Chastiser* before acceptance by the RN under Lend/Lease arrangements.

Summary of service

02.08.43 Commissioned in Vancouver; defect rectifications and alterations
22.11.43 Work completed
04.01.44 Passed through Panama Canal
19.01.44 Sailed from New York for Liverpool with 1837 and 1838 NAS (Corsair) embarked
01.02.44 Clyde for refit
03.03.44 Allocated to 1 ACS, EF; embarked 1839 (Corsair), 1844 (Hellcat) and 815 and 817 (Barracuda) NAS for passage
26.04.44 Arrived in Colombo; initially used to ferry aircraft
11.06.44 Commenced AS sweeps as part of Force 66 with 832 NAS (Avenger/ Wildcat) embarked
16.01.45 Sailed for UK
20.02.45 Clyde for refit; allocated to BPF as ferry carrier
17.04.45 Sailed as part of KMF.43 with 721 (Vengeance) and 1701 (Sea Otter) NAS embarked for passage
05.06.45 Arrived in Sydney
15.06.45 Arrived in Manus with replacement aircraft
02.07.45 In Trincomalee; allocated to EIF as DLT carrier operating in Ceylon area
23.10.45 Sailed for UK
10.11.45 De-storing in Clyde
11.12.45 Sailed for USA via Portsmouth
05.01.46 Returned to USN at Norfolk, Va
16.04.47 Sold by USN; renamed *Raki*
00.00.66 Renamed *I Yung*
00.03.74 Broken up in Taiwan

Biter (D97) Avenger *Class Escort Carrier*

Laid down: 28 December 1939
Launched: 18 December 1940
Completed: 1 May 1942

Builder: Sun Shipbuilding and Drydock Corp., Chester; completed by Atlantic Basin Iron Works, Brooklyn
Machinery: 1 shaft; 2 Doxford diesels; 8,500bhp = 16 knots
Displacement: 12,150 tons standard; 15,700 tons full load
Dimensions: 492ft overall x 70ft max beam x 26ft 4in max draught
Gun armament: 3 single 4in US Mk 9 (3); 10 single 20m Oerlikon (10)
Fuel: 3,205 tons diesel
Endurance: 14,550 miles @ 10 knots
Complement: 555
Protection: None
Flight deck: 442ft x 70ft wood-covered steel
Arrester wires: 9 x 10,000lb @ 60 knots; 3 barriers
Hangar: 190ft x 47ft x 16ft
Catapults: 1 x H2 hydraulic, 7,000lb @ 61 knots (tail down method only)
Lifts: *Aft* 34ft long x 42ft wide; 12,000lb
Aircraft: Up to 15 could be operated; up to 90 could be ferried
Aircraft fuel: 36,000 gallons AVGAS
Air weapons: 18in torpedoes; Mk XXIV mines (homing torpedoes); 500lb SAP bombs; 250lb SAP bombs; 250lb GP bombs; 3in RP; Mk 7 depth charges; .5in gun ammunition; flares and pyrotechnics

Notes: Laid down as mercantile *Rio Parana*. Taken up incomplete by USN as unit of *Avenger* class (BAVG-3) for the RN under Lend/Lease arrangements. Sister-ship *Charger* retained by USN for aircrew training.

Summary of service

06.04.42 Commissioned in Brooklyn
00.06.42 Arrived in UK; allocated to HF and, after modifications, embarked 800 NAS (Sea Hurricane) to work up for operations in Mediterranean
22.10.42 Sailed with KMF.1 for Mediterranean; 833A Flight (Swordfish) embarked for passage to give AS defence but disembarked at Gibraltar
00.11.42 Operation 'Torch' (invasion of North Africa); ship formed part of the Centre Naval Task Group off Oran with *Furious* and *Dasher*; on completion, returned to UK for refit; allocated to WAC
21.04.43 Commenced AS operations with 811 NAS

HMS *Biter* at Lamlash in 1944. The structure that supported the flight deck above the basic hull is clear in this view. (G. M. Hughes via FAA Museum)

	(Swordfish/Wildcat) embarked in company with 5th Escort Group
22.04.43	Supported ONS.4
25.04.43	*U203* sunk by aircraft attack followed by depth-charge attack by destroyer *Pathfinder* and *Biter* herself (first occasion on which escort carrier did so)
05.05.43	Supported HX.237 and SC.129
11.05.43	Aircraft shared in sinking of *U89* (in all, 8 U-boats attacked in this period at sea, one of them twice by different aircraft)
19.10.43	Sailed from Clyde with 7th Support Group to support ON.207 westbound
07.11.43	Sailed from Argentia to support HX.265 and SC.146 (one attack carried out and both convoys sailed through U-boat concentration unscathed)
16.11.43	Swordfish crashed close alongside; its Mk XXIV mine (homing torpedo) did not detonate but broke loose and struck and damaged ship's rudder (damage took one month to repair)
12.02.44	Operated west of Finisterre with *Tracker* and 7th and 9th Escort Groups in support of OS.68, KMS.42 and ONS.29
16.02.44	811 NAS Wildcats shot down Junkers 290 that had carried out an ineffectual glider bomb attack on the force; later same day ship controlled interception by Beaufighter of No 235 Squadron, RAF Coastal Command, when a second Ju 290 was destroyed (believed to be only occasion on which an escort carrier controlled a successful interception by a shore-based fighter)
00.03.44	Supported SL.150 and MKS.41
00.04.44	Supported OS.73 and KMS.47
14.04.44	*U448*, while trying to attack *Biter*, sunk by *Pelican*
00.06.44	Employed in supporting Gibraltar convoys with *Activity*, *Nairana*, *Emperor*, *Campania*, *Searcher*, *Vindex* and *Fencer*
00.08.44	At Greenock for conversion to ferry carrier (U-boat threat to convoys in the Atlantic considered to have ceased—at least temporarily—and thus no further escort carriers employed on trade protection)
21.08.44	Allocated to MN for ferry duties
24.08.44	Major fire whilst alongside at Greenock; no dockyard capacity available for repairs, so

ship laid up in care and maintenance

09.04.45 Returned to USN custody in Clyde; refitted by USN and loaned to French Navy; renamed *Dixmude* and employed, initially, in ferrying aircraft from USA to France

00.00.46 Saw action off Indo-China, striking at Viet Minh irregulars in support of land forces; on completion reverted to ferrying duties (to 00.00.48)

00.00.56 Became accommodation ship for labourers

00.00.66 Returned to USN for disposal and subsequently scrapped

Bonaventure (CVL-22) Majestic *Class Light Fleet Carrier*

HMCS *Bonaventure*. Note the sponsons rebuilt to take the twin 3in mountings, the extensive array of sensors on the island (which was much modified from the original design) and the deck recognition number '22', rather than a letter, painted on deck. (Canadian Department of National Defence)

Laid down: 27 November 1943
Launched: 27 February 1945
Completed: 17 January 1957

Builder: Harland & Wolff, Belfast
Machinery: 2-shaft Parsons geared turbines; 4 Admiralty 3-drum boilers; 40,000shp = 24.5 knots
Displacement: 16,000 tons standard; 19,950 tons deep load
Dimensions: 704ft overall x 128ft max beam x 25ft max draught
Gun armament: 4 twin US 3in Mk 33 (8); 4 single 3pdr saluting (4)
Fuel: 3,200 tons FFO
Endurance: 12,000 miles @ 14 knots
Complement: 1,370
Protection: Armoured mantlets over torpedo warheads
Flight deck: 704ft x 80ft average; 8-degree angled deck
Arrester wires: 6 x 20,000lb @ 104 knots; emergency nylon barriers
Hangar: 273ft (plus 63ft extension aft of aft lift) x 52ft x 17ft 6in
Catapults: 1 x BS4 (103ft stroke); 40,000lb @ 78 knots
Lifts: *Fwd* 54ft long x 34ft wide; *aft* 54ft long x 34ft wide; both 24,000lb, 23-second cycle

Aircraft: 34
Aircraft fuel: 97,000 gallons AVCAT; 146,000 gallons AVGAS
Air weapons: Sidewinder AAM; Mk 30/44/46 homing torpedoes; 540lb bombs; 5in RP; depth charges; 20mm cannon ammunition; flares and pyrotechnics

Notes: Laid down and built as *Powerful* of the *Majestic* class. Purchased in 1952 and renamed *Bonaventure*, the first carrier owned outright by Canada.

Summary of service

17.01.57 Commissioned in Belfast by Mrs Ralph Campney, wife of Canadian Minister of National Defence
04.03.57 Sailed to Devonport to store and ammunition
02.04.57 Flying trials in English Channel with Banshee and Tracker aircraft flown across Atlantic for purpose; Whirlwind planeguard delivered by HMCS *Magnificent*
19.06.57 Sailed for Canada
26.06.57 Arrived in Halifax
30.09.57 Commenced work-up with VF-870 (Banshee) and VS-881 (Tracker) CNAS embarked and planeguard Whirlwind; air group could be modified to include mix of ASW helicopters from HS-50 (Whirlwind) CNAS
20.01.58 Sailed for training period in Caribbean
10.03.58 Flying exercises with HMS *Bulwark* off Bermuda, including cross-decking
01.05.58 Exercise 'New Broom VIII'
19.05.58 Refit in St John, New Brunswick
08.09.58 Sailed for post-refit work-up
00.10.58 NATO exercises in Mediterranean
26.11.58 Visited Portsmouth
15.12.58 Returned to Halifax
15.01.59 Sailed for exercises off Bermuda with VS-881 (Tracker) and HS-50 (Whirlwind) CNAS embarked
25.03.59 Exercise 'New Broom IX'
04.04.59 Visited Norfolk, Va
00.10.59 NATO Exercise 'Sharp Squall IV' followed by visits to British ports
00.01.60 Refit in St John, New Brunswick
00.03.60 Work-up off Bermuda
00.07.60 Further refit at St John
00.11.60 Re-joined fleet for work-up; air group now consisted of mix of VF-870 (Banshee), VS-880 (Tracker) and HS-50 (Whirlwind) CNAS plus SAR Whirlwind
00.02.61 Exercise 'Tout Droit'
00.07.61 Exercises with US Atlantic Fleet
00.10.61 Exercise 'Trapline'; ASW operations in north Canadian waters
16.04.62 10,000th arrested deck landing by Tracker '550'.
00.07.62 Exercise 'Fleetex 2' followed by refit in Champion Drydock in Lauzon PQ
00.09.62 VF-870 CNAS disbanded, ending fighter operations in RCN; air group then became specialist ASW force with VS-880 (Tracker) and HS-50 (Whirlwind) CNAS and SAR Whirlwind
17.09.62 Involved in search for survivors from 'Flying Tiger' Super Constellation which had ditched off Land's End (ship had been en route to Rotterdam with other units of Canadian Fleet)
00.10.62 Exercise 'Sharp Squall VI' with RN, Danish and Norwegian units
00.11.62 Operations in Atlantic north of Cuba during Missile crisis together with units of the USN
00.01.63 Refit in St John, New Brunswick; modified to operate ASW Sea Kings to replace Whirlwinds (Whirlwind retained for SAR duties)
00.05.63 Operations in Western Atlantic
00.08.63 Boiler uptake explosion whilst flashing up in Halifax, NS; repairs took 6 weeks
25.09.63 Sailed to cross Atlantic for NATO Exercise 'Sharp Squall' (AS training period in Greenland–Iceland–UK gap
00.10.63 Cross-deck operations with Dutch carrier *Karel Doorman*
12.12.63 Alongside in Halifax
16.01.64 Exercise 'Gooey Duck' (AS training off Bermuda)
00.02.64 Entered Mediterranean for visit to Toulon and Exercise 'Magic Lantern'
07.03.64 Withdrawn from exercise and returned to Halifax in order to ferry Canadian troops to Cyprus, where they were to form part of UN peacekeeping force
18.03.64 Operation 'Snow Goose' (ship ferried 54 vehicles, 400 tons of stores and 95 soldiers to Cyprus; retained 12 Trackers of VS-880 CNAS and could operate them despite vehicles and stores)
30.03.64 Anchored off Famagusta to disembark military equipment
22.04.64 Trials with Skyhawk aircraft off Norfolk (aircraft seen as a possible Banshee replacement)

HMCS *Bonaventure* in Grand Harbour, Valletta, Malta. The aircraft on deck are Trackers and Whirlwinds. (Canadian Department of National Defence)

00.05.64	Exercise 'Silex' (combined RCN/USN ASW training period in Atlantic)
14.05.64	Returned to Halifax
30.07.64	Refit in St John, New Brunswick
07.12.64	Carrier trials with new CHSS-2 Sea King helicopters of HS-50
09.01.65	'Don Messer' country and western TV show filmed on board
13.01.65	Sailed for AFWR with VS-880 (Tracker) and HS-50 (Sea King) CNAS embarked plus single planeguard HO4S-3 from HU-21 and COD Tracker from VU-32
00.02.65	Exercise 'Springboard' off Puerto Rico
00.03.65	Exercise ''Maple Springboard' with frigates of Canadian Atlantic Fleet
14.05.65	Visited Portsmouth
25.05.65	Sailed to visit Baltic and Scandinavian ports
14.06.65	Visited Belfast; on completion took part in a work-up based on JASS at Londonderry
09.07.65	Returned to Halifax for self-maintenance period
08.09.65	Sailed for exercises with *Ark Royal* and *Karel Doorman* in SWAPPS
19.11.65	Returned to Halifax
12.01.66	Sailed with AOR *Provider*, repair ship *Cape Scott* and 6 frigates for the largest yet Canadian training period in West Indies and South American waters
07.02.66	Visited Rio de Janeiro and Montevideo with Canadian task force
25.03.66	Returned to Halifax
00.04.66	Lauzon, Quebec, for major 'half life' refit
01.09.67	Refit completed
15.09.67	Took on stores and ammunition at Halifax
00.10.67	Flying work-up
01.11.67	Operational work-up
31.01.68	RCN ceased to exist; *Bonaventure* and Canadian naval aviation became part of integrated CAF
00.02.68	Exercise 'Maple Spring' in AFWR
22.02.68	Sea King '305' ditched and, for first time in any navy, was salvaged at sea, being craned on to *Bonaventure*'s flight deck
01.03.68	Visited New Orleans for 'Canada Week'
00.05.68	Returned to Halifax
00.06.68	Amphibious Exercise 'Racer Run' with USN
00.08.68	EASTLANT deployment with visit to Belfast before NATO command and control Exercise 'Silver Tower' with *Eagle* and escorts
28.09.68	'Wash up' in Rosyth
00.10.68	Visited Portsmouth
30.10.68	Returned to Halifax
26.01.69	Sailed for Exercise 'Maple Spring' in AFWR
22.03.69	Returned to Halifax
00.09.69	'Shop window' for Canadian Parliamentary sub-commitee looking into the future of

	carrier aviation; followed by NATO Exercise 'Peace Keeper' off west coast of Ireland, during which ship logged record number of flying hours in atrocious weather; then visited Holland and Norway
14.10.69	Visited Portsmouth
22.10.69	Sailed for Canada
28.10.69	Last night landing by fixed-wing aircraft
00.12.69	Visited Boston
12.12.69	Last fixed-wing launch
00.01.70	Carried troops of Loyal 22nd Regiment to Jamaica for exercises ashore
00.02.70	Acted as AOR for Exercise 'Maple Spring' with 6 Sea Kings of HS-50 embarked.
00.04.70	Collected Canadian military forces from Narvik after Exercise 'Arctic Express'; on completion, visited Portsmouth for last time
03.07.70	Paid off in Halifax
00.03.71	Towed to Taiwan and broken up by Tung-Chen Iron and Steelworks Co.

Bulwark (R08) Centaur *Class Commando Carrier*

Laid down: 10 May 1945
Launched: 22 June 1948
Completed: 4 November 1954

Builder: Harland & Wolff, Belfast
Machinery: 2-shaft Parsons geared turbines; 4 Admiralty 3-drum boilers; 76,000shp = 28 knots
Displacement: 22,000 tons standard; 27,800 tons deep load
Dimensions: 737ft overall x 123ft 6in max beam x 28ft 3in max draught
Gun armament: 4 twin 40mm Bofors (8); 4 single 3pdr saluting (4)
Fuel: 4,085 tons FFO
Endurance: 6,000 miles @ 20 knots
Complement: 1,800 (inc. commandos and NAS)
Protection: 1in–2in flight deck; 1in uptakes; 1in magazine crowns
Flight deck: 733ft x 84ft steel
Arrester wires: None as commando carrier
Hangar: 274ft (plus 55ft extension fwd of fwd lift) x 62ft x 17ft 6in
Catapults: None as commando carrier
Lifts: *Fwd* 54ft long x 44ft wide; *aft* 54ft long x 44ft wide; both 35,000lb
Aircraft: 30 helicopters (in 1971)
Aircraft fuel: 299,000 gallons AVCAT; 50,000 gallons AVGAS/MOGAS
Air weapons: SS.11 ATG missiles; AS.12 ATG missiles; Mk 44 torpedoes; 2in RP; Mk 11 depth charges; 7.62mm MG ammunition; flares and pyrotechnics

Notes: Originally built as a light fleet carrier (for details before conversion to commando carrier see *Albion*). A second commando could be carried in austere conditions for a 'quick dash' to an operating area. She had a splendid record in action and in peacetime exercises and stands as an example of what can be achieved with a comparatively simple design.

Summary of service

00.00.48	Named by Countess Granville, sister of HM Queen Elizabeth the Queen Mother
29.10.54	Commissioned in Belfast
00.11.54	Fitted with mirror landing sight in Portsmouth; relieved *Illustrious* as trials and training carrier
07.02.55	First arrested landing, by Avenger of 703 NAS from RNAS Ford
01.06.55	Summer cruise with HF: visited Oslo with 800 and 811 (Sea Hawk) and 751 (Avenger) NAS embarked
06.08.56	Deployed from UK to join MF with 804, 897 and 810 (Sea Hawk) NAS embarked
01.11.56	Operation 'Musketeer' (Suez landings): aircraft struck at Egyptian targets in support of Anglo-French landings, flying nearly 600 sorties
18.12.56	Returned to Portsmouth for refit
00.05.57	Re-joined HF with 820 (Gannet AS), 891 (Sea Venom), 849D (Skyraider) and 801 and 898 (Sea Hawk) NAS embarked
27.08.57	845 NAS (Whirlwind) joined air group
00.09.57	NATO Exercise 'Strikeback' with *Ark Royal*; first carrier to use flight deck magnetic loop communication system
02.12.57	820 NAS disembarked and disbanded
00.01.58	Training in Caribbean
09.03.58	Flag of CinC HF transferred to ship from *Maidstone* for first phase of Exercise 'Maple Royal' with RCN

HMS *Bulwark* assisting the tanker *Melika* in September 1958. A Whirlwind helicopter, Sea Hawks and Sea Venoms are parked on deck and the frigate HMS *Puma* is visible in the background. (Author)

00.05.58	Deployed to FEF
00.07.58	Involved in Middle East crisis; cut short visit to Mombasa and carried infantry battalion with its stores and vehicles from Kenya to Aden
00.08.58	Ferried further infantry battalion from Aden to Aqaba in Jordan
13.09.58	Aircraft rendered assistance to two tankers on fire after collision off Persian Gulf; took one, *Melika*, in tow to Muscat (845 NAS won Boyd Trophy for 1958 for efforts in connection with this salvage)
05.11.58	Disembarked air group and returned to Portsmouth
00.01.59	Entered Portsmouth Dockyard for conversion to commando carrier
23.01.60	Recommissioned at Portsmouth; embarked 848 NAS (Whirlwind) and 42 RM Cdo; sailed for work-up in Mediterranean
02.04.60	Visited in Mediterranean by Admiral of the Fleet the Earl Mountbatten of Burma
25.04.60	HRH the Duke of Edinburgh witnessed exercises landing on Libyan beaches
01.07.61	Operation 'Vantage': landed 42 RM Cdo during Kuwait crisis (ship had been visiting Karachi and arrived off Kuwait within 24 hours of request for British aid, having made a high-speed dash into the Persian Gulf); fixed-wing air support provided by *Victorious*; by 08.07.61 it was clear that amphibious operation had succeeded and that Iraqi threat to invade Kuwait had receded
01.10.61	Recommissioned in Singapore (first carrier since WW2 to commission away from its UK base port)
00.01.62	Exercise 'Tombstone' (42 RM Cdo landed in north-west Australia)

00.03.62 Exercised in Persian Gulf
00.04.62 Wessex of 815 NAS embarked from *Ark Royal* for familiarisation
00.05.62 Exercise 'Common Assault 3' (training Hong Kong garrison troops in helicopter landing techniques in New Territories)
00.07.62 Refit in Singapore followed by Exercise 'FOTEX 62'
00.10.62 Visited Kuwait after further exercises with Amphibious Warfare Squadron in Persian Gulf
20.11.62 Transferred stores to *Albion* off Aden
17.12.62 Arrived in Devonport for refit
03.12.63 Recommissioned at Devonport; sailed with 706 (*Bulwark*) Flight with Wessex helicopters and 43 RM Cdo.
00.03.64 Exercise 'Sandfly 2' off North African coast
23.03.64 Relieved *Albion* in FEF off Aden; 706B amalgamated with 845 NAS (Wessex) transferred from *Albion*
00.04.64 Provided support for operations in Borneo during confrontation with Indonesia; half of 845 NAS operated ashore at Sibu, Nanga Gaat and Simanggang (for these efforts, 845 NAS awarded Boyd Trophy for 1964)
00.03.65 Exercise 'FOTEX 65' with *Melbourne*, *Victorious* and *Eagle* in Singapore areas (combined force included units of RN, RAN, RNZN and Royal Malaysian Navy)
00.04.65 Maintenance period in Singapore, followed by visit to Western Australia
03.09.65 Arrived in Plymouth for refit
22.04.66 Recommissioned in Plymouth
18.06.66 Carried out sea trials with Kestrel (forerunner of Sea Harrier)
00.06.66 Embarked 845 NAS (now equipped with Wessex 5 helicopters) and 42 RM Cdo for Exercise 'Dry Fly' on west coast of Scotland
28.08.66 Relieved *Albion* in FEF south of Suez Canal
00.10.66 Embarked 845 NAS detachment from Borneo after end of confrontation, followed by Exercise 'Barrawinga' off Queensland
00.06.67 Landed 3 Cdo Bde at Kuantan in eastern Malaysia with *Fearless* in company
00.08.67 Drydocked in Singapore
23.10.67 Recommissioned in Singapore
00.03.68 Sailed for UK via South Africa
03.06.68 Exercise 'Polar Express' off Norway with 845 NAS (Wessex) and 45 RM Cdo embarked
00.08.68 Commenced major refit in Portsmouth, ship's company being accommodated in *Centaur*

After her conversion to a commando carrier, HMS *Bulwark* carried out trials with the Hawker P.1127, forerunner of the Sea Harrier, seen here right aft, turning on to a white line painted along the axis of the former angled deck. The white circles are helicopter landing spots. Two Wessexes and a Whirlwind are parked forward. (Author)

HMS *Bulwark* refuelling the minesweeper HMS *Woolaston* during operations with the FEF off Borneo. Whirlwind helicopters are spotted on deck, with commando transport parked aft. (FAA Museum)

17.04.69 Sailed to Plymouth to embark 41 RM Cdo group; once aboard, ship sailed for the Mediterranean still with 845 NAS embarked
00.04.69 Landed 845 NAS and 41 RM Cdo in Cyprus for Exercise 'Grecian Vase', followed by Exercise 'Olympic Express' off Salonika
15.08.69 Returned to Portsmouth
10.11.69 Recommissioned at Devonport
21.01.70 Sailed for Far East with 848 NAS (Wessex) embarked
00.06.70 Exercise 'Bersatu Padu', involving over 50 ships, 200 aircraft and 20,000 men from Australia, New Zealand, Malaysia, Singapore and UK; 40 RM Cdo landed at Penarek from *Bulwark*; on completion, ship sailed for UK via Djakarta, Fremantle, Durban and Gibraltar
20.08.70 Arrived in Devonport for refit
13.05.71 Embarked 845 NAS (Wessex) and sailed for Stockholm and Helsinki flying flag of CinC WF
12.06.71 Exercise 'Dry Fly III' in Loch Fyne with 41 RM Cdo
30.06.71 Transited Gibraltar for Mediterranean and Exercise 'Deep Furrow 71' in which *Bulwark* and *Fearless* landed 41 RM Cdo Group in Turkish Thrace (forces from Turkey, Italy and USA also took part)
26.11.71 Fire damaged 'B' boiler room; repairs carried out in Devonport Dockyard
13.01.72 Sailed for Malta to act as HQ ship for Operation 'Exit' (planned withdrawal of British forces); spent two and a half months moored in Grand Harbour, during which 845 NAS carried out over 1,000 deck landings (in the event, Malta was retained as base for further seven years)
00.03.72 Sailed across Atlantic for Exercise 'Rum Punch' on Vieques Island east of Puerto Rico (USMC training area); on completion, 41 RM Cdo returned to Malta and 845 NAS transferred to *Albion*
17.06.72 DED in Portsmouth.
17.07.72 Exercise 'West Hoe' with other fleet units
00.09.72 Deployed to Mediterranean with 848 NAS (Wessex) and 42 RM Cdo in company with *Fearless* and *Intrepid*
10.01.73 Embarked 40 RM Cdo in Plymouth and sailed for USA and Caribbean to exercise with USMC
00.02.73 Visited Charleston, SC, flying flag of FOCAS (largest warship to sail under Cooper Bridge); on completion, took part in Exercise 'Rum Punch 73' on Vieques Island
25.04.73 Deployed to Mediterranean to embark 41 RM Cdo from Malta for exercises in Cyprus; on completion, sailed into North Atlantic, exchanging 848 NAS for 814 and 820 (Sea King) NAS off RNAS Culdrose; participated in Anglo-US AS exercises inside Arctic Circle
00.07.73 Exercise 'Sally Forth 73' (combined RN/RAF demonstration of versatility to government ministers and NATO Military Committee in Firth of Forth)
26.07.73 Alongside in Devonport
04.09.73 Deployed to Mediterranean with 848 NAS and 42 RM Cdo for Exercise 'Deep Furrow 73' (major NATO effort involving 54 ships and 50,000 Marines and troops from UK, USA, Greece, Turkey and Italy)
00.01.74 Deployed to Caribbean with force of Dutch Marines embarked
16.01.74 Damaged by storms north-east of Azores (Sea State 9)
00.02.74 Visited Willemstad, Curacao, while Dutch Marines exercised ashore; in same deployment, became largest warship to visit Cartagena, Colombia
15.02.74 Exercise 'Caribtrain' (gathering of 14 RN and RFA ships off Virgin Gorda, with both First Sea Lord and CinC Fleet present)
08.03.74 Entered Devonport Dockyard for refit
07.02.75 Refit completed
10.03.75 Portland work-up; on completion, deployed to Mediterranean for exercises with US Sixth Fleet with 848 NAS and 41 RM Cdo
25.04.75 Cracked propeller exchanged for a new one in drydock in Gibraltar
00.06.75 Exercise 'Dawn Patrol' with 1 ACG RNethMC as well as 41 RM Cdo
03.07.75 Returned to Portsmouth
01.09.75 Deployed to Mediterranean again with 848 NAS and 40 RM Cdo for Exercise 'Deep Express 75' (landings in Turkish Thrace) followed by visit to Istanbul with *Hermes*
00.11.75 Exercise 'Triple Jubilee' with US and Dutch Marines on Dartmoor, Lulworth and Salisbury Plain supported by amphibious task force in Channel
00.01.76 Deployed to Caribbean with 848 NAS, 40 RM Cdo, Band of Royal Green Jackets and 1 ACG for exercises with Dutch forces in Curacao, USMC off Puerto Rico and Marine wing of Royal Bahamian Police Force

09.04.76 Cermonial return to Portsmouth, followed by Farewell Ball
00.05.76 Reduced to reserve status (preservation by operation) in Portsmouth with ship's company of about 200
20.03.78 Taken in hand in Portsmouth for refit to prepare ship for further operational service (last commission made necessary by the new *Invincible* class carriers' not being ready when *Ark Royal* paid off)
23.02.79 Recommissioned in Portsmouth in presence of HRH the Prince of Wales
27.02.79 Commenced work-up with 846 (Sea King Commando) and 826 (Sea King ASW) NAS
28.06.79 Sailed for Baltic and Exercise 'Whiskey Venture' with 820 (Sea King ASW) NAS added to air group, 45 RM Cdo and 1 ACG
19.09.79 Deployed to Mediterranean to exercise with garrison in Cyprus
04.01.80 Deployed to USA with 814, 820 and part of 846 NAS embarked (only carrier in commission in the RN at the time)
22.02.80 Exercise 'Safe Pass' (ASW exercise off US East Coast)
15.03.80 'A1' boiler room destroyed by fire (never repaired)
02.04.80 Returned to Portsmouth
00.04.80 Embarked 45 RM Cdo and deployed to Mediterranean for Exercise 'Dawn Patrol' off Sardinia; on completion, returned to Portsmouth for maintenance period
00.08.80 Deployed 40 RM Cdo to exercises in Norway and took part in Exercise ' Teamwork 80' (NATO ASW training period in North Atlantic)
09.11.80 Major fire damaged forward hangar and several messdecks whilst alongside in Portsmouth; concern about wiring led to withdrawal from service 6 months earlier than expected; planned deployment to USA cancelled but, with 42 RM Cdo embarked, ship took part in Exercise 'Cold Winter' off Norwegian coast in early 1981
27.03.81 Entered Portsmouth for last time
00.04.81 De-stored for disposal
10.04.84 Taken in tow from Portsmouth to breaker's yard
17.04.84 Arrived at Cairnryan for scrapping

Campania (1944) (R48) *Escort Carrier*

Laid down: 12 August 1941
Launched: 17 June 1943
Completed: 7 March 1944

Builder: Harland & Wolff, Belfast
Machinery: 2 shafts; 2 Burmeister and Wain diesels; 13,250bhp = 18 knots
Displacement: 13,000 tons standard; 15,970 tons deep load
Dimensions: 540ft overall x 70ft max beam x 23ft 7in max draught
Gun armament: 1 twin 4in Mk XVI HA (2); 4 quadruple 2pdr pompom (16); 8 twin 20mm Oerlikon (16)
Fuel: 2,230 tons diesel
Endurance: 17,000 miles @ 17 knots
Complement: 639
Protection: 1in magazine crowns; empty oil drums in voids to provide measure of torpedo protection
Flight deck: 515ft x 70ft steel
Arrester wires: 4 x 15,500lb @ 60 knots; 1 barrier
Hangar: 198ft x 63ft 6in x 17ft 6in
Catapults: None
Lifts: *Aft* 45ft long x 34ft wide; 15,000lb
Aircraft: 20
Aircraft fuel: 52,000 gallons AVGAS
Air weapons: Mk XXIV mines (homing torpedoes); 18in torpedoes; 250lb GP bombs; 3in RP; Mk 7 depth charges; aircraft mines; .5in gun ammunition; .303in gun ammunition; flares and pyrotechnics

Notes: Taken over by the Admiralty on 29 July 1942 after she had been on the stocks for nearly a year building as a merchant ship. Some structure had to be dismantled and internal decks were made watertight with additonal transverse bulkheads added. Unlike US escort carriers, the hangar and flight deck were built up as part of the structure of the hull and not added as superstructure. The lack of a second lift proved a liability and made ranging aircraft from the forward end of the hangar difficult. This, coupled with the lack of parking space in Fly 1 forward of the single barrier, limited to 20 the effective air group that could be operated. *Campania* and her half-sisters *Nairana* and *Vindex*

HMS *Campania* in 1944. (Author)

were used in arctic operations because it was felt that their riveted hulls would be less susceptible to fracture and cracking in sub-zero temperatures than the welded hulls of US-built CVEs. She was equipped for fighter direction and with flight deck lighting to support night flying.

Summary of service

09.02.44	Commissioned in Belfast
08.03.44	Sailed for work-up in Clyde area
16.04.44	Engine defect repairs in Belfast
23.05.44	Completed work-up
03.06.44	Allocated to WAC with 813 NAS (Swordfish/Fulmar NF/Wildcat) embarked; sailed to cover OS.79, KMS.53, SL.160 and MKS.51
02.07.44	Covered OS.82, KM.56, SL.163 and MKS.54
03.08.44	Covered OS.85, KMS.59, SL.166 and MKS.57
19.09.44	Defect repairs in Belfast
14.09.44	Deployed to Scapa Flow, attached to HF
16.09.44	Sailed from Scapa Flow as part of escort with JW.60 to North Russia (Operation 'Rigmarole')
28.09.44	Sailed from Kola with cover for RA.60
30.09.44	Aircraft sank *U921*
21.10.44	Arrived in Scapa Flow
23.10.44	Sailed with *Fencer* and *Trumpeter* for minelaying operations by HF off Trondheim
27.10.44	In Scapa Flow
01.11 44	Sailed with cover for JW.61A to North Russia (Operation 'Golden')
10.11 44	Sailed from Kola with cover for RA.61A; suffered weather damage
27.11.44	In Scapa Flow
30.11 44	Sailed with cover for JW. 62 (Operation 'Acumen')
10.12.44	Sailed from Kola with cover for RA.62
13.12.44	Aircraft sank *U365*
20.12.44	Repairs in Clyde
16.01.45	In Scapa Flow
28.01.45	Sailed with carriers *Nairana* and *Trumpeter* for anti-shipping strike off Norway by HF with 4 Wildcats of 842 NAS added to air group
03.02.45	Sailed from Scapa Flow with cover for JW.64
17.02.45	Sailed from Kola with cover for RA.64
01.03.45	Clyde for repairs
12.03.45	Sailed from Scapa Flow with cover for JW.65
23.03.45	Sailed from Kola with cover for RA.65
07.04.45	Clyde for repairs
05.06.45	Hit dock on leaving
10.06.45	London for damage repairs
11.08.45	In The Nore; allocated for trooping duties
09.09.45	Sailed from Devonport for Trinidad trooping with no aircraft

28.09.45	Sailed from Trinidad for Clyde trooping
29.10.45	Sailed from Clyde for Trinidad trooping
19.11.45	Sailed from Trinidad for Clyde trooping
10.12.45	Arrived in Devonport; de-stored into reserve
30.12.45	Laid up in reserve (Category B) in Rosyth
00.00.47	Considered for conversion to RFA-manned ferry carrier but no action taken
00.00.50	Converted to exhibition ship
00.00.51	Toured UK as floating exhibition ship for Festival of Britain
00.00.52	Fitted out as HQ ship for British atomic bomb tests at Monte Bello Island
00.10.52	Atomic tests carried out
00.00.53	Laid up in reserve at Chatham
11.11.55	Breaking-up commenced at Blyth

Centaur (R06) *Light Fleet Carrier*

Laid down: 30 May 1944
Launched: 22 April 1947
Completed: 1 September 1953

Builder: Harland & Wolff, Belfast
Machinery: 2-shaft Parsons geared turbines; 4 Admiralty 3-drum boilers; 76,000shp = 28 knots

Displacement: 20,260 tons standard; 27,800 tons deep load
Dimensions: 737ft overall x 123ft max beam x 28ft 3in max draught
Gun armament: 4 twin 40mm Bofors (8); 2 single 40mm Bofors (2); 4 single 3pdr saluting (4)
Fuel: 3,500 tons FFO

HMS *Centaur* was the only ship of her class to complete to the original 1943 design, without an angled deck. She is seen here on initial trials off Portsmouth in October 1953. (FAA Museum)

HMS *Centaur* in the Brisbane River during Centenary celebrations in 1959. (FAA Museum)

Endurance: 5,040 miles @ 20 knots
Complement: 1,390
Protection: 1in–2in flight deck; 1in uptakes; 1in magazine crowns
Flight deck: 733ft x 123ft steel; 6-degree angled deck
Arrester wires: 6 x 35,000lb @ 103 knots; emergency nylon barriers
Hangar: 274ft (plus 55ft extension fwd of fwd lift) x 62ft x 17ft 6in
Catapults: 2 x BS4 (139ft stroke); 40,000lb @ 94 knots
Lifts: *Fwd* 54ft long x 44ft wide, 37,000lb; *aft* 54ft long x 44ft wide, 40,000lb; both 22-second cycle
Aircraft: Up to 42
Aircraft fuel: 295,000 gallons AVCAT; 50,000 gallons AVGAS
Air weapons: Firestreak AAM; Sidewinder AAM; Bullpup ASM; Mk 30/44/46 homing torpedoes; 2,000lb MC bombs; 1,000lb MC bombs; 500lb GP bombs; 3in RP; 2in RP; Mk 11 depth charges; 30mm cannon ammunition; 20mm cannon ammunition; Glowworm illuminant RP; flares and pyrotechnics

Notes: *Centaur* was the only ship of her class to be completed to the original 1943 design with an axial flight deck. She was modified to take an interim angled deck after initial sea trials. Steam catapults were fitted in [illegible] and improved arresting gear to take the Scimitar in 1960–61. In her last refit in 1963, Type 965, an improved air warning radar, was fitted. The details show *Centaur* as she was in 1964.

Summary of service

22.04.47	Launched by HRH the Duchess of Kent
17.09.53	Commissioned at Belfast to original design
Win. 53/4	Engaged in trials in Portsmouth area, on completion of which ship was taken in hand in February 1954 to have 5.5-degree angled deck fitted
14.05.54	Operation 'Loyalty' (escort for HM Queen Elizabeth II in HMY *Britannia* passing up-Channel on completion of her Australian tour)
00.09.54	Embarked 806 (Sea Hawk), 810 (Sea Fury) and 820 (Avenger) NAS (plus SAR Dragonfly of Ship's Flight) and worked up with MF
00.10.54	Embarked British troops during withdrawal from Trieste
00.01.55	Exercised with US Sixth Fleet in Western Mediterranean
07.06.55	Arrived in Portsmouth for DED
10.01.56	Sailed for FEF with 803 and 806 (Sea Hawk) and 814 (Gannet) NAS embarked plus Dragonfly of Ship's Flight
15.05.56	Returned to Devonport; taken in hand for limited modernisation
03.09.58	Recommissioned; for remainder of 1958 was engaged in trials and exercises with HF; air group comprised 801 (Sea Hawk), 810 (Gannet AS.4) and 891 (Sea Venom) NAS
00.05.59	Visited Copenhagen before sailing to join FEF

00.07.59	Visited Karachi
00.08.59	Hoisted flag of FO2 FEF; (largest Commonwealth naval exercise since 1945)
00.10.59	Visited Subic Bay, then Australia
00.03.60	Exercise 'Jet 60'
00.04.60	Operation 'Damon' (strikes against arms smugglers in Western Aden)
24.04.60	Returned to Devonport
00.06.60	Flying exercises in UK waters
29.08.60	Portsmouth Dockyard for refit
03.03.61	Recommissioned; worked up and embarked 807 (Scimitar), 893 (Sea Vixen), 849A (Gannet AEW) and 824 (Whirlwind) NAS; sailed for deployment to MF
00.07.61	Passed through Suez Canal to relieve *Victorious* off Kuwait following threatened Iraqi invasion
00.09.61	Returned to Devonport.
00.10.61	Sailed for the Middle East station
00.11.61	Flood relief operations in Kenya (helicopters operated 'flying doctor' service to remote areas and evacuated casualties)
00.01.62	Joined FEF
27.01.62	Went to aid of Greek tanker *Stanvac Sumatra* which had broken in two 250 miles south-east of Saigon in South China Sea
00.02.62	Maintenance period in Singapore
00.03.62	Exercise 'Jet 62'
00.04.62	Returned to UK, exercising with MF en route
17.05.62	Arrived in Portsmouth
23.07.62	Sailed for MF
00.08.62	Exercise 'Riptide', followed by visits to Mediterranean ports
26.10.62	Returned to Portsmouth
21.11.62	DED in Portsmouth
00.02.63	Embarked 892 (Sea Vixen), 849A (Gannet AEW) and 815 (Wessex ASW) NAS and sailed for FEF
00.05.63	Returned to Portsmouth for refit
00.11.63	Refit completed
20.12.63	Sailed to join FEF
00.01.64	Carried 45 RM Cdo, 16/5 Lancers, 2 RAF Belvedere helicopters and their vehicles plus ship's full air group from Aden to quell mutiny by units of Tanganyika Rifles (operation completely successful—and an excellent demonstration of how flexible a carrier can be)
00.03.64	Rescued survivors from the Greek liner *Lakonia*
25.04.64	Carried out strikes against rebelling tribesmen in Radfan, north of Aden
21.12.64	Returned to Portsmouth
00.04.65	Flagship of MF

HMS *Centaur* proceeding at speed from Aden to Dar-es-Salaam on 24 January 1964. Despite the sizeable embarked military force, she remained capable of operating her air group of Sea Vixens, Gannets and Wessexes—although it would have been a tight squeeze. (FAA Museum)

00.12.65	Paid off at Portsmouth; used as accommodation ship for *Victorious*'s refit
00.10.66	Employed as accommodation ship in Devonport Dockyard during *Eagle*'s refit
15.03.67	Tender to HMS *Drake* as accommodation ship
31.05.67	Towed to Portsmouth for use as accommodation ship during *Hermes*' refit
24.04.70	Towed to Plymouth; continued to be used as accommodation ship
11.08.72	Sold to Shipbreaking (Queenborough), Kent, and broken up

Chaser (D32) Attacker *Class Escort Carrier*

Laid down: 28 June 1941
Launched: 15 January 1942
Completed: 9 April 1943

Builder: Ingalls Shipbuilding Corp., Pascagoula
Machinery: 1-shaft Westinghouse geared turbine; 2 Foster Wheeler boilers; 8,500shp = 18 knots
Displacement: 10,200 tons standard; 14,170 tons deep load
Dimensions: 495ft 9in x 102ft max beam x 26ft max draught
Gun armament: 2 single 4in US Mk 9 (2); 4 twin 40mm Bofors (8); 4 twin 20mm Oerlikon (8); 4 single 20mm Oerlikon (4)
Fuel: 3,270 tons FFO
Endurance: 27,300 miles @ 11 knots
Complement: 646
Protection: Splinter protection for bomb room
Flight deck: 442ft x 102ft wood-covered steel
Arrester wires: 9 x 19,800lb @ 55 knots; 3 barriers
Hangar: 262ft x 62ft x 18ft
Catapults: 1 x H2 hydraulic; 7,000lb @ 61 knots (tail-down method only)
Lifts: *Fwd* 42ft long x 34ft wide; *aft* 34ft long x 42ft wide; both 14,000lb
Aircraft: Up to 20 could be operated; up to 90 could be ferried
Aircraft fuel: 52,800 gallons AVGAS
Air weapons: Mk XXIV mines (homing torpedoes); 18in torpedoes; 500lb SAP bombs; 250lb SAP bombs;

HMS *Chaser* as a ferry carrier with the BPF in July 1945. Corsairs, Seafires and Avengers are parked on deck. (FAA Museum)

250lb GP bombs; 3in RP; Mk 11 depth charges; 20mm gun ammunition; .303in gun ammunition; flares and pyrotechnics

Notes: Laid down as the mercantile *Mormacgulf*. Acquired before launch for conversion and built as USS *Breton* (AVG-10) of the USN *Bogue* class. Transferred to the RN under Lend/Lease arrangements.

Summary of service

09.04.43 Commissioned in Pascagoula
23.04.43 Arrived in Norfolk, Va
31.05.43 Work-up in Chesapeake Bay area
23.06.43 Embarked 845 NAS (Avenger) for passage and sailed for UK with HX.245
06.07.43 Arrived in Clyde
07.07.43 Boiler explosion (repairs in Rosyth)
29.10.43 Allocated to WAC; commenced work-up in Clyde area; embarked 835 NAS (Swordfish/Sea Hurricane) and carried out flying work-up based on Scapa Flow
29.11.43 Repairs on Clyde
21.02.44 Sailed from Scapa Flow as part of escort of JW.57 with 816 NAS (Swordfish/Wildcat) embarked
02.03.44 Escorted RA.57
04.03.44 Swordfish 'B' sank *U472* with 3in RP 27 miles from convoy (destroyer *Onslaught* fired at stricken U-boat on surface)
05.03.44 Swordfish 'F' sank *U366* with 3in RP
06.03.44 Swordfish 'X' sank *U973* with 3in RP
13.03.44 Dragged anchor and grounded; towed off next day
18.03.44 Rosyth for refit and repairs, followed by conversion to ferry role in Belfast
04.02.45 Allocated to BPF as replenishment carrier; sailed for Far East in KMF.41 to Gibraltar and thence via Suez, Aden, Cochin and Colombo
00.05.45 Arrived in Sydney; sailed for Manus Island
18.05.45 Employed in replenishment operations off Okinawa.
00.07.45 Ferried aircraft from Leyte to operational areas off Japan (aircraft load was 9 Seafires, 7 Avengers, 6 Corsairs, 1 Hellcat and 1 Firefly)
31.07.45 With Replenishment Group off Japan
00.08.45 In Manus
03.10.45 Repairs in Sydney
00.03.46 In Soerabaya
12.05.46 Returned to USN; sold as mercantile *Aagtekerk*; later renamed *E Yung*
04.12.72 Foundered
00.00.73 Salvaged and broken up in Taiwan

HMS *Colossus* on 25 September 1945 whilst serving with the BPF. Two Barracudas are parked aft, with two Corsairs forward. (FAA Museum)

Colossus (15) Colossus *Class Light Fleet Carrier*

Laid down: 1 June 1942
Launched: 30 September 1943
Completed: 16 December 1944

Builder: Vickers-Armstrong, Newcastle-upon-Tyne
Machinery: 2-shaft Parsons geared turbines; 4 Admiralty 3-drum boilers; 40,000shp = 25 knots
Displacement: 13,190 tons standard; 18,040 tons deep load
Dimensions: 695ft overall x 112ft 6in max beam x 23ft 5in max draught
Gun armament: 6 quadruple 2pdr pompom (24); 11 twin 20mm Oerlikon (22); 10 single 20mm Oerlikon (10); 4 single 3pdr saluting (4)
Fuel: 3,196 tons FFO
Endurance: 8,300 miles @ 20 knots
Complement: 1,300
Protection: Armoured mantlets over torpedo warheads in magazine

Flight deck: 690ft x 80ft steel
Arrester wires: 8 x 15,000lb @ 60 knots; 2 barriers
Hangar: 275ft (plus 57ft extension aft of aft lift) x 52ft x 17ft 6in
Catapults: 1 x BH3; 16,000lb @ 66 knots
Lifts: *Fwd* 45ft long x 34ft wide; *aft* 45ft long x 34ft wide; both 15,000lb
Aircraft: 42 in 1945
Aircraft fuel: 80,000 gallons AVGAS
Air weapons: 18in torpedoes; 2,000lb bombs; 500lb SAP bombs; 500lb MC bombs; 250lb B bombs; Mk 11 depth charges; mines; .5in gun ammunition; .303in gun ammunition; flares and pyrotechnics

Notes: Name-ship of the first class of 1942 light fleet carriers. Based on experience with maintenance carrier *Unicorn*, which she resembled, but with only one hangar deck. Hull and fittings built to Lloyd's Register standards for merchant ships, thus enabling the class to be

The hangar in HMS *Colossus* laid out with camp beds ready to receive former POWs from Japanese camps. (FAA Museum)

built quickly and in shipyards not normally used for naval work. The detailed design work was carried out by Vickers.

Summary of service

01.12.44 Commissioned in Walker Naval Yard, Tyneside
16.12.44 Trials and work-up in Tyne area
12.03.45 Sailed to join 11 ACS, BPF
26.07.45 Part of Task Group 111.2 with 1846 (Corsair) and 827 (Barracuda) NAS embarked; saw no action but after VJ Day was used to repatriate British and Australian former POWs to Australia
22.11.45 Transferred to East Indies Station
23.07.46 Returned to UK and then paid off in Portsmouth
06.08.46 Transferred to French Navy on loan for five years (renamed *Arromanches*)
00.00.49 Deployed to South-East Asia with Seafire and Dauntless aircraft to support military operations in Indo-China
00.00.51 Purchased outright by France
00.00.53 Air group comprised Hellcats and Helldivers supplied by USN
00.11.56 Part of Anglo-French task force off Suez with air group of Corsairs
00.00.57 Modernised with 4-degree angled deck (to 00.00.58)
00.00.68 Refitted as ASW helicopter carrier
00.00.73 Paid off into reserve at Toulon
31.10.74 Original ship's bell returned to RN during service in *Hermes* during visit to Toulon
00.00.78 Broken up in Toulon

Courageous (50) Courageous *Class Fleet Carrier*

Laid down: 28 March 1915
Launched: 5 February 1916
Completed: 4 November 1916 as battlecruiser; 5 May 1928 as carrier

Builder: Sir W. G. Armstrong Whitworth & Co., Newcastle-upon-Tyne
Machinery: 4-shaft Parsons geared turbines; 18 Yarrow small-tube boilers; 90,670shp = 30 knots
Displacement: 22,500 tons standard; 27,560 tons deep load
Dimensions: 786ft 6in overall x 110ft max beam x 28ft max draught
Gun armament: 16 single 4.7in QF Mk VIII HA (16); 4 single 3pdr (3); 10 single .303in MG (10)
Fuel: 3,685 tons FFO
Endurance: 2,920 miles @ 24 knots
Complement: 1,260
Protection: 3in side belts; 3in fwd and 2in aft bulkheads; 1.75in over machinery spaces; 0.75in funnel uptakes; 1.75in over steering gear; external anti-torpedo bulges designed to defeat torpedo warheads up to 440lb
Flight deck: 530ft x 91ft 6in steel
Arrester wires: 4 x 11,000lb @ 53 knots; no barrier
Hangar: *Upper* 550ft x 50ft x 16ft; *lower* 550ft x 50ft x 16ft
Catapults: 2 hydraulic, 10,000lb @ 52 knots (fitted in 1936)
Lifts: *Fwd* 46ft long x 47ft wide; *aft* 46ft long x 47ft wide
Aircraft: 48
Aircraft fuel: 35,700 gallons AVGAS
Air weapons: 18in torpedoes; 500lb SAP bombs; 250lb SAP bombs; 250lb GP bombs; 100lb GP bombs; 100lb AS bombs; 20lb bombs; 8.5lb bombs; .303in gun ammunition; flares and pyrotechnics

Notes: Served as light battlecruiser in WW1 with an armament of 4 x 15in, 18 x 4in and 2 x 3in guns and 14 x 21in torpedo tubes. Converted to fleet carrier in Devonport Dockyard 1924–28. 'Slip' flight deck forward designed to allow fighters to launch directly out of upper hangar when flight deck was crowded with aircraft (impractical and seldom used). Lifts cross shaped rather than rectangular, designed to allow aircraft to be struck down into hangar whilst still spread. *Courageous*'s tragic loss constituted a lesson in how not to use an aircraft carrier under conditions of modern naval warfare: the experiment of 'trailing a coat' with such a valuable ship was not repeated.

Summary of service

00.00.17 Served in 1CS, GF, with *Glorious*
00.00.19 Employed as turret drill ship in Portsmouth
00.06.24 Taken in hand for conversion to a fleet carrier in Devonport
21.02.28 Recommissioned in Portsmouth
06.06.28 Deployed to join MF
00.00.28 Visited Skiathos, Argostoli, Zara, Venice, Taranto and Athens; air group comprised 404 and 407 (Flycatcher), 445 and 446 (Fairey IIIF) and 463 and 464 (Dart) Flights (to 00.00.29)
00.08.29 Embarked 2nd Bn South Staffordshire Regiment for passage to Jaffa, where they restored order after outbreak of inter-racial violence
28.08.29 Part of air group disembarked to Gaza to support military force ashore
12.10.19 Passed through Dardanelles to visit Constantinople with MF
18.10.29 Air group gave Constantinople its first-ever flying display
00.00.30 Returned to UK for refit
00.00.32 Allocated to HF
00.00.35 Flying trials and training in Mediterranean (tactics that led to successful attack on Taranto in 1940 were worked out by ship's air group in this period and number of successful exercises showed how naval air operations were essential to modern fleet)
25.02.36 Reallocated to HF
21.06.37 HF visited Copenhagen and HM the King of Denmark spent day on board
00.00.38 Paid off for refit
31.07.39 Recommissioned and formed part of Channel Force at Portland
31.08.39 Part of force that escorted BEF to France
16.09.39 Sailed from Plymouth with 4 destroyers to carry out offensive AS operations in Atlantic with 811 and 822 (Swordfish) NAS embarked
17.09.39 Sunk by one (possibly two) contact torpedo hits from *U29* whilst in South-West Approaches, in 50° 18' N 14° 47' W; 518 officers and men, including CO, lost out of complement of 1,260

HMS *Courageous* as originally completed. The ship is alongside Walker Naval Yard on the Tyne. (FAA Museum)

HMS *Courageous* after her conversion to an aircraft carrier, moored to a buoy in Plymouth Sound. Note that the door from the upper hangar on to the 'slip' flight deck forward is open. The palisades aft of the island were intended to stop aircraft from going over the side after a bad landing. (Author)

Dasher (D37) Avenger *Class Escort Carrier*

Laid down: 14 March 1940
Launched: 12 April 1941
Completed: 1 July 1942

Builder: Sun Shipbuilding and Drydock Corp., Chester; completed by Tietjens & Lang Drydock Co.
Machinery: 1 shaft; 2 Doxford diesels; 8,000bhp = 17 knots
Displacement: 12,150 tons standard; 15,700 tons full load
Dimensions: 492ft overall x 70ft max beam x 26ft 3in max draught
Gun armament: 3 single 4in US Mk 9 (3); 10 single 20m Oerlikon (10)
Fuel: 3,205 tons diesel
Endurance: 14,550 miles @ 10 knots
Complement: 555
Protection: None
Flight deck: 442ft x 70ft wood-covered steel
Arrester wires: 9 x 8,000lb @ 53 knots; 3 barriers
Hangar: 190ft x 47ft x 16ft
Catapults: 1 x 7,000lb @ 60 knots (tail-down method only)
Lifts: *Aft* 34ft long x 42ft wide; 12,000lb
Aircraft: 18 in 1943
Aircraft fuel: 29,000 gallons AVGAS
Air weapons: 18in torpedoes; 500lb SAP bombs; 250lb SAP bombs; 250lb GP bombs; Mk 7 depth charges; .303in gun ammunition; flares and pyrotechnics

Notes: Laid down as mercantile *Rio de Janeiro*. Taken over by USN on 22 November 41 for completion as an *Avenger* class carrier for RN (BAVG-5) under Lend/Lease arrangements. Petrol vapour explosion which destroyed her was felt, by Admiralty, to be due to inadequate protection provided for her AVGAS tanks. This followed normal USN practice of using internal hull tanks like those provided for FFO with its higher flash-point. All subsequent escort carriers allocated to the RN were modified to British standards, with a consequent reduction of about half the quantity of aviation fuel.

Summary of service

01.07.42 Handed over to USN by Hoboken Navy Yard
02.07.42 Transferred to RN and commissioned
00.07.42 Engine trials and defect rectification; fire broke out on board while in dockyard and further repairs necessary
30.08.42 Sailed for Clyde in company with HX.205 with 837 NAS (Swordfish) embarked
11.09.42 Taken in hand on Clyde for modifications
27.10.42 Sailed for Mediterranean, where ship formed part of Eastern Naval Task Force during Operation 'Torch' (invasion of North Africa); 802 and 883 NAS (Sea Hurricane) embarked
00.11.42 Sailed from Gibraltar for Clyde as part of MKF.1

HMS *Dasher* launching a Sea Hurricane. (FAA Museum)

20.11.42	Arrived in Liverpool for repairs and fitting of air defence room; allocated to HF
01.02.43	Arrived in Scapa Flow for work-up
15.02.43	Sailed as part of escort for JW.53 with 891 (Sea Hurricane) and 816 and 837 (Swordfish) NAS embarked
17.02.43	Suffered severe weather damage off Iceland; proceeded to Dundee for repairs
24.03.43	Recommenced work-up in the Clyde area
27.03.43	Sank at 1645 off Little Cumbrae Island (55° 40' N 04° 57' W) following massive petrol vapour explosion and fire whilst refuelling aircraft; went down in 3 minutes with only 149 survivors

Eagle (1924) (94) *Fleet Carrier*

Laid down: 20 February 1913
Launched: 8 June 1918
Completed: 20 February 1924 (23 April 1920 for trials)

Builder: Sir W. G. Armstrong Whitworth & Co., Newcastle-upon-Tyne; completed by Portsmouth Dockyard
Machinery: 4-shaft Brown-Curtis HP turbines; Parsons LP turbines; 32 Yarrow boilers; 50,000shp = 24 knots
Displacement: 22,600 tons standard in 1924; 27,500 tons deep load in 1942
Dimensions: 667ft 6in overall x 115ft max beam x 26ft 8in max draught
Gun armament: 9 single 6in Mk XVII (9); 5 single 4in Mk V HA (5); 4 single 3pdr saluting guns (4); 2 twin .303in MG as built (4); 2 octuple 2pdr (16) added in 1937; 12 single 20mm Oerlikon (12) added in 1942
Fuel: 3,750 tons FFO as built; 2,810 tons FFO in 1942
Endurance: 3,000 miles @ 17.4 knots in 1942
Complement: 988
Protection: 4.5in waterline; 4in bulkheads; 1.5in main deck; 1.5in hangar deck; 1.5in flight deck; 3in gun shields; underwater protection against 750lb torpedo warhead
Flight deck: 652ft x 96ft armoured steel
Arrester wires: 6 x 11,000lb @ 53 knots (fitted in 1936)
Hangar: 400ft x 66ft x 20ft 6in
Catapults: None
Lifts: *Fwd* 46ft long x 47ft wide; *aft* 46ft long x 33ft wide; both 14,000lb
Aircraft: 22 in 1942
Aircraft fuel: 8,300 gallons AVGAS in 1924; 17,750 gallons AVGAS in 1942
Air weapons: 18in torpedoes; 500lb SAP bombs; 250lb SAP bombs; 250lb B bombs; 100lb AS bombs; Mk 7 depth charges; aircraft mines; .303in gun ammunition; flares and pyrotechnics

Notes: Laid down as the battleship *Almirante Cochrane* for Chile but suspended on the outbreak of war in 1914. Completed for the RN as a fleet carrier after the war. Her sister-ship *Almirante Latorre* was further advanced and completed for the RN as the battleship *Canada*; she was returned to Chile after hostilities. When partially completed in 1920, *Eagle* carried out flying trials to validate the starboard side island design. On 1 May 1925 she used 1,525 gallons of AVGAS in one day's flying off Malta.

Summary of service

11.11.19	Approval given to complete ship for trials
03.03.20	Steam raised for first time
23.04.20	Left Tyne for Portsmouth
28.05.20	Trials carried out in English Channel by specially formed 'Eagle' Flight based at Gosport
01.06.20	First deck landing carried out by Sopwith 2F.1 Camel (other trial aircraft included Panther, Bristol Fighter, Cuckoo and D.H.9A); latter part of the trial sought and found bad weather in Pentland Firth; 143 landings carried out with only 12 minor accidents and no casualities
24.09.20	Admiralty agreed to complete ship as aircraft carrier in view of success of flying trials
27.10.20	Trials completed
16.11.20	Trial crew paid off in Devonport
21.02.21	Transferred to Portsmouth for completion
00.09.23	Completed for full sea trials
05.10.23	Flying trials started
26.02.24	Commissioned for service in MF; started work-up
07.06.24	Relieved *Ark Royal* in MF; air group

comprised 402 (Flycatcher), 422 (Blackburn), 460 (Dart) and 440 (Seagull III) Flights

00.01.25 Fairey IIIDs replaced 440's Seagulls

00.00.26 Refit in Devonport, during which original fore and aft arrester gear (unused since 1924) was removed

00.00.27 Re-joined MF, 448 Flight (Bison) having replaced 422; carried out trials of carrier task group operations with *Courageous*

00.00.28 Refit, during which hangar spray system installed (to 00.00.29); on completion, returned to Mediterranean

00.00.30 Limited night flying trials successfully carried out

08.01.31 Left Malta for UK, where ship embarked special Flight with Nimrods, Ospreys and Ripons

14.03.31 Supported British Industries Exhibition in Buenos Aires (opened by HRH the Prince of Wales)

00.08.31 Paid off for major refit in Devonport, during which ship was re-boilered and fitted with improved close-range AA weapons

28.11.32 Refit completed 33 days ahead of schedule, but shortage of manpower delayed recommissioning

09.01.33 Recommissioned for service in Far East

00.07.33 Passed through Red Sea; air group now comprised 824 (Fairey IIIF) and 803 (Osprey) NAS (this commission was spent on China Station based on Hong Kong and

HMS *Eagle* as first completed for flying trials in 1920. (J. D. Brown via Author)

HMS *Eagle* in her China Station paint scheme during 1933. Note the large crane abaft the island, originally intended to operate seaplanes. (Author)

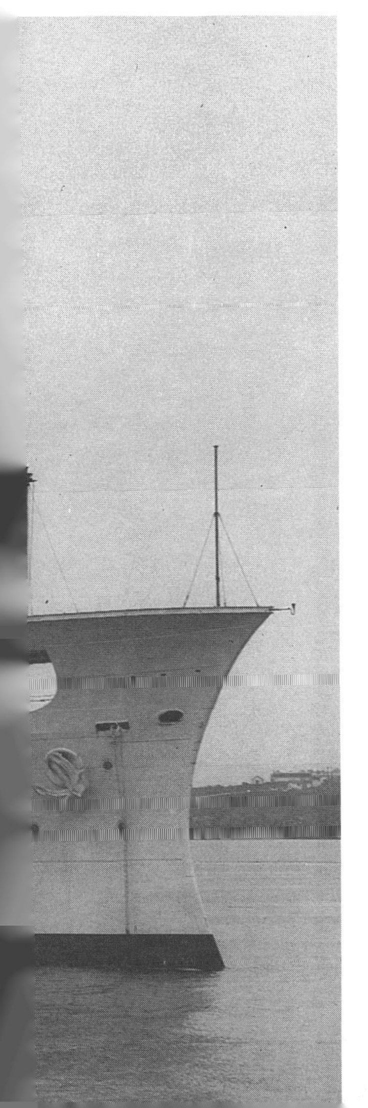

Wei-Hai-Wei; aircraft used to search for and stop pirate junks as well as to carry out attacks on robber bands on coast at request of Chinese authorities)

08.10.34 824 NAS renumbered 825 NAS; *Eagle* relieved *Furious* in Mediterranean, having been relieved by *Hermes* in Far East; air group now comprised 825 and 811 NAS (Baffin), which had transferred from *Furious*

00.06.35 Returned to Devonport to pay off into reserve prior to refit

00.00.36 Refit in Devonport, during which arrester wires fitted, air weapon stowage extended and expanded, extra close-range AA weapons fitted and flight deck lighting added to facilitate night flying

00.02.37 Recommissioned and sailed for Far East with 813 NAS (Swordfish) embarked; relieved *Hermes* at Hong Kong in summer, from which 824 NAS (Seal) transferred

00.00.38 824 NAS re-equipped with Swordfish

00.00.39 Refit in Singapore

00.09.39 Teamed with cruisers *Cornwall* and *Dorsetshire* to form Force I, hunting for raiders in Indian Ocean trade routes

00.12.39 Boiler clean in Durban

01.02.40 Sailed from Colombo with battleship *Ramillies* as part of escort for first Australian troop convoy

08.02.40 Left Australian convoy in Aden to re-join Force I in Bay of Bengal

14.03.40 250lb bomb detonated as it was being returned to bomb room, killing 13 men and wounding 3; flash penetrated hangar and sprays were used to put out fires; ship was able to operate aircraft en route to Singapore, where she was repaired

09.05.40 Sailed from Singapore to join MF, replacing *Glorious* which had joined HF

26.05.40 Passed through Suez Canal into Mediterranean en route for Malta

11.06.40 Searched for Italian units in Eastern Mediterranean and supported convoy movements

29.06.40 Aircraft attacked submarine unsuccessfully

05.07.40 While ship was in Alexandria, 813 NAS attacked shipping in Tobruk, sinking 4 ships (including liner *Liguria*) and damaging 2

07.07.40 Covered convoys carrying evacuees and stores from Malta to Alexandria; 813 NAS had 3 Sea Gladiator fighters added to it

09.07.40 Action off Calabria: 813 NAS spotted for Fleet's guns while 824 NAS carried out two unsuccessful torpedo attacks on Italian Fleet

10.07.40 813 NAS attacked Augusta harbour, sinking destroyer and damaging oiler

11.07.40 During Italian air attacks on Fleet, 813 NAS (Sea Gladiators) shot down four SM.79 bombers and damaged 3 others

20.07.40 824 NAS disembarked to Sidi Barrani while ship was in Alexandria and carried out devastating attack on Italian submarines and their depot ship in Gulf of Bomba

04.09.40 Struck at Rhodes in concert with *Illustrious* (*Eagle*'s target was Maritsa airfield, where aircraft and hangars were damaged on ground, but four 813 NAS Swordfish lost to Italian fighters)

28.09.40 Air group damaged freighter at Bomba whilst based ashore; ship near-missed by bombs which caused shock damage which was not fully appreciated at time

27.10.40 Struck at seaplane station on Stampalia as part of operations covering first Commonwealth troop movements to Crete; on completion, urgent repairs to the aircraft fuel system had to be carried out in Alexandria and ship was not, therefore, available for planned strike on Taranto with *Illustrious* but 5 aircraft and 8 experienced crews were transferred for attack

16.11.40 At sea covering convoy movements in Eastern Mediterranean

26.11.40 8 Swordfish dive-bombed large freighter alongside in Tripoli

00.12.40 813 and 824 NAS operated in Western Desert whilst disembarked

11.01.41 Sailed to harass Axis forces in Eastern Mediterranean while *Illustrious* lay damaged in Malta; 2 Skuas added to Sea Gladiator Flight of 813 NAS

21.02.41 Landed 4 Swordfish and the Skuas and replaced them with Flight from 805 NAS (Fulmar)

25.03.41 Air group disembarked to Port Sudan for strikes against Italian warships in Red Sea

03.04.41 2 destroyers sunk, 2 others and torpedo boat damaged and run aground

12.04.41 Air group re-embarked

13.04.41 Passed through Suez Canal into Red Sea

00.04.41 Search operations against raider *Admiral Scheer* in Indian Ocean

13.05.41 Planned boiler clean cancelled; left Cape Town with all dispatch in company with battleship *Nelson* as 'long stop' in case battleship *Bismarck* broke into South Atlantic

06.06.41 Swordfish found and sank *Elbe*, one of *Bismarck*'s supply ships

13.06.41 Second supply ship, *Lothringen*, surrendered intact to aircraft; *Eagle* remained in South Atlantic, searching for raiders and their supply ships

20.09.41 Serious hangar fire destroyed 13 aircraft whilst ship was operating off St Helena (refit needed in UK to repair damage); on passage home ship embarked two Sea Hurricanes of 804 NAS for air defence

26.10.41 Arrived in Clyde and disembarked aircraft

30.10.41 Entered refit with Cammell Laird at Birkenhead (work included fitting of air, surface and fire control radar, Type 72 aircraft homing beacon and improved close-range AA weapons; AVGAS stowage improved at expense of FFO)

09.01.42 Refit completed; new air group comprised 824 (Swordfish) and 813 (Swordfish/Sea Hurricane) NAS

23.02.42 Arrived in Gibraltar to join Force H; employed to support convoys and missions to ferry Spitfires to Malta

08.04.42 Docked in Gibraltar for repair work

00.05.42 Flew off Spitfires to Malta with USS *Wasp*

11.06.42 Operation 'Harpoon' (with *Argus* to support convoy to Malta); some Swordfish transferred to *Argus* and in return *Eagle* embarked part of 807 (Fulmar) and 801 (Sea Hurricane) NAS from *Argus*

13.06.42 *Eagle*'s fighters broke up number of attacks and shot down 9 confirmed enemy aircraft

10.08.42 Joined escort for Operation 'Pedestal' (largest convoy to be fought through to Malta); *Indomitable* and *Victorious* also part of fighting escort, *Furious* ferried Spitfires; *Eagle* embarked 801 NAS (Sea Hurricane) and 813 Fighter Flight (Sea Hurricane); largest British carrier operation of war to date

11.08.42 At 1311, hit by 4 torpedoes fired by *U73* 584 miles west of Malta (38° 05' N 03° 02' E); ship sank at 1315, taking 2 officers and 158 men; 789 survivors plus 4 Sea Hurricanes of Red Section 801 NAS airborne at time (recovered to other carriers)

Eagle (1951) (R05) *Fleet Carrier*

Laid down: 24 October 1942
Launched: 19 March 91946
Completed: 1 October 1951

Builder: Harland & Wolff, Belfast
Machinery: 4-shaft Parsons SR geared turbines; 8 Admiralty 3 drum boilers; 152,000shp = 30.5 knots
Displacement: 41,200 tons standard; 49,950 tons deep load
Dimensions: 803ft 9in overall x 112ft 9in max beam x 35ft 7in max draught
Gun armament: 8 twin 4.5in Mk 6 DP (16) ; 8 sextuple 40mm Bofors (48); 2 twin 40mm Bofors (4); 9 single 40mm Bofors (9); 4 single 3pdr saluting (4)
Fuel: 5,500 tons FFO
Endurance: 7,000 miles @ 14 knots
Complement: 2,750
Protection: 4.5in waterline belt; 1.5in–4in flight deck; 1.5in hangar side; 1in–2.5in hangar deck
Flight deck: 800ft x 112ft armoured steel
Arrester wires: 16 x 30,000lb @ 75 knots; 3 barriers
Hangar: *Upper* 364ft (plus+ 45ft extension fwd of fwd lift) x 67ft x 17ft 6in; *lower* 172ft x 54ft x 17ft 6in
Catapults: 2 x BH5; 30,000lb @ 75 knots
Lifts: *Fwd* 54ft long x 44ft wide; *aft* 54ft long x 33ft wide; both 40,000lb, 35-second cycle
Aircraft: Up to 100
Aircraft fuel: 103,000 gallons AVGAS; 279,000 gallons AVCAT
Air weapons: 18in torpedoes; 1,000lb MC bombs; 500lb SAP bombs; 500lb GP bombs; 3in RP; 2in RP; Mk 11 depth charges; 20mm cannon ammunition; flares and pyrotechnics

AS REBUILT 1959–64:
Builder: Devonport Dockyard
Machinery: 4-shaft Parsons SR geared turbines; 8 Admiralty 3-drum boilers; 152,000shp = 30.5 knots
Displacement: 43,000 tons standard; 50,536 tons deep load

HMS *Eagle* as first completed, with axial flight deck, turning into wind to launch a range of Attackers, Sea Hornets, Fireflies, Firebrands and a Skyraider. (FAA Museum)

Dimensions: 813ft 5in overall x 171ft max beam x 34ft 6in max draught
Missile/gun armament: 4 twin 4.5in Mk 6 DP (8); 6 quadruple GWS 22 Seacat SAM (24); 4 single 3pdr saluting (4)
Fuel: 3,200 tons FFO
Endurance: 7,000 miles @ 14 knots
Complement: 2,750
Protection: 4.5in waterline belt; 1.5in–4in flight deck; 1.5in hangar side; 1in–2.5in main deck
Flight deck: 800ft x 160ft armoured steel; 8-degree angled deck
Arrester wires: 4 x 35,000lb @ 103 knots; emergency nylon barriers
Hangar: *Upper* 364ft (plus 45ft extension fwd of fwd lift) x 67ft x 17ft 6in; *lower* 172ft x 54ft x 17ft 6in
Catapults: *Fwd* BS5 steam, 50,000lb @ 91 knots, 151ft stroke; *waist* BS5 steam, 50,000lb @ 105 knots, 199ft stroke
Lifts: *Fwd* 54ft long x 44ft wide; *aft* 54ft long x 33ft wide; both 40,000lb, 35-second cycle
Aircraft: 44 in 1964
Aircraft fuel: 487,480 gallons AVCAT
Air weapons: Tactical nuclear bombs; nuclear depth bombs; Red Top AAM; Firestreak AAM; Sidewinder AAM; Bullpup ASM; Mk 30/44/46 homing torpedoes; 1,000lb MC bombs; 500lb MC bombs; 28lb practice bombs; 2in RP; Mk 11 depth charges; 30mm cannon ammunition; flares and pyrotechnics

Notes: Completed to the original 1942 straight-deck design; effectively an improved *Implacable*. Was fitted with an interim 5.5-degree angled deck and mirror landing aid in 1954–55 refit. Between 1959 and 1964 she was completely rebuilt with full 8-degree angled deck, steam catapults and more powerful arrester gear. Reconstruction, based on that given to *Victorious*, altered *Eagle* to such an extent that details are given separately above. In 1964 she was one of the world's most capable carriers. She had a modern air group, had the powerful Type 984 three-dimentional radar and was the first ship in the RN to take a computer-aided action information system to sea (ADAWS 1).

Summary of service

01.03.52 Accepted into RN; commenced trials in Portsmouth area
00.05.52 DLTs conducted with prototypes of new aircraft (including Gannet, Sea Venom and Sea Hawk)
00.06.52 Exercise 'Castanets' (designed to test wartime NATO command arrangements in HF area)
00.08.52 Replaced *Indomitable* as flagship of Heavy Squadron, HF
02.09.52 Sailed from Devonport for HF autumn cruise and embarked 800, 803 and 890 (Attacker), 827 (Firebrand) and 812 and 814 (Firefly) NAS
13.09.52 NATO Exercise 'Mainbrace' (largest ever peacetime naval exercise)
27.09.52 Post-exercise discussion on board *Eagle* at Oslo
20.01.53 Sailed for HF spring cruise; 890 NAS had by now disbanded, but air group was augmented by 809 (Sea Hornet NF.21) and 849A (Skyraider AEW) NAS; proceeded to Mediterranean via Gibraltar for combined HF/MF fleet exercises
26.03.53 Returned to Devonport for docking and repairs
15.05.53 HF summer cruise
09.06.53 Coronation Review at Spithead, on completion of which ship visited Blackpool and then returned to Devonport (to 16.06.53)

00.09.53 Embarked new air group for autumn cruise: 800 and 803 (Attacker), 825 and 814 (Firefly), 809 (Sea Hornet) and 849C (Skyraider AEW) NAS
22.09.53 Took part in Exercise 'Mariner' with over 300 warships and 100 aircraft
26.01.54 Sailed for spring cruise with 800 and 803 (Attacker), 806 (Sea Hawk), 815 (Avenger ASW), 849A and 849B (Skyraider AEW) and 809 (Sea Hornet NF.21) NAS embarked
00.03.54 Detached from HF to 2 ACS, MF
08.04.54 Joined other ships of MF to search for wreckage and bodies from BOAC Comet airliner which had crashed in sea 60 miles north of Straits of Messina (5 bodies recovered)
14.04.54 Arrived in Malta
18.05.54 Left MF and returned to Devonport to prepare for refit; FO Heavy Squadron, HF, transferred to *Glory*
28.02.55 Refit completed; commenced trials in home waters
21.05.55 Embarked 826 (Gannet), 802 and 804 (Sea Hawk), 813 and 827 (Wyvern) and 849A (Skyraider AEW) NAS and sailed for work-up in Mediterranean
23.08.55 Air group flew record 201 sorties in one day (still unsurpassed in RN)
08.09.55 Returned to HF, flying flag of FO Aircraft Carriers, HF
21.09.55 NATO Exercise 'Sea Enterprise' with ships from UK, Canada, USA and Norway (RN contributed 5 carriers, 26 surface ships and 6 submarines)
00.10.55 Exercise 'Phoenix I' (test of air defence of HF against high-lying jet bombers)
00.11.55 Returned to Devonport for repairs
00.04.56 Repairs complete; sailed for MF with 812 (Gannet), 849A (Skyraider AEW), 897 and 899 (Sea Hawk) and 830 (Wyvern) NAS; 892 and 893 NAS (Sea Venom), delayed by technical problems, joined in July
00.05.56 Embarked FOAC and carried out live firing demonstration off Izmir, Aegean
00.06.56 Exercise 'Maltex' (to test air defences of Malta)
31.10.56 Preparation for Operation 'Musketeer' (Anglo-French landings in Suez); FOAC (Vice-Admiral Manley Power) embarked
01.11.56 Aircraft struck at Egyptian targets in support of landings; 898 (Sea Hawk), 849A (Skyraider), 830 (Wyvern) and 892 and 893 (Sea Venom) NAS embarked

HMS *Eagle* off Malta on 10 October 1956, working up for Operation 'Musketeer'. She is about to launch a range of Sea Venoms, Sea Hawks and Wyverns. Note the interim angled deck and the partial plating over of the port forward 4.5in mountings. (FAA Museum)

00.01.57 Returned to Devonport for improvements and repairs
14.06.57 Sailed for post-refit trials
00.09.57 Joined HF for autumn cruise with 849A (Skyraider AEW), 813 (Wyvern), 803 and 806 (Sea Hawk), 814 (Gannet) and 894 (Sea Venom) NAS embarked
17.09.57 Participated in Exercises 'Strike Back', 'Pipe Down' and 'Phoenix II'
02.12.57 Returned to Devonport to give leave
28.01.58 Sailed for MF with same air group plus 701A SAR Flight (Whirlwind)
00.03.58 Exercise 'Dawn Breeze IV'
00.07.58 Took part in operations to land British troops in Jordan following *coup* in Iraq
04.09.58 Exercise 'Petrel I' (combined amphibious exercise with Libyan Army)
03.12.58 Returned to Devonport to give leave
00.01.59 Returned to Mediterranean
00.03.59 Exercise 'Dawn Breeze V'
00.04.59 Returned to UK, visiting Brest on way, with 806, 802 and 898 (Sea Hawk), 814 (Gannet AS), 849A (Skyraider AEW) and 894 (Sea

HMS *Eagle* after her full modernisation, seen on Beira Patrol duties on 4 April 1966. She is replenishing at sea with the tanker *Tidepool* to port and the air stores ship *Reliant* to starboard. The aircraft on deck are Sea Vixens, Buccaneers and Scimitars. (FAA Museum)

Venom) NAS embarked
11.05.59 Paid off for modernisation.
30.10.59 Taken under dockyard control
14.05.64 Recommissioned at Devonport and started post-refit trials and work-up in UK waters
01.12.64 Sailed for FEF with 800 (Buccaneer), 800B (Scimitar), 820 (Wessex AS), 849D (Gannet AEW) and 899 (Sea Vixen) NAS embarked
08.12.64 Passed through Suez Canal
13.12.64 Work-up off Aden
00.03.65 Exercise 'FOTEX 65' in Singapore area with ships from the RN, RAN, RNZN and Royal Malaysian Navy
00.04.65 Sailed for UK
24.05.65 Arrived at Devonport for repairs
00.08.65 Sailed for FEF
12.11.65 Arrived in Singapore
00.01.66 Sailed for Middle East to relieve *Ark Royal* on Beira patrol (intended to cut off supplies to Rhodesia which had recently declared UDI from Britain); aircraft from *Eagle* provided surveillance and cover up to 350 miles from Beira and helped to identify over 770 ships including 116 tankers in area (2 tankers, *Enterprise* and *Manuella*, deterred from entering port)
10.05.66 Arrived in Singapore, having set peacetime record for RN carrier with 71 days at sea during which ship flew 1,880 sorties and steamed 30,000 miles
00.06.66 Flying exercises off Singapore and Penang
14.07.66 Sailed for UK
22.08.66 Arrived in Devonport
03.10.67 Taken in hand for refit
06.04.67 Refit completed; embarked 800 (Buccaneer), 820 (Wessex AS), 849D (Gannet AEW) and 899 (Sea Vixen) NAS and sailed for FEF on completion of work-up; after exercises, ship returned to UK for maintenance
18.06.68 Arrived in Devonport
16.09.68 NATO Exercise 'Silver Tower': major command and control exercise, flying flag of FOAC and Com Car Strike Group 2 (Rear-Admiral M. F. Fell DSO DSC)
04.10.68 Returned to Devonport for improvements to steam catapults and arrester wires to enable ship to carry out trials with new Phantom fighter
05.03.69 Recommissioned for trials.
10.03.69 Phantoms from A&AEE Boscombe Down carried out 81 'touch and go' landings
00.04.69 Work-up in Moray Firth with same air group
00.05.69 Further work-up in South-West Approaches
00.06.69 Further Phantom trials in Lyme Bay
02.06.69 First arrested landing by RN Phantom
03.06.69 First catapult launch by RN Phantom
00.06.69 Visited Norfolk, Va, and Boston, Massachusetts
29.07.69 New colours presented to WF by HM Queen Elizabeth II on board *Eagle* at Torbay
00.09.69 Deployed to Mediterranean for Exercises 'Peace Keeper' and 'Deep Furrow 69'
05.12.69 Returned to Devonport for SMP
10.01.70 Sailed for Mediterranean for flying exercises
27.02.70 Visited Liverpool
00.03.70 Carried out flying exercises in English Channel with Harrier aircraft from A&AEE Boscombe Down
00.04.70 Entered Devonport for DED
00.09.70 DED complete, commenced work-up; 826 NAS (Sea King) replaced 820 NAS
07.02.71 Rendered assistance to burning Cypriot merchant ship *Byzantium* in Gibraltar

00.05.71 Sailed for FEF
08.07.71 Arrived in Singapore
00.08.71 Responded to distress call from SS *Steel Vendor*, aground and breaking up off Loatia Island, west of Philippines, after Typhoon 'Elaine' had passed through (4 Sea Kings from 826 NAS winched all 40 crewmen to safety despite appalling conditions)
00.10.71 Exercised with USN in Subic Bay area
00.11.71 Exercises off west coast of Malaysia before sailing for UK for last time
26.01.72 Arrived in Portsmouth to pay off for disposal
00.02.72 De-stored and de-equipped
06.08.72 Towed to Plymouth, where she was moored for six years to be cannibalised for spares to support *Ark Royal*
00.10.78 Towed away to breaker's yard on Clyde

Emperor (D98) Ruler *Class Assault Escort Carrier*

Laid down: 23 June 1942
Launched: 7 October 1942
Completed: 6 August 1943

Builder: Seattle-Tacoma Shipbuilding Corp., Seattle; completed by Puget Sound Navy Yard
Machinery: 1-shaft General Electric geared turbine; 2 Foster Wheeler boilers; 8,500shp = 18.5 knots
Displacement: 11,200 tons standard; 15,400 tons deep load
Dimensions: 494ft 9in overall x 108ft 6in max beam x 25ft 6in max draught
Gun armament: 2 single 5in US Mk 12 (2); 8 twin 40mm Bofors (16); 27 single 20mm Oerlikon (27)
Fuel: 3,290 tons FFO
Endurance: 27,500 miles @ 11 knots
Complement: 646
Protection: Splinter protection for bomb room
Flight deck: 450ft x 88ft wood-covered steel
Arrester wires: 9 x 19,800lb @ 55 knots; 3 barriers
Hangar: 260ft x 62ft x 18ft
Catapults: 1 x H4C; 16,000lb @ 74 knots (tail-down method only)
Lifts: *Fwd* 42ft long x 34ft wide; *aft* 34ft long x 42ft wide; both 14,000lb
Aircraft: Up to 30 could be operated; up to 90 could be ferried
Aircraft fuel: 48,000 gallons AVGAS
Air weapons: 500lb SAP bombs; 120lb MC bombs; .5in gun ammunition; flares and pyrotechnics

Notes: Provisionally named *Stinger* by the RN. One of a class of 24 ships, 23 of which served with the RN. Laid down as carrier but hull based on C3 mercantile design. Built as USS *Pybus* (CVE-34), she served as such for three months before being transferred to the RN under Lend/Lease arrangements. The single ship that remained with the USN was *Prince William*, nameship of the original class.

Summary of service

06.08.43 Commissioned in New York City
03.09.43 Arrived in Clyde; allocated to WAC
07.09.43 Arrived in Belfast for conversion to RN standards, followed by flying work-up in Clyde area with 800 and 804 NAS (Hellcat)
00.02.44 To Norfolk, Va, and return via Argentia
18.03.44 Allocated to HF
30.03.44 Part of Operation 'Tungsten' (strike on battleship *Tirpitz* in her anchorage in Kaafjord); 800 and 804 NAS (Hellcat) embarked; ship also took part in HF attacks on Bodø, Kristiansund and Rorvik
23.05.44 Returned to WAC for convoy work; escorted SL.158 and MKS.49
18.06.44 804 NAS absorbed into 800 NAS
15.07.44 Sailed for Mediterranean with 800 NAS (Hellcat) and single Walrus from 700 NAS embarked
12.08.44 Operation 'Dragoon' (invasion of Southern France) as part of Task Group 88.1
02.09.44 Based on Alexandria, carried out Operations 'Outing', 'Cablegram', 'Manna' and 'Contempt' in Aegean with *Attacker*, *Hunter*, *Stalker*, *Khedive*, *Pursuer* and *Searcher*; fighters flew 1,500 sorties and gained invaluable results for negligible losses
20.11.44 Returned to UK for refit in Newport
01.03.45 Sailed from Newport; allocated to 21 ACS EIF; 800 NAS (Hellcat) embarked.
25.03.45 Arrived in Colombo
04.04.45 Operation 'Sunfish' in company with *Khedive* (photographic reconnaissance of

	Port Swettenham area and strike on Emmahaven); 800 NAS augmented by detachment of 808 (Hellcat) and 845 (Avenger) NAS
21.04.45	Operation 'Dracula' (strikes on Rangoon and Tenasserim coast) with *Khedive*, *Hunter* and *Stalker*; 800 NAS embarked
02.07.45	Operation 'Collie' (strikes on Nicobar Islands and cover for minesweeping forces off Phuket) in company with *Ameer*; 1 Walrus of 1700 NAS embarked with 800 NAS
04.09.45	Operation 'Zipper' (re-occupation of Singapore)
10.09.45	Anchored in Keppel Harbour off Singapore with 21 ACS, *Khedive*, *Ameer*, *Empress*, *Hunter* and *Stalker*
30.10.45	Sailed for UK via Colombo and Bombay
04.12.45	Arrived in Clyde; later commenced de-storing
08.01.46	Arrived in Plymouth
23.01.46	Sailed for USA
12.02.46	Returned to USN at Norfolk, Va; subsequently sold for scrap

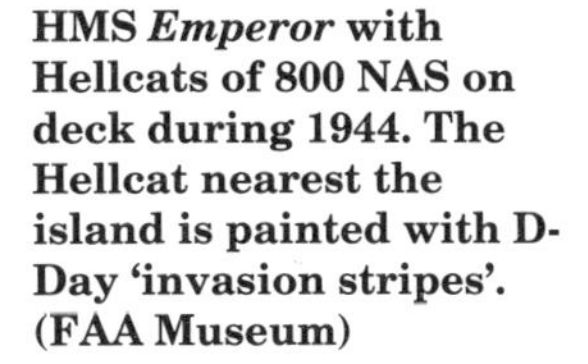

HMS *Emperor* with Hellcats of 800 NAS on deck during 1944. The Hellcat nearest the island is painted with D-Day 'invasion stripes'. (FAA Museum)

Empress (1943) (D42) Ruler *Class Assault Escort Carrier*

Laid down: 9 September 1942
Launched: 30 December 1942
Completed: 13 August 1943

Builder: Seattle-Tacoma Shipbuilding Corp., Seattle
Machinery: 1-shaft Allis-Chalmers geared turbine; 2 Foster Wheeler boilers; 8,500shp = 18.5 knots
Displacement: 11,400 tons standard; 15,400 tons deep load
Dimensions: 494ft 9in overall x 108ft 6in max beam x 25ft 6in max draught
Gun armament: 2 single 5in US Mk 12 (2); 8 twin 40mm Bofors (16); 14 twin 20mm Oerlikon (28); 7 single 20mm Oerlikon (7)
Fuel: 3,290 tons FFO
Endurance: 27,500 miles @ 11 knots
Complement: 646
Protection: Splinter protection for bomb room
Flight deck: 450ft x 88ft wood-covered steel
Arrester wires: 9 x 19,800lb @ 55 knots; 3 barriers
Hangar: 260ft x 62ft x 18ft
Catapults: 1 x H4C; 16,000lb @ 74 knots (tail-down method only)
Lifts: *Fwd* 42ft long x 34ft wide; *aft* 34ft long x 42ft wide; both 14,000lb, 50-second cycle
Aircraft: Up to 30 could be operated; up to 90 could be ferried
Aircraft fuel: 43,200 gallons AVGAS
Air weapons: 500lb SAP bombs; 250lb MC bombs; .5in gun ammunition; flares and pyrotechnics

Notes: Laid down as a carrier but hull based on US C3 mercantile design. Built as USS *Carnegie* (CVE-38). Tranferred to RN under Lend/Lease arrangements.

Summary of service

12.08.43 Commissioned in Vancouver; modified to RN standards
17.02.44 Sailed for New York
09.03.44 Passed through Panama Canal
26.03.44 Sailed from New York with 850 NAS (Avenger) embarked for passage
08.04.44 Arrived in Clyde
11.04.44 Allocated to WAC but spent considerable period in Clyde yards and Rosyth undergoing repairs
06.01.45 Allocated to EIF; sailed with KMF.38 to Gibraltar
04.02.45 Arrived in Trincomalee; formed part of 21 ACS
22.02.45 Operation 'Stacey' (photographic reconnaissance of Sumatra and Kra Isthmus) in company with *Ameer*; 888 (Hellcat PR) and 845 (Avenger) NAS and Flight of 804 (Hellcat) NAS embarked
27.04.45 Operation 'Bishop' (strikes on Nicobar and Andaman Islands and on Burma coast) in company with *Shah*; 804 NAS (Hellcat) and Walrus of 1700 NAS embarked.

HMS *Empress* in the Clyde during late 1944 prior to sailing to join the EIF. (FAA Museum)

19.07.45 Operation 'Livery' (strikes on northern Malaya and cover for minesweeping operations off Phuket Island) in company with *Ameer*; same air group
08.09.45 Operation 'Zipper' (re-occupation of Singapore) with 896 NAS (Hellcat) and the Walrus of 1700 NAS
11.10.45 In Colombo
03.11.45 Visited Wellington
23.11.45 Returned to Colombo
27.11.45 Sailed for UK
19.12.45 Arrived in Clyde; commenced de-storing
06.01.46 Sailed for USA
04.02.46 Returned to USN at Norfolk, Va
21.06.46 Sold for scrap

Fencer (D64) Attacker *Class Escort Carrier*

Laid down: 5 September 1941
Launched: 4 April 1942
Completed: 20 February 1943

Builder: Western Pipe & Steel Corp., San Francisco
Machinery: 1-shaft GEC geared turbine; 2 Foster Wheeler boilers; 8,500shp = 18 knots
Displacement: 10,200 tons standard; 14,400 tons deep load
Dimensions: 495ft 9in x 102ft max beam x 26ft max draught
Gun armament: 2 single 4in US Mk 9 (2); 4 twin 40mm Bofors (8); 4 twin 20mm Oerlikon (8); 7 single 20mm Oerlikon (7)
Fuel: 3,123 tons FFO
Endurance: 27,300 miles @ 11 knots
Complement: 646
Protection: Splinter protection for bomb room

Flight deck: 442ft x 102ft wood-covered steel
Arrester wires: 9 x 19,800lb @ 55 knots; 3 barriers
Hangar: 262ft x 62ft x 18ft
Catapults: 1 x H2 hydraulic; 7,000lb @ 61 knots (tail-down method only)
Lifts: *Fwd* 42ft long x 34ft wide; *aft* 34ft long x 42ft wide; both 14,000lb
Aircraft: Up to 20 could be operated; up to 90 could be ferried
Aircraft fuel: 41,000 gallons AVGAS
Air weapons: 22.4in torpedoes; 18in torpedoes; Mk XXIV mines (homing torpedoes); 500lb SAP bombs; 250lb SAP bombs; 250lb GP bombs; 3in RP; Mk 11 depth charges; aircraft mines; .5in gun ammunition; .303in gun ammunition; flares and pyrotechnics

Notes: Originally laid down as a C3 merchant ship. Acquired by USN and completed as USS *Croatan* (CVE-

14) of the *Bogue* class. Transferred to the RN under Lend/Lease arrangements.

Summary of service

20.02.43 Commissioned into USN
27.02.43 Transferred to RN
01.03.43 Commissioned in San Francisco
02.05.43 Arrived in New York; sailed with HX.238 to UK
22.05.43 Allocated to WAC; refitted to British standards in Liverpool
31.07.43 Worked up in Clyde with 842 NAS (Swordfish/Seafire) embarked
03.10.43 Operation 'Alacrity' (occupation of Azores for use as maritime air base)
05.11.43 Returned to Clyde
19.11.43 Supported SL.139 and MKS.30 but was not present for glider bomb attack on 21 November by 8 HE 177s
26.11.43 Supported OS.60 and KMS.34 (Wildcats replaced Seafires in 842 NAS and they shot down FW 200 shadower; Swordfish flew constant night AS patrols)
06.12.43 Supported SL.141 and MKS.32
11.12.43 Supported OS.61 and KMS.35
17.12.43 Supported SL.142 and MKS.33
24.12.43 Repairs in Clyde
08.02.44 Supported ON.223 and HX.278
10.02.44 Swordfish sank *U666*
26.02.44 Supported SL.149 and MKS.40
17.03.44 Allocated to HF and arrived at Scapa Flow
30.03.44 Sailed from Scapa Flow to provide support for JW.57 and RA.57
03.04.44 Provided AS support for Operation 'Tungsten' (FAA attack on battleship *Tirpitz*), still with 842 NAS (Swordfish/Wildcat) embarked
19.04.44 Escorted RA.59 to North Russia
01.05.44 Swordfish sank *U277*
02.05.44 Swordfish sank *U674* and *U959*; Bv 138C shadowing aircraft shot down
05.05.44 Repairs in Clyde
20.06.44 Strike in Norwegian waters with 842 and 881 NAS (Wildcat) embarked
13.07.44 Returned to WAC; supported OS.83 and KM.57 with 842 NAS embarked
22.07.44 Supported SL.164 and MKS.55
08.08.44 AS sweep off west coast of Scotland
28.09.44 AS support for strikes in Norwegian coastal waters with 842 NAS embarked
13.10.44 Minelaying operations off Norway with 852 NAS (Avenger) embarked
31.10.44 Allocated to BPF as ferry carrier and sailed from Clyde
22.11.44 Arrived in Trincomalee; used to ferry aircraft between Ceylon and Australia
31.03.45 Sailed from Sydney to Leyte with replacement aircraft
13.06.45 Sailed for repairs in Simonstown; allocated to 30 ACS
31.08.45 In Colombo
04.09.45 Sailed for UK
25.09.45 Arrived in Clyde
30.09.45 Arrived in London docks; modified for trooping duties; allocated to Rosyth Command
13.12.45 Sailed for Colombo
20.02.46 Arrived in Plymouth
21.02.46 Sheerness for defect rectification
21.11.46 Returned to USN; sold as mercantile *Sydney*
00.00.67 Renamed *Roma*
00.00.70 Renamed *Galaxy Queen*
00.00.72 Renamed *Lady Dina*
00.02.73 Renamed *Caribia*
01.09.75 Commenced breaking-up at Spezia

HMS *Fencer* during Operation 'Tungsten', the first air attack on *Tirpitz* by the Home Fleet in April 1944. HMS *Furious* is visible in the background at left. (FAA Museum)

Formidable (R67) Illustrious *Class Fleet Carrier*

HMS *Formidable* in the Captain Cook Dry Dock in Sydney in 1945. (FAA Museum)

Laid down: 17 June 1936
Launched: 17 August 1939
Completed: 24 November 1940

Builder: Harland & Wolff, Belfast
Machinery: 3-shaft Parsons SR geared turbines; 6 Admiralty 3-drum boilers; 111,000shp = 30.5 knots
Displacement: 23,207 tons standard; 28,619 tons deep load
Dimensions: 740ft 9in overall x 106ft 9in max beam x 28ft 2in max draught
Gun armament: 8 twin 4.5in QF Mk III HA (16); 6 octuple 2pdr pompom (48); 20 twin 20mm Oerlikon (40); 14 single 20mm Oerlikon (14)
Fuel: 4,854 tons FFO
Endurance: 14,000 miles @ 12 knots
Complement: 1,997 in 1945
Protection: 3in NC flight deck; 2.5in NC hangar deck; 4.5in hangar sides; 4.5in main belt; internal protection against 750lb torpedo charge
Flight deck: 740ft x 95ft 9in armoured steel
Arrester wires: *Aft 7* 11,000lb @ 55 knots; *aft, 2 furthest fwd* 20,000lb @ 60 knots; *fwd 2* 20,000lb @ 60 knots; 3 barriers (*aft 2* 10,000lb; *fwd 1* 20,000lb)
Hangar: 456ft x 62ft x 16ft
Catapults: 1 x BH3; 14,000lb @ 66 knots (tail-down method); 14,000lb @ 60 knots (with trolley)
Lifts: *Fwd* 45ft long x 22ft wide; *aft* 45ft long x 22ft wide; both 14,000lb
Aircraft: 54 in May 1945
Aircraft fuel: 40,540 gallons AVGAS
Air weapons: 18in torpedoes; 1,000lb MC bombs; 500lb SAP bombs; 250lb SAP bombs; 250lb B bombs; 100lb AS bombs; Mk 11 depth charges; aircraft mines; .5in gun ammunition; .303in gun ammunition; flares and pyrotechnics

HMS *Formidable* in 1942. (FAA Museum)

Notes: Second of *Illustrious* class to complete. Three extra arrester wires, aft of the original six, were added shortly before completion. After 1946 a number of schemes were put forward to modernise or convert her to other roles but lack of funds and her deteriorating material state led to their being abandoned.

Summary of service

17.08.39 Launched by Lady Kingsley-Wood
24.11.40 Commissioned in Belfast
00.01.41 Hunting for German surface raiders off St Helena
00.02.41 After work-up, replaced damaged sister-ship *Illustrious* in MF; took passage around Cape and en route struck at targets at Kismayn, Mogadishu and Massawa in Italian Somaliland
10.03.41 Passed through Suez Canal
28.03.41 Battle of Matapan with 803 and 806 (Fulmar), 826 (Albacore) and 829 (Albacore/Swordfish) NAS embarked; aircraft from *Formidable* and 815 NAS (Swordfish) from RNAS Maleme in Crete carried out 3 strikes on Italian Fleet, damaging battleship *Vittorio Veneto* and stopping cruiser *Pola* in water (*Pola*, *Zara* and *Fiume* subsequently sunk by gunfire from heavy units)
00.04.41 Covered convoys during evacuation of Commonwealth forces from Greece
26.05.41 Struck at airfield on Scarpanto during operations off Crete; 6 enemy aircraft shot down by *Formidable*'s fighters but others got through and ship damaged by two 2,000lb bomb hits; proceeded to USA for repairs in Norfolk, Va
12.12.41 NAS disembarked to North Africa and served ashore with distinction
16.12.41 Collided with *Illustrious* on completion of repairs; allocated to EF; 888 (Martlet) and 820 (Albacore) NAS embarked
00.09.42 Returned to Clyde for refit
08.11.42 Formed part of Force H covering Operation 'Torch' (North African landings) with 885 (Seafire), 888 and 893 (Martlet) and 820 (Albacore) NAS embarked
25.11.42 One of ship's Albacores torpedoed and sank *U331* on surface in Western Mediterranean
10.07.43 Covered Operation 'Husky' (invasion of Sicily) with Force H
09.09.43 Provided cover for Operation 'Avalanche' (Salerno landings) with Force H
00.10.43 Belfast for refit
00.07.44 Allocated to HF
17.07.44 Operation 'Mascot' (strike on battleship *Tirpitz* in anchorage in Kaafjord) with 1841 (Corsair) and 827 and 830 (Barracuda) NAS embarked in company with *Furious* and *Indefatigable*
00.08.44 Operation 'Goodwood' (further strikes on *Tirpitz*) with 1841 and 1842 (Corsair) and 826 and 828 (Barracuda) NAS embarked in company with *Furious*, *Indefatigable*, *Nabob* and *Trumpeter*
00.09.44 Joined MF
01.03.45 Joined 1 ACS, BPF, in Sydney with 1841 and 1842 (Corsair) NAS (6 Naval Fighter Wing) and 848 (Avenger) NAS embarked; relieved *Illustrious*
26.03.45 Operation 'Iceberg' (strikes on Sakashima Gunto and Formosa in support of US landings on Okinawa)
04.05.45 'Zeke' Kamikaze aircraft crashed on to flight deck with 600lb bomb off Sakashima Gunto; fires caused damage to radar and flight deck, which were out of action for 5 hours while temporary repairs were carried out
09.05.45 Damaged by Kamikaze aircraft off Sakashima Gunto; aircraft dived from astern and hit carrying 600lb bomb; 6 aircraft on deck wrecked by blast and fire, 10 others damaged in hangar by fire

HMS *Formidable* (far left) seconds before being hit by a Kamikaze aircraft on 9 May 1945—and (left) seconds after being hit. (FAA Museum)

01.07.45 Flagship of Rear-Admiral Sir Phillip Vian, FO1 ACS (to 11.07.45)
17.07.45 Strikes on Tokyo Plain, Japan, with 1841 and 1842 (Corsair), 1844 (Hellcat) and 848 (Avenger) NAS embarked
09.08.45 Lt R. H. Gray DSC RCNVR, Senior Pilot of 1841 NAS, awarded VC for leading attack on Japanese shipping in Onagawa Wan
23.08.45 Disembarked air group off Sydney; used to ferry former Allied POWs from Japan to Australia; then sailed for UK as troopship
00.00.46 Made two round trips UK–Australia returning servicemen for demobilisation
00.11.46 Returned to Portsmouth to de-store into reserve
00.03.47 Paid off into unmaintained reserve in Portsmouth
00.00.53 Sold for breaking up in Inverkeithing

Furious (47) *Fleet Carrier*

Laid down: 8 June 1915
Launched: 15 August 1916
Completed: 4 July 1917

Builder: Sir W. G. Armstrong Whitworth & Co., Newcastle-upon-Tyne; engined by Wallsend Slipway and Newcastle-upon-Tyne Engineering Co.
Machinery: 4-shaft Brown-Curtis geared turbines; 18 Yarrow boilers; 90,820shp = 30 knots
Displacement: 22,450 tons standard; 27,165 tons deep load
Dimensions: 786ft 5in overall x 90ft 1in max beam x 29ft 11in max draught
Gun armament: 6 twin 4in Mk XVI HA (12); 4 octuple 2 pdr pompom (32) ; 4 twin 20mm Oerlikon (8); 7 single 20mm Oerlikon (7)
Fuel: 3,830 tons FFO
Endurance: 3,700 miles @ 20 knots
Complement: 1,218
Protection: 2in–3in side belt; 2in–3in bulkheads; 0.75in–3in deckheads; 1in steel plate flight deck; 1in–2in magazine crowns; 3in magazine sides; bulges designed to defeat torpedo warhead up to 440lb
Flight deck: 576ft x 91ft 6in steel; length extended to 596ft in 1943
Arrester wires: 4 x 11,000lb @ 60 knots (installed in 1933); no barrier
Hangar: *Upper* 520ft x 50ft x 15ft; *lower* 550ft x 50ft x 15ft
Catapults: None
Lifts: *Fwd* 34ft long x 45ft wide; *aft* 34ft long x 45ft wide
Aircraft: 33 in 1939
Aircraft fuel: 20,800 gallons AVGAS
Air weapons: (1944–45) 18in torpedoes; 1,600lb AP bombs; 500lb SAP bombs; 250lb SAP bombs; 250lb GP bombs; Mk 7 depth charges; aircraft mines; .5in gun ammunition; .303in gun ammunition; flares and pyrotechnics

Notes: *Furious* had a long and distinguished career in the forefront of naval aviation. The forward flying-off deck was intended to enable fighters to launch directly out of the upper hangar when the main flight deck was not available. It was never a success and was discarded in the 1930s. Details show her as she was in 1940.

HMS *Furious* in 1918, with a flying-off deck forward and a landing-on deck aft. Note the 'goalpost' abaft the funnel, intended to stop aircraft from crashing into the midship superstructure if they failed to stop within the limits of the deck. (FAA Museum)

Summary of service

04.07.17	Completed and joined GF at Scapa Flow; used to carry out flying trials in Scapa Flow
02.08.17	Sqn Cdr Dunning twice landed Sopwith Pup on flying-off deck
07.08.17	Dunning killed trying a further landing
00.11.17	Returned to builders to have after 18in gun replaced by landing-on deck
15.03.18	Recommissioned in Rosyth for Flying Squadron, GF, flying flag of Admiral Commanding Aircraft
00.04.18	Further flying trials carried out but only 3 of 13 landings attempted by Pup aircraft were successful and deck was deemed unusable, even for wartime service; air group of 1½-Strutters and 2F.1 Camels carried (could launch but not land on)
19.07.18	7 Camels struck at Tondern airship base in Schleswig-Holstein, destroying Zeppelins *L54* and *L60*
00.12.18	Allocated to AF
Early 19	Served in Baltic in support of White Russian forces
21.11.19	Reduced to reserve in Rosyth
00.07.20	Admiralty agreed to proceed with reconstruction as flush-deck carrier
00.06.22	Steamed in stripped-down condition from Rosyth to Devonport for reconstruction
01.08.25	Work completed
00.09.25	Joined AF with 404A, 405 and 406 (Flycatcher) Fighter Flights, 420 (Blackburn) and 421 (Bison) Spotter Flights, 443 (Fairey IIID) Reconnaissance Flight and 461 and 462 (Dart) Torpedo Flights embarked; ship took part in every major exercise with AF during late 1920s
01.07.30	Refit at Devonport
00.05.31	Re-joined AF
00.11.31	Allocated to newly named HF, where she remained apart from six months with MF in 1934; based at Rosyth in September 1939
22.09.39	Aircraft attacked U-boat east of Fair Isle
00.11.39	Air group comprised 801 (Skua) and 816 and 818 (Swordfish) NAS; operated with battlecruiser *Repulse* as anti-U-boat hunting group in Atlantic
10.12.39	Sailed from Halifax as part of escort for first Canadian troop convoy

A Sopwith Pup being hoisted out of the hatch at the after end of HMS *Furious*'s flying-off deck during 1917. (FAA Museum)

00.04.40	Operations off Norway, including strike, fighter and reconnaissance missions as well as misemployment ferrying RAF Gladiators and Hurricanes
00.06.40	Crossed Atlantic alone, ferrying £18,000,000 of gold bullion to Canada
01.07.40	Sailed from Halifax for UK, ferrying 40 Martlets and Buffaloes and spares
00.09.40	Aircraft struck at Tromsø and Trondheim
00.10.40	Strikes on Norwegian coastal targets
15.11.40	Sailed from Liverpool, ferrying aircraft to Takoradi
15.12.40	Returned to Liverpool
00.12.40	Further ferrying operations to Takoradi with WS.5A, during which she flew unsuccessful searches for *Admiral Hipper*; 801 NAS (Skua) embarked
00.01.41	Further ferry operation to Takoradi
04.05.41	Damaged by bomb whilst refitting in Belfast
12.05.41	Arrived in Gibraltar for ferry operations to Malta with Force H; 807 (Fulmar) and 827 (Swordfish) NAS embarked
00.07.41	Allocated to HF with 800 (Fulmar), 812 (Swordfish) and 817 (Albacore) NAS and 880A (Sea Hurricane) Flight embarked; struck at Petsamo (2 Fulmars and 1 Albacore lost)
00.08.41	Anti-shipping strikes in Varanger Fjord
00.09.41	Ferry operation to Malta
07.10.41	Arrived in Philadelphia for refit
12.04.42	Arrived in Clyde; further refit work carried out
00.07.42	Re-joined HF with 801 and 807 (Seafire) and 822 (Albacore) NAS embarked
11.08.42	Ferried aircraft to Malta
17.08.42	Again ferried aircraft to Malta
00.11.42	Operation 'Torch' (North African landings): formed part of Centre Naval Task Group with 801 and 807 (Seafire) and 828 (Albacore) NAS embarked; afterwards joined Force H based on Gibraltar
00.01.43	Covered convoys to Algiers
00.02.43	Re-joined HF
07.07.43	Operations off Norwegian coast as strategic diversion during Sicilian landings; on completion, refitted in Liverpool
00.10.43	Re-joined HF with 801 (Seafire) and 827 and 830 (Barracuda) NAS embarked
11.02.44	Anti-shipping strikes in Norwegian waters
03.04.44	Operation 'Tungsten' (strike on *Tirpitz*) with 801 and 880 (Seafire) and 830 and 831 (Barracuda) NAS embarked (830 formed part of 8 TBR Wing and 831 part of 52 TBR Wing; the other halves of these wings were embarked in *Victorious*)
22.08.44	Operation 'Goodwood' (further strike on *Tirpitz*) in Norwegian waters with 801 and 880 (Seafire) and 827 (Barracuda) NAS embarked
00.09.44	Aerial mining operations off Norwegian coast
15.09.44	Paid off into reserve (special signal was sent to CinC HF from Admiralty recalling great services ship had performed for more than quarter of century; by then, however, she was mechanically so run down that she could not continue in service)
00.00.45	Berthed at Loch Striven near Rothesay and used for ship target trials to analyse result of explosions on her hull
00.00.48	Sold to British Iron and Steel Corporation for scrap; towed to Troon for final breaking-up (not completed until 1954)

HMS *Furious* as she was in the 1930s. Note the open door at the forward end of the upper hangar, allowing two Flycatchers to be ranged for take off from the 'slip' deck. The wind break is being lowered to allow them to launch and the ship is already into wind. The cruciform-shaped lift at the forward end of the main flight deck was intended to allow aircraft to be struck down with their wings spread in order to speed up recovery times before the introduction of the barrier. Note, too, the soot aft from the funnel gas exhaust arrangements and the black-painted ship's side, intended to mask the effects of the gas when 'smoking down' during flying operations. 'Smoking up' allowed smoke through vents in the deck aft when no flying was in progress. (J. D. Brown)

Glorious (77) *Fleet Carrier*

Laid down: 1 May 1915
Launched: 20 April 1916
Completed: 14 October 1916

Builder: Harland & Wolff, Belfast
Machinery: 4-shaft Parsons geared turbines; 18 Yarrow boilers; 91,162shp = 30 knots
Displacement: 22,500 tons standard; 27,400 tons deep load
Dimensions: 786ft 5in overall x 91ft 6in max beam x 28ft max draught
Gun armament: 12 single 4.7in QF Mk VIII HA (12); 3 quadruple .5in MG (12)
Fuel: 3,450 tons FFO
Endurance: 2,490 miles @ 24 knots
Complement: 1,200
Protection: 3in side belt; 3in fwd ends; 2in aft ends; 0.75in funnel casings and uptakes; 1.75in over machinery spaces; 1.5in over steering gear; external bulges designed to defeat torpedo warhead up to 440lb
Flight deck: 576ft x 91ft 6in steel
Arrester wires: 4 x 11,000lb @ 53 knots (installed in 1934); no barriers
Hangar: *Upper* 550ft x 50ft x 15ft; *lower* 550ft x 50ft x 15ft
Catapults: 2 x hydraulic; 10,000lb @ 52 knots
Lifts: *Fwd* 46ft long x 47ft wide (cruciform); *aft* 46ft long x 47ft wide (cruciform); both 14,000lb
Aircraft: 48 in 1940
Aircraft fuel: 35,700 gallons AVGAS
Air weapons: 18in torpedoes; 500lb SAP bombs; 250lb SAP bombs; 250lb GP bombs; 100lb GP bombs; 100lb AS bombs; 20lb bombs; .303in gun ammunition; flares and pyrotechnics

Notes: Similar to the rebuilt *Courageous* and a half-sister to *Furious*. The ship was originally armed with four 15in guns in two turrets; when removed from *Courageous* and *Glorious*, these guns and mountings were kept in store and were eventually used to equip the battleship *Vanguard* (those from *Courageous* being mounted forward and those from *Glorious* aft). The short flight deck forward was intended to allow fighters to be launched from the upper hangar while the flight deck was full of strike aircraft. *Glorious* landed her air group in the UK in 1940 to provide space for ferrying aircraft to Norway, but this was a terrible misuse of the ship, which was never allowed to fulfil her potential.

Summary of service

14.10.16	Commissioned as large light cruiser
23.10.16	Left Belfast for trials but struck buoy and had to be docked for repairs
19.11.16	Struck by steamer *Corib* whilst still in Harland and Wolff yard; further repairs required
30.12.16	Sailed for Clyde for trials
06.01.17	Joined GF at Rosyth, forming part of 1 CS with *Courageous*
17.11.17	Intercepted German forces and saw action off Heligoland
00.02.18	Refit in Devonport, including fitting of flying-off platforms on main turrets and some structural stiffening
05.11.18	Seaplane carrier *Campania* dragged anchor in Firth of Forth during gale and collided with battleship *Royal Oak* and both ships dragged on to *Glorious*, causing damage which, whilst not serious for *Glorious*, caused *Campania* to founder
21.11.18	With GF force that escorted German High Seas Fleet into internment
00.00.19	Paid off into reserve
00.01.21	Recommissioned as turret drill ship for Plymouth Gunnery School
00.04.21	Flagship of RF Devonport
01.02.24	Arrived in Rosyth for conversion to aircraft carrier; work completed in Devonport Dockyard
07.01.30	Recommissioned as aircraft carrier at Devonport
15.02.30	Carried out trials and work-up
06.03.30	Flying trials started; air group arrived in stages and eventually comprised 406 and 408 (Flycatcher) Flights, 461 and 462 (Ripon) Flights and 441 and 447 (Fairey IIIF) Flights
02.07.30	Arrived in Malta to join MF (three turbines damaged on journey out and repairs took until December 1930 with air group disembarked at Hal Far)
08.12.30	Shakedown cruise off Crete
08.01.31	Exercises in Adriatic (*Glorious* in 'Blue Fleet' and *Eagle* in opposing 'Red Fleet')
13.03.31	Combined AF/MF exercises off Gibraltar
01.04.31	Collided with French liner *Florida* north-east of Gibraltar; landed *Florida*'s passengers at Malaga, then proceeded to

Gibraltar for temporary repairs
02.04.31 In Gibraltar
23.05.31 Permanent repairs in Malta
21.09.31 Having completed repairs, sailed for exercises
16.01.32 Formed part of squadron with *Courageous* under Rear-Admiral Aircraft Carriers based in Mediterranean to practise carrier task force techniques
19.01.32 Aircraft from *Glorious* and *Courageous* 'struck' at remainder of fleet which was anchored in a southern Greek port; results very encouraging, with 'hits' on battleships and cruisers (concept of future FAA attack on Taranto grew out of practices such as this)
22.02.32 Sailed for Gibraltar; Nimrods replaced Flycatchers in 408 Flight
25.04.32 Returned to Malta
23.06.32 Summer exercises in Greek waters with MF
00.09.32 Visited Alexandria
01.11.32 Sailed for refit in UK
10.11.32 Paid off in Devonport
06.01.33 Recommissioned in Devonport
25.01.33 Re-joined MF
01.03.33 Combined exercises practising strike operations with *Furious* and *Courageous* detached from HF
03.04.33 Old Flight numbering system abolished and *Glorious*'s air group restructured as 802 (Nimrod/Osprey), 812 (Ripon) and 823 and 825 (Fairey IIIF) NAS
27.04.33 Arrived in Malta
27.06.33 Exercises and MF regatta
23.10.33 Arrived back in Malta for winter
00.03.34 Combined exercises with HF in Atlantic
11.03.34 Storm-force waves smashed through hangar door into upper hangar, destroying 6 aircraft
23.04.34 Left Malta for UK
01.05.34 Refit in Devonport, including fitting of Mk III arrester gear, extension of flight deck aft supported by a distinctive 'W' bracket on quarterdeck and two catapults forward
23.07.35 Recommissioned at Devonport
19.08.35 Flying trials
28.08.35 Arrived in Malta; Baffins replaced Ripons in 812 NAS (aircraft had been stored at Hal Far after service in *Eagle*)
03.09.35 Sailed for Alexandria
05.09.35 Arrived in Alexandria, air group disembarking to Aboukir (MF concentrated there during deepening crisis over Abyssinia; ships were stored for war and there was reinforcement from HF and other stations)
15.09.35 Reinforced MF put to sea for exercises and training
05.10.35 Italy invaded Abyssinia
11.10.35 Sanctions agreed against Italy by League of Nations
18.11.35 Sanctions came into force but did not prove effective
Xmas 35 Ship returned to Malta for docking
03.01.36 Returned to Alexandria
15.07.36 Sanctions against Italy ended
18.07.36 MF sailed for Malta.
00.09.36 Cruise to Greece and Crete, returning to Malta on completion
00.07.36 825 NAS re-equipped with Swordfish (first squadron to do so)
Aut. 36 Night flying trials using new visual landing aids designed on board (these comprised pillar lights and sector lights; both concepts still in use today)
00.03.37 Combined exercises with HF in Atlantic, with over 100 ships taking part (emphasis on night flying and especially torpedo strikes)
05.05.37 In Portsmouth for Coronation Review of HM King George VI with 140 other ships (ship's NAS took part in fly-past on 21 May)
24.06.37 Re-embarked air group
26.06.37 Arrived in Falmouth for start of major trade defence exercise
16.07.37 Arrived in Malta
24.08.37 Major exercise in Eastern Mediterranean
18.09.37 Deployed to Western Mediterranean to protect international shipping during Spanish Civil War
18.10.37 Returned to Malta and disembarked air group to Hal Far
25.10.37 Sailed for Devonport to pay off
04.01.38 Recommissioned at Devonport
15.01.38 Re-joined MF
24.01.38 Arrived in Malta
00.03.38 Combined exercise with HF off Gibraltar (over 80 ships took part)
Aut. 38 Cruise in Eastern Mediterranean
00.02.39 Combined exercises with HF off Gibraltar (to 00.03.39)
00.04.39 Based at Alexandria
00.05.39 Sea Gladiators replaced Ospreys in 802 NAS
04.07.39 Exercises in Greek waters
11.09.39 Exercises in Eastern Mediterranean

HMS *Glorious* at anchor in Plymouth Sound during 1935. Note the flying control position hinged out from the port side of the island, the forerunner of the modern 'flyco', from which Commander 'Flying' controlled operations on deck. It could be hinged back against the island to provide a clear deck for aircraft recovery operations. The box-like structures in the fore part of the flight deck supported the forward end of the catapult mechanisms. (Author)

16.09.39 Returned to Alexandria (planned refit in Malta cancelled)
09.10.39 Passed through Suez Canal
13.10.39 Arrived in Aden to refit before hunting for German raiders in Indian Ocean
10.12.39 Arrived in Colombo for rest and to collect replacement aircrew
Xmas 39 In Trincomalee
29.12.39 Covered French convoy from Indo-China with *Kent* and *Suffren*
07.01.40 Arrived in Aden
17.01.40 Malta for delayed docking and refit (300 men travelled by ship to Marseilles and then by train across France to UK)
31.03.40 Sailed for Alexandria with *Ark Royal*
04.04.40 Arrived in Alexandria
08.04.40 At sea for period of intensive training (cancelled when Germany invaded Norway)
09.04.40 *Glorious* and *Ark Royal* ordered to Malta
13.04.40 In Gibraltar; hoisted Flag of Vice-Admiral L. V. Wells CB DSO, Vice-Admiral Air, who transferred from *Ark Royal*
14.04.40 Ordered to join HF for operations off Norway
18.04.40 Arrived in Clyde
21.04.40 812 and 825 NAS (Swordfish) flown off to Prestwick, leaving 802 (Sea Gladiator) and 823 (Swordfish) NAS on board; sailed from Clyde and embarked 18 Gladiator fighters of No 263 Squadron RAF (landed-on by naval pilots)
22.04.40 823 disembarked and 804 (Sea Gladiator) and 803 (Skua) NAS embarked
23.04.40 Sailed from Scapa Flow with *Ark Royal* for Operation 'DX' to provide fighter cover off Namsos and Aandalsnes and fly off No 263 Squadron RAF to frozen Lake Lesjaskou
27.04.40 Remaining 4 Skuas of 803 NAS transferred to *Ark Royal*; *Glorious* then returned to Scapa Flow to refuel and embark replacement fighters
28.04.40 Arrived in Scapa Flow
30.04.40 Embarked 18 Sea Gladiators for 802 and 804 NAS plus 823 NAS (Swordfish)

01.05.40 Re-joined task force off Norwegian coast to cover evacuation from Aandalsnes; later that day ordered to withdraw by CinC HF (remaining Skuas transferred to *Ark Royal*)
03.05.40 Arrived in Scapa Flow briefly before sailing on to Greenock
09.05.40 18 Hurricanes of No 46 Squadron RAF lightered on board; ship also embarked 802 (Sea Gladiator), 823 (Swordfish) and 701 (Walrus) NAS (to 11.05.40)
14.05.40 Sailed in company with *Furious*
18.05.40 Joined *Ark Royal* off Narvik and disembarked 701 NAS to Harstad but bad weather prevented No 46 Squadron from flying off
22.05.40 Withdrew from Norwegian waters with Hurricanes still on board
23.05.40 Arrived in Scapa Flow to refuel
24.05.40 Sailed, still with No 46 Squadron embarked
26.05.40 Flew off No 46 Squadron Hurricanes to Skaanland (they flew on to Bardufoss)
28.05.40 3 Sea Gladiators of 802 NAS shot down shadowing He 115 floatplane
30.05.40 Entered Scapa Flow to refuel
31.05.40 Sailed in company with *Ark Royal* for Operation 'Alphabet' (evacuation of BEF from Narvik area); again, *Glorious* had only embarked 802 and 823 NAS in order to leave space for such RAF aircraft as could be recovered from ashore
07.06.40 Recovered 10 Gladiators of No 263 and 7 Hurricanes of No 46 Squadrons RAF (first time high-performance monoplane fighters had landed on British carrier)
08.06.40 Sunk by gunfire from German battlecruisers *Scharnhorst* and *Gneisenau* between 1600 and 1730 south-west of Narvik (68° 45' N 04° 30' E) whilst on passage back to UK (ship's escorts, destroyers *Ardent* and *Acasta*, also sunk)

Glory (R62) Colossus *Class Light Fleet Carrier*

Laid down: 27 August 1942
Launched: 27 November 1943
Completed: 2 April 1945

Builder: Harland & Wolff, Belfast
Machinery: 2-shaft Parsons geared turbines; 4 Admiralty 3-drum boilers; 40,000shp = 25 knots
Displacement: 13,190 tons standard; 18,040 tons deep load
Dimensions: 695ft overall x 112ft 6in max beam x 23ft 5in max draught
Gun armament: 4 quadruple 2pdr pompom (16); 16 single 40mm Bofors (16); 4 single 3pdr saluting (4)
Fuel: 3,196 tons FFO
Endurance: 8,300 miles @ 20 knots
Complement: 1,300
Protection: Armoured mantlets over torpedo warheads in magazine
Flight deck: 690ft x 80ft steel
Arrester wires: 10 x 15,000lb @ 60 knots; 2 barriers
Hangar: 275ft (plus 57ft extension aft of aft lift) x 52ft x 17ft 6in
Catapults: 1 x BH3 (twin-track); 16,000lb @ 66 knots
Lifts: *Fwd* 45ft long x 34ft wide; *aft* 45ft long x 34ft wide; both 15,000lb
Aircraft: 42
Aircraft fuel: 98,600 gallons AVGAS
Air weapons: 18in torpedoes; 1,000lb MC bombs; 500lb SAP bombs; 500lb MC bombs; 250lb B bombs; 3in RP with 28lb and 60lb warheads; Mk 11 depth charges; aircraft mines; 20mm cannon ammunition; flares and pyrotechnics

Notes: One of sixteen 1942 light fleet carriers designed to mercantile standards below the hangar deck so that they could be built quickly and cheaply in yards that did not normally specialise in warship construction. They had twice the AVGAS stowage of the fleet carriers and a flight deck and hangar nearly as big. Gun armament was limited to close-range AA weapons to save time, cost and complexity in build. For the first time in a British carrier design, the light fleet carriers recognised that aircraft formed the main armament. Considered for conversion to a commando carrier in 1958, but nothing came of the idea. Details apply to *Glory* as she was in 1951.

Summary of service
02.04.45 Commissioned in Belfast
14.05.45 Sailed from Greenock for Malta to work up in Mediterranean
21.05.45 Allocated to 11 ACS, BPF, under Rear-

Admiral C. H. J. Harcourt, with *Venerable*, *Colossus* and *Vengeance*

16.07.45 Arrived in Trincomalee after work-up with 1831 (Corsair) and 837 (Barracuda) NAS embarked

00.08.45 Arrived in Sydney

00.09.45 In response to a request from Australian government, led Task Goup 111.5 to Rabaul for surrender of Japanese forces there

06.09.45 Ceremony of surrender took place on flight deck at 0147 GMT whilst ship was moored in St George's Channel 28 miles south-east of Rabaul; Gen. B. A. H. Sturdee of Australian Army took surrender of all Japanese forces in New Britain

00.10.45 Employed in repatriating former POWs to Canada and Australia (ship remained operational with BPF until September 1947)

02.09.47 Left Singapore for UK

00.10.47 Paid off into reserve

00.02.48 Major refit in Devonport during which bridge was rebuilt and 16 single 40mm Bofors replaced Oerlikons fitted on build

00.00.49 Allocated to HF

23.04.51 Entered Sasebo Dockyard in Japan after passage from Mediterranean via Hong Kong

26.04.51 Sailed for first operational patrol off west coast of Korea with 804 (Sea Fury) and 812 (Firefly) NAS plus SAR Dragonfly embarked; as well as CAP and AS patrols, both NAS flew strikes against railways and interdiction targets

09.05.51 Returned to Sasebo for operational turn-round

11.05.51 Sailed for second operational patrol; junks attacked as well as inland targets

14.05.51 Stoker McPherson, who had fallen overboard, rescued by SAR helicopter (first such rescue in RN)

20.05.51 Arrived in Sasebo for operational turn-round and repairs to defective stern gland

22.05.51 Entered drydock for repair and bottom scrape

25.05.51 Moved out to buoy for further defect rectification

03.06.51 Sailed from Sasebo for third operational patrol, relieving USS *Bataan* off west coast; junks attacked and CAS provided

HMS *Glory*, a few days after her completion in May 1945. (FAA Museum)

14.06.51 Relieved off west coast by USS *Sicily*; proceeded to Kure and secured alongside *Unicorn* to replace defective aircraft

21.06.51 Sailed for West Korean waters; CAS sorties flown over eastern part of the Allied lines; Fireflies used 1,000lb bombs on bridge-blasting sorties; both NAS spotted for shore bombardments by frigates

03.07.51 Replenishment period in Sasebo

10.07.51 Armistice discussions commenced between UN and North Korea

11.07.51 Sailed for fifth operational patrol in West Korean waters; attacks on railway trucks, junks and barracks and at least one 'moving haystack' set on fire

20.07.51 Search carried out for ditched MiG-15, which was located and marked for recovery off Chodo

22.07.51 Returned to Kure for rest period

24.07.51 Sailed in haste to reinforce USS *Sicily* off west coast of Korea to provide show of force as backdrop to armistice negotiations (which were proceeding with difficulty); bad weather limited flying

05.08.51 Returned to Sasebo for rest period

07.08.51 *Warrior* arrived from UK with replacement aircraft and aircrew

10.08.51 Sailed for Kure via Iwakuni Air Base (which she used as 'spare deck' for DLP session)

13.08.51 Sailed from Kure for seventh patrol off Korea

18.08.51 Operated off south-west tip of Korea to avoid Hurricane 'Marge'

21.08.51 Steamed off Okinawa to avoid 100mph winds

25.08.51 Arrived in Kure for rest period

31.08.51 Sailed to relieve USS *Sicily* off Korea; targets ranged from Taedong Gang in north to Yonan in south (catapult gave trouble so many take-offs had to use RATOG)

09.09.51 New record of 84 sorties in single day, 66 offensive and 18 defensive (100 per cent serviceability maintained)

11.09.51 Returned to Sasebo

16.09.51 Sailed for operations off east coast of Korea

21.09.51 Transferred to west coast for strikes in Taedong area

22.09.51 804 NAS completed 1,000 accident-free deck landings

25.09.51 Last day of operations on this tour

27.09.51 Arrived in Kure and berthed alongside *Sydney* to transfer aircraft and equipment (in this tour, ship's CAG flew total of 2,875 flying hours in 107 days at sea; 2,871 deck landings were achieved with only 9 accidents, and aircraft expended 94 x 1,000lb bombs, 1,450 x 500lb bombs, 9,242 x 3in RP and 538,000 rounds 20mm cannon ammunition; targets destroyed included 679 junks, 794 ox carts and 236 rail trucks)

01.02.52 Returned to Hong Kong with same air group after refit and rest period in Australia; took over stores, aircraft and equipment from *Sydney*

05.02.52 Arrived in Sasebo

06.02.52 Sailed for operations off west coast of Korea (including defence of Allied-held islands off enemy coast, in particular Chodo and Paengyong-do)

09.02.52 Fireflies successfully blocked rail tunnel north of Haejn; Sea Furies spotted for bombardment by cruiser *Ceylon*

16.02.52 Returned to Sasebo for replenishment; relieved off coast of Korea by USS *Bairoko*

24.02.52 Resumed operations off west coast of Korea

25.02.52 Sea Furies attacked communist troop concentrations at Sogang-ni while Fireflies attacked buildings at Yonchodo-ri

01.03.52 Lt Fraser's Sea Fury suffered engine failure whilst 'slotting' to starboard of carrier and ditched; he was immediately rescued by USN planeguard helicopter and on flight

Former British and Australian prisoners of the Japanese embarked in HMS *Glory* for repatriation during October 1945. (Jack Waterman)

deck only 1½ minutes after hitting water

04.03.52 Proceeded to Kure for replenishment

12.03.52 Sailed for operations flying flag of Admiral Scott-Moncrieff, FO2 FEF; deep-penetration raids flown to vicinity of Anak which destroyed number of ground targets

17.03.52 Record number of sorties flown to break up attack on Sok-to: 804 NAS flew 65 and 812 NAS 40, a total of 105 (previous best was 89 by *Sydney*); serviceability 100 per cent

21.03.52 Sea Furies supported landing by South Korean Marines at Pongwha-ri

23.03.52 Arrived in Sasebo for replenishment (during this period the Sea Furies were modified to carry 500lb bombs; 804 NAS pilots carried out bombing practice at Iwakuni)

31.03.52 Resumed operations with TF.95.11 off west coast of Korea after stormy passage from Sasebo

01.04.52 Flying commenced with both Sea Furies and Fireflies carrying 500lb bombs and cannon on armed reconnaissance sorties (attacks on warehouses at Simpo and Kyomipo particularly successful)

04.04.52 Sea Furies carried out CAS sorties north of Imjin River in support of 1 Commonwealth Division

06.04.52 Sea Furies bombed and destroyed rail bridge north of Chinnampo

09.04.52 CAS supplied for 1 US Marine Division

11.04.52 Arrived in Kure to take on stores and replacement aircraft from *Unicorn*

17.04.52 Sailed for fifth and last patrol of this deployment

22.04.52 Fireflies destroyed centre of village of Singsongdong and Sea Furies destroyed factory near Pyongyang; bad weather prevented flying for much of this period

27.04.52 Sea Furies destroyed one span of the strongly built rail bridge near Sariwon

01.05.52 Left Korean waters for Hong Kong, where ship transferred pilots, aircraft and stores to *Ocean*, which relieved her on station

06.05.52 Sailed for Singapore (during two tours in Korean waters, *Glory*'s aircraft had flown 4,835 sorties for the loss of 27 aircraft and 9 aircrew; totals of ammunition expended rose to 886,300 rounds of 20mm cannon ammunition, 126 x 1,000lb bombs, 3,114 x 500lb bombs and 13,098 x 3in RP; targets taken out included 796 junks, 1,001 ox carts and 308 rail trucks)

11.05.52 Left FEF for MF

23.10.52 Returned to Hong Kong with 801 (Sea Fury) and 821 (Firefly) NAS embarked

04.11.52 Rendezvoused with *Ocean* for Exercise 'Taipan' to test air defence of Hong Kong; on completion, pilots, stores and aircraft transferred from *Ocean* to *Glory*

06.11.52 Sailed from Hong Kong for Sasebo

10.11.52 Sailed from Sasebo for first patrol of third tour of operations off Korea (ground targets strictly controlled because of peace talks in progress ashore; AAA proved particularly heavy during this period)

20.11.52 Arrived in Sasebo to take on aircraft and stores from *Unicorn*

28.11.52 Sailed to relieve USS *Badoeng Strait* off Western Korea (much of flying was intended to protect islands of Chodo and Sok-to which were threatened again; bad weather caused flying to be cancelled on four days)

09.12.52 Arrived in Kure for replenishment

15.12.52 Sailed for operational area

16.12.52 SAR Dragonfly and crew lost when crosswind caused it to crash over starboard side

17.12.52 Interdiction sorties given priority, with emphasis on railway tunnels

20.12.52 Firefly carried out 10,000th deck landing since *Glory* left UK in May 1951

26.12.52 Left operational area for Iwakuni, where ship took on replacement Fireflies by lighter; on completion, sailed for Sasebo

04.01.53 Sailed for Korean waters (priority targets this time were villages where enemy troops were reported to be billeted; rail communications also cut successfully)

11.01.53 Left operational area for Kure via Iwakuni, where replacement aircraft were taken on

19.01.53 Sailed for fifth patrol of this tour (flying effort concentrated on enemy troops billeted in villages)

28.01.53 Returned to Sasebo for replenishment

05.02.53 Sailed for sixth patrol; possible threat of communist submarines led to continuous daylight AS patrols by Fireflies

10.02.53 Sea Furies attacked by section of MiG-15s (none lost)

17.02.53 Sailed for replenishment period in Kure

25.02.53 Returned to operational area in some of worst weather encountered during war; targets included troop concentrations and transport

04.03.53 Leaflet raids carried out on larger villages and towns
05.03.53 Pre-dawn strikes carried out on MT convoys
06.03.53 Left operational area for Sasebo
15.03.53 Sailed for eighth patrol
17.03.53 Attacks concentrated on road and rail communications
24.03.53 Left operational area for Kure, where ship took on aircraft and stores from *Unicorn*
03.04.53 Sailed for west Korean waters; new 3in RP with shaped-charge warheads used for first time
05.04.53 123 sorties flown in the day, equalling record set by *Ocean* (this involved all squadron pilots flying four sorties and Cdr (Air), FDO and LSO flying two; targets destroyed included 7 road and rail bridges, 28 houses and 5 ox carts with 4 bridges and 3 gun positions damaged; 104 x 500lb bombs and 384 x 60lb 3in RPs expended)
12.04.53 Arrived in Sasebo for replenishment
19.04.53 Sailed for tenth patrol of this deployment (operations severely restricted as sick and wounded POWs were being exchanged at Panmunjon); CAS provided for Commonwealth Division
20.04.53 Admiral Sir Charles Lambe, CinC FEF, visited ship and flew over North Korea in Firefly of 821 NAS
29.04.53 Arrived at Kure for replenishment; replacement aircraft lightered to ship from NASU at Iwakuni
05.05.53 Sailed for eleventh patrol of this deployment and twenty-fifth patrol off Korea (war was drawing to close and Cdr Seventh Fleet ordered that no unnecessary risks be taken by aircraft attacking heavily defended targets)
14.05.53 Last day of operational flying
17.05.53 Arrived in Sasebo to pass over some aircraft, personnel and stores to *Ocean* (*Glory* had made a greater contribution to the Korean War than any other carrier: since leaving UK in May 1951 she had steamed 157,000 miles and flown 13,700 sorties, 9,500 of which were operational over Korea; her aircraft had destroyed 70 bridges, 392 vehicles and 49 railway trucks for the loss of 20 aircrew; ordnance expended included 278 x 1,000lb bombs, 7,080 x 500lb bombs, 24,238 x 3in RP and 1,441,000 rounds of 20mm ammunition)
08.07.53 Arrived in Portsmouth for refit; on completion, joined MF with same air group
09.03.54 Returned to Portsmouth for minor refit
00.08.54 Employed as ferry carrier without air group (used to carry aircraft and equipment to Far East)
00.01.55 Acted as base ship for naval helicopters carrying out relief operations for Scotland, which was snowbound (operated mainly in Loch Eriboll, supported by frigate *Urchin*)
00.00.56 Paid off into maintained reserve at Rosyth
00.00.57 Placed on disposal list
00.00.61 Broken up at Inverkeithing

HMS *Glory* with Sea Furies on deck. Flying operations are not imminent, however, as the range is not manned and the jackstaff is rigged forward. (FAA Museum)

Hermes (1924) (I95) *Fleet Carrier*

Laid down: 15 January 1918
Launched: 11 September 1919
Completed: 18 February 1924

Builder: Sir W. G. Armstrong Whitworth & Co., Newcastle-upon-Tyne; completed by Devonport Dockyard
Machinery: 2-shaft Parsons geared turbines; 40,000 shp = 25 knots
Displacement: 10,850 tons standard; 13,700 tons deep load
Dimensions: 600ft overall x 90ft max beam x 26ft 7in max draught
Gun armament: 6 single 5.5in LA (6); 3 single 4in HA (3); 2 quadruple 0.5in AA (8)
Fuel: 2,000 tons FFO
Endurance: 2,930 miles @ 18 knots
Complement: 700
Protection: 3in waterline belt; 1in flight deck
Flight deck: 570ft x 90ft steel
Arrester wires: 4 x 11,000lb @ 53 knots (fitted in 1934); no barriers
Hangar: 400ft x 50ft x 16ft
Catapults: None
Lifts: *Fwd* 46ft long x 47ft wide (cruciform); *aft* 46ft long x 47ft wide (cruciform); both 14,000lb
Aircraft: 12 in 1939
Aircraft fuel: 7,500 gallons AVGAS
Air weapons: 18in torpedoes; 100lb GP bombs; 65lb bombs; 6lb bombs; explosive darts; Mk 7 depth charges; .303in gun ammunition; flares and pyrotechnics

Notes: The first ship in the world to be designed, ordered and built as an aircraft carrier. After lift opened on to the open-sided quarterdeck which was originally intended to be used as seaplane operating area, accessible from hangar by steel shutter door. Round down was exaggerated by a hump in after flight deck, intended to form rear anchor of original fore and aft arrester wire system.

Summary of service

11.09.19	Launched by Mrs Cooper (daughter of First Lord of Admiralty, Mr Walter Long)
00.07.20	Towed from Elswick to Devonport Dockyard for fitting out
00.00.23	Steaming trials in Plymouth Sound
18.02.24	Commenced trials in UK waters with 403 (Flycatcher) Flight and Panther spotter aircraft
03.06.25	Commissioned for operational service and sailed to join MF via Portland and Gibraltar; during this period air group comprised 442 and 440 (Fairey IIID) and 403 (Flycatcher) Flights; after short period in Mediterranean, ship deployed to China Station based on Hong Kong
13.12.27	Paid off in Devonport after being relieved on station by *Eagle*
15.12.27	Refit at Chatham
00.00.28	Re-joined China Station with same air group but with Fairey IIIFs having displaced IIIDs in 440 Flight
00.08.30	Left Hong Kong for UK
00.12.30	Sailed to re-join China Station with 440 (Fairey IIIF) and 403 (Flycatcher) Flights
22.09.33	Paid off for long refit at Devonport, during which arrester wires were fitted
01.11.34	Recommissioned with 803 (Osprey) and 824 (Seal) NAS and returned to Far East
06.05.35	Jubilee Review in Hong Kong
09.11.35	Assisted Kingsford-Smith and other record-breakers on their flights to Australia; ship based in Singapore
03.05.37	Arrived in Devonport
20.05.37	Royal Review of the Fleet at Spithead; on completion, paid off into reserve at Devonport (retained skeleton complement and used as harbour training ship)
00.08.39	Recommissioned for operational service with 814 NAS (Swordfish); used at first with Channel Force, covering passage of BEF to France
14.10.39	Joined French squadron led by battlecruiser *Strasbourg*, based on Dakar; hunted German raiders in South Atlantic shipping lanes
00.06.40	After fall of France, blockaded French Fleet in Dakar
08.07.40	One of ship's boats carried out unsuccessful attack on French battleship *Richelieu* with depth charges (intended to damage rudder/propellers but they failed to explode due to shallow water)
10.07.40	Collided with AMC *Corfu* in dense fog, suffering damage to bows; initial repairs carried out in Freetown

HMS *Hermes* (1924) in her China Station paint scheme after a Devonport refit, moored near the breakwater in Plymouth Sound in November 1934. (Author)

00.08.40 Full repairs carried out in Simonstown
00.11.40 Resumed hunting operations for enemy raiders in South Atlantic and Indian Oceans (12 Swordfish of 814 NAS remained her air group throughout wartime service)
00.04.41 Supported British/Indian force that defeated German intervention in Iraq
00.05.41 Employed on trade protection in Indian Ocean
00.11.41 Refit in Simonstown
02.01.42 Joined Australian Squadron
00.02.42 Transferred to EIF; retained in Colombo area while *Indomitable* ferried aircraft to Far East
08.04.42 Ordered to clear Trincomalee harbour without aircraft embarked to escape reportedly imminent Japanese air attack; sailed with destroyer *Vampire* and ordered to be at least 40 miles south by next dawn
09.04.42 Sighted by Japanese reconnaissance aircraft and attacked by about 50 aircraft at 0500 off Batticaloa in Ceylon; sank in 7° 45' N 81° 48' E with loss of 19 officers and 288 men

Hermes (1959) (R12) *Light Fleet Carrier*

Laid down: 21 June 1944
Launched: 16 February 1953
Completed: 18 November 1959

Builder: Vickers-Armstrong, Barrow-in-Furness
Machinery: 2 Parsons geared turbines; 4 Admiralty 3-drum boilers; 76,000shp = 28 knots
Displacement: 24,900 tons standard; 27,800 tons deep load
Dimensions: 774ft 3in overall x 147ft 11in max beam x 27ft 10in max draught
Missile/gun armament: 2 quadruple GWS.22 Seacat SAM (8); 4 single 3pdr saluting (4)
Fuel: 3,500 tons FFO
Endurance: 5,040 miles @ 20 knots
Complement: 2,100
Protection: 1in–2in flight deck; 1in uptakes; 1in magazine crowns

HMS *Hermes* (1959) in 1968. The aircraft on deck are Gannets, Wessexes, Sea Vixens and Buccaneers. (Author)

Flight deck: 744ft 6in x 144ft 6in steel; 8-degree angled deck
Arrester wires: 5 x 35,000lb @ 103 knots; emergency nylon barriers
Hangar: 356ft x 62ft x 17ft 6in
Catapults: 2 x BS4; *port* 50,000lb @ 94 knots (175ft stroke); *starboard* 50,000lb @ 94 knots (151ft stroke)
Lifts: *Side* 54ft long x 35ft wide, 30-second cycle; *aft* 54ft long x 44ft wide, 25-second cycle; both 40,000lb
Aircraft: 28
Aircraft fuel: 332,000 gallons AVCAT
Air weapons: Tactical nuclear bombs; nuclear depth bombs; Firestreak AAM; Red Top AAM; Sidewinder AAM; Bullpup ASM; Mk 30/44/46 homing torpedoes (Stingray homing torpedoes after 1982); 1,000lb MC bombs; 500lb MC bombs; 28lb practice bombs; 3in RP with 60lb warheads; 2in RP; Glowworm illuminant RP; 30mm cannon ammunition; 7.62mm MG ammunition; flares and pyrotechnics

Notes: *Hermes*' construction was suspended in 1945 and resumed in 1952 to clear the slipway. She was laid up after launch until 1957 when work started again to a revised design. When delivered in 1959 she was very different from her three half-sisters *Albion*, *Bulwark* and *Centaur* and was closely comparable with the modernised *Victorious*. When converted to the Commando role her catapults, arrester wires and aircraft direction facilities were removed. Originally to have been named *Elephant*, she was given the name *Hermes* in 1945 in order to keep the famous carrier name alive when 4 further units of the *Centaur* class (*Arrogant*, *Hermes*, *Monmouth* and *Polyphemus*) were cancelled. Details apply to *Hermes* as she was in 1968.

Summary of service

16.02.53	Launched by Mrs Winston Churchill
25.11.59	Commissioned in Portsmouth and sailed for shakedown cruise following day
00.07.60	Embarked air group with 804 (Scimitar), 890 (Sea Vixen), 814 (Whirlwind) and 849C (Gannet AEW) NAS; deployed to Mediterranean for work-up in Malta area
07.11.60	Arrived back in UK for SMP before joining FEF
31.12.60	Arrived in Singapore
24.02.61	Exercise 'Jet 61' in Trincomalee area with other Commonwealth warships

HMS *Hermes* refuelling at sea from RFA *Orangeleaf* in the South China Sea in 1968. (Author)

19.04.61	Arrived back in UK
00.07.61	NATO Exercise 'Fairwind 6'
16.10.61	Entered Portsmouth Dockyard for refit
16.04.62	Refit completed
00.05.62	Sea trials with Buccaneer aircraft before deploying to Mediterranean
00.07.62	Visited Beirut with destroyer *Scorpion*
09.08.62	Exercise 'Riptide' with British, US and French ships
05.10.62	Returned to Portsmouth for SMP
00.11.62	Sailed for FEF
06.01.63	Exercised with USN off Subic Bay in Philippines
00.04.63	Commonwealth Exercise 'Jet 63'; then SEATO Exercise 'Sea Serpent' with 60 Commonwealth, US and Thai warships (to 00.05.63)
29.08.63	Arrived back in UK after SMP in Mombasa
00.01.64	Exercise 'Phoenix' (test of HF air defences against high-flying jet bombers); on completion, carried out sea trials with Sea Vixen FAW.2
24.02.64	Entered Devonport Dockyard for major refit
00.05.66	Sailed for trials and work-up
13.01.67	Sailed for Mediterranean with 809 (Buccaneer S.2), 892 (Sea Vixen FAW.2), 826 (Wessex AS) and 849B (Gannet AEW) NAS embarked
00.06.67	Joined FEF temporarily as part of force covering withdrawal from Aden
02.10.67	Returned to UK for docking in Portsmouth
10.05.68	Sailed for trials and work-up
00.08.68	Re-joined FEF with 801 (Buccaneer S.2), 893 (Sea Vixen FAW.2), 814 (Wessex AS) and 849A (Gannet AEW) NAS embarked.
00.09.68	Docking in Singapore
00.10.68	Exercise 'Coral Sands' (Australian-directed maritime and amphibious exercise); on completion, visited Sydney
00.11.68	Visited Hong Kong
14.12.68	Alongside in Singapore
00.00.69	Returned to UK via Perth and Cape Town
00.04.69	Arrived in Portsmouth for docking
02.09.69	Sailed to join WF
00.01.70	Exercises with *Eagle*
00.06.70	NATO Exercise 'Dawn Patrol'
22.06.70	Returned to Portsmouth
14.07.70	Paid off into care and maintenance
00.10.70	Towed to Devonport for conversion to a commando carrier
01.03.71	Taken in hand for conversion
18.08.73	Recommissioned in Devonport.; after working up she embarked 845 (Wessex Commando) and 814 (Sea King AS) NAS
00.10.73	Operation 'Swift Move' off Norway
00.01.74	Exercises off northern Norway, followed by Exercise 'Dawn Patrol' in Mediterranean (to 00.02.1974)
00.06.74	Commando training in Canada
00.07.74	Evacuated 900 British nationals from Cyprus during fighting between Greek and Turkish forces
00.09.74	NATO Exercise 'Northern Merger'

25.02.75	Sailed from Devonport; Exercises in WESTLANT with 42 RM Cdo embarked with normal air group (deployment ended with visits to Montreal and Quebec)
26.06.75	Returned to Devonport
12.09.75	Exercise 'Deep Express' in Aegean
00.11.75	NATO Exercise 'Ocean Safari' (large-scale anti-submarine exercise in Norwegian Sea)
28.11.75	Docking and maintenance at Devonport
12.01.76	Sailed for Norwegian exercises with 845 and 814 NAS and 45 RM Cdo,followed by Exercise 'Atlas Express'
10.05.76	Taken in hand in Devonport Dockyard for conversion to anti-submarine carrier (although retaining commando capability)
10.12.76	Recommissioned in Devonport
00.01.77	Trials in English Channel, culminating in embarkation of 4 Harriers and prototype equipment to enable them to operate at night and in poor weather (to 00.02.77)
00.03.77	Sailed for ASW work-up in Mediterranean
00.06.77	Took part in HM Queen Elizabeth II's Silver Jubilee Review of the Fleet at Spithead, flying flag of FOCAS; on completion, took part in Exercise 'Highwood' (maritime air exercise)
00.10.77	NATO Exercise 'Ocean Safari 77'
00.02.78	Exercise 'Springtrain'
00.03.78	Exercise 'Safe Pass'
00.05.78	Exercise 'Open Gate'
00.09.78	Exercise 'Northern Wedding'
00.11.78	Further Harrier trials
00.12.79	Trials in Irish Sea with development Sea Harriers and operational trials with 700A NAS (Sea Harrier), the IFTU
00.00.80	Taken in hand in Portsmouth Dockyard to be modified to operate Sea Harriers (included fitting of 12-degree 'ski-jump', workshops and improved air weapon stowage; *Hermes* could operate twice the number of aircraft that an *Invincible* class ship could, despite having hull of smaller internal volume)
00.06.81	Sailed for trials and embarked 800 (Sea Harrier) and 826 (Sea King AS) NAS
00.03.82	Portsmouth for SMP
05.04.82	Sailed as flagship of South Atlantic Task Force for operations to recover Falkland Islands following Argentine invasion (Operation 'Corporate'); enhanced air group comprised 800 and 899 (Sea Harrier) and 826 and 846 (Sea King) NAS; ship spent 108 days at sea and, whilst deployed, air group was further increased by helicopters from 815 NAS (Lynx) and Harriers of No 1 Squadron RAF
21.07.82	Returned to rapturous welcome in Portsmouth
00.00.83	Carried out exercises off Norway and USA and in Mediterranean
00.12.83	Portsmouth for refit
00.04.84	Post-refit trials, after which she became harbour training ship in Portsmouth at nominal 30 days' notice for sea
00.00.86	Purchased by India and refitted for IN in Devonport
Early 87	Renamed *Viraat* and sailed to form part of IN Western Fleet; capable of operating mix of up to 30 Sea Harriers and Sea Kings
00.00.95	Extant in IN

HMS *Illustrious* steams past *Hermes* on the latter's return from South Atlantic waters to the UK in 1982 at the end of the Falklands War. Many of *Hermes*' ship's company line the flight deck to port, with Sea Harriers and Sea Kings on deck. (*Fly Navy*)

Hunter (D80) Attacker *Class Assault Escort Carrier*

Laid down: 15 May 1941
Launched: 22 May 1942
Completed: 11 January 1943

Builder: Ingalls Shipbuilding Corp., Pascagoula
Machinery: 1-shaft General Electric geared turbine; 2 Foster Wheeler boilers; 8,500shp = 18 knots
Displacement: 10,200 tons standard; 14,170 tons deep load
Dimensions: 492ft x 102ft max beam x 24ft 8in max draught
Gun armament: 2 single 4in US Mk 9 (2); 4 twin 40mm Bofors (8); 8 twin 20mm Oerlikon (16); 4 single 20mm Oerlikon (4)
Fuel: 2,423 tons FFO
Endurance: 27,300 miles @ 11 knots
Complement: 646
Protection: Splinter protection for bomb room
Flight deck: 442ft x 88ft wood-covered steel
Arrester wires: 9 x 19,800lb @ 55 knots; 3 barriers
Hangar: 262ft x 62ft x 18ft
Catapults: 1 x H2 hydraulic; 7,000lb @ 70 knots (tail-down method only)
Lifts: *Fwd* 42ft long x 34ft wide; *aft* 34ft long x 42ft wide; both 14,000lb
Aircraft: Up to 20 could be operated; up to 90 could be ferried
Aircraft fuel: 45,400 gallons AVGAS
Air weapons: 500lb SAP bombs; 250lb SAP bombs; 250lb GP bombs; 20mm cannon ammunition; .303in gun ammunition; flares and pyrotechnics

Notes: Laid down as the US mercantile *Mormacpen*. Acquired for conversion and built as USS *Block Island* (AVG-8) before transfer to the RN under Lend/Lease arrangements. Originally to have been called *Trailer* by the RN.

Summary of service

09.01.43 Commissioned in Pascagoula
31.01.43 Commenced trials in West Indies
05.03.43 Sailed with UGF.6 from Norfolk, Va, to Casablanca
12.04.43 Arrived in Dundee for alterations to RN standard, followed by work-up in Clyde
05.09.43 Arrived in Malta
09.09.43 Formed part of Force V with *Attacker*, *Battler*, *Stalker* and *Unicorn*; provided tactical air support for Operation 'Avalanche' (Salerno landings); 899 and part of 834 (Seafire) NAS embarked
12.09.43 5 Seafires landed to operate from forward airstrip at Paestum
30.09.43 Sailed to Dundee for repairs
03.12.43 Hangar deck plating fractured whilst undocking in Dundee
07.12.43 Clyde for further repair work
01.03.44 Work-up in Scapa Flow with 807 NAS (Seafire) embarked
14.05.44 Sailed for Mediterranean
15.08.44 Operation 'Dragoon' (invasion of southern France): ship formed part of Task Group 88.2 with *Stalker* and US CVEs *Tulagi* and *Kasaan Bay*
09.09.44 Based on Alexandria for Operations 'Outing', 'Cablegram', 'Manna' and 'Contempt' (strikes on German shipping and garrisons in Aegean) with 807 NAS (Seafire) embarked in company with *Attacker*, *Stalker* and *Khedive* (their combined Seafire NAS constituted 4 Naval Fighter Wing; *Emperor*, *Pursuer* and *Searcher* operated Hellcats and Wildcats which constituted 7 Naval Fighter Wing); 1,500 fighter sorties flown, for minimal losses
10.11.44 Returned to UK
29.11.44 Sailed to join 21 ACS, EIF
06.12.44 Refit in Malta
21.02.45 Sailed for Trincomalee
08.03.45 Arrived in Trincomalee with 807 NAS (Seafire) embarked
30.04.45 Operation 'Dracula' (strikes on Rangoon and Tenasserim Coast) in company with *Emperor*, *Khedive* and *Stalker*
00.09.45 Part of covering force for Operation 'Zipper' (reoccupation of Singapore) in company with *Khedive*, *Emperor*, *Ameer*, *Empress* and *Stalker*
10.09.45 Entered Singapore
09.10.45 Sailed for UK
31.10.45 Arrived in Clyde; allocated to Rosyth Command and de-stored into reserve
28.11.45 Sailed for Portsmouth
02.12 45 Sailed from Portsmouth for USA
29.12.45 Returned to USN at Norfolk, Va; sold by USN as mercantile *Almdijk*
02.11.65 Arrived at Valencia to be broken up

HMS *Illustrious* shortly after her completion in 1940. (Author)

HMS *Hunter* shortly after entering service with the Royal Navy. (FAA Museum)

Illustrious (1940) (R87) Illustrious *Class Fleet Carrier*

Laid down: 27 April 1937
Launched: 5 April 1939
Completed: 25 May 1940

Builder: Vickers-Armstrong, Barrow-in-Furness
Machinery: 3-shaft Parsons SR geared turbines; 6 Admiralty 3-drum boilers; 111,000shp = 30.5 knots

Displacement: 23,207 tons standard; 28,619 tons deep load
Dimensions: 740ft overall x 106ft 9in max beam x 28ft 2in max draught
Gun armament: (In 1945) 8 twin 4.5in QF Mk III HA (16); 5 octuple 2pdr pompom (40); 3 single 40mm Bofors (3); 19 twin 20mm Oerlikon (38); 14 single 20mm Oerlikon (14)

Fuel: 4,850 tons FFO
Endurance: 11,000 miles @ 12 knots
Complement: 1,997 in 1945
Protection: 3in flight deck; 3in hangar deck; 4.5in waterline belt; 4.5in hangar sides; underwater protection against 750lb torpedo
Flight deck: 740ft x 95ft 9in armoured steel
Arrester wires: *Aft* 7 x 11,000lb @ 55 knots; *fwd* 2 x 20,000lb @ 60 knots; 3 barriers (*aft 2* 10,000lb, *fwd 1* 20,000lb)
Hangar: 456ft x 62ft x 16ft
Catapults: 1 x BH3; 14,000lb @ 66 knots (tail-down method), 14,000lb @ 60 knots (with trolley)
Lifts: *Fwd* 45ft long x 22ft wide; *aft* 45ft long x 22ft wide; both 14,000lb
Aircraft: 54 in 1945
Aircraft fuel: 50,540 gallons AVGAS
Air weapons: 18in torpedoes; 500lb SAP bombs; 500lb GP bombs; 250lb SAP bombs; B bombs; Mk 11 depth charges; aircraft mines; .5in gun ammunition; .303in gun ammunition; flares and pyrotechnics

Notes: First of eight carriers completed for RN with protected hangars, a concept which was unique to Britain (the USN and IJN armoured flight decks in some cases but never hangar sides). In the rearmament programme of the late 1930s the easy option would have been to build repeat *Ark Royal*s, but Admiral Chatfield (First Sea Lord) and Admiral Henderson (Controller) foresaw the need to provide better protection for aircraft carriers and their vulnerable fuel against intense land-based air attack, especially in the North Sea and Mediterranean. Given the low performance of RN fighters at the outbreak of war, their concept had merit and the fact that *Illustrious* survived the attack on 10 January 1941 spoke eloquently for the design. On RAF advice, the armour was proof against 500lb bombs although, in the event, no bomb that small was used against it. Once radar had advanced and better fighters became available to improve fleet air defence, the paramount need was to get more aircraft to sea. This was not easy in the cramped space available in the armoured carriers. The armour proved its worth again against Kamikazes in the Pacific, but post-war it proved costly and complicated to modernize even the newest ships and only *Victorious* completed the many modernisations planned for the *Illustrious* group. Unable to operate jet aircraft because of her small lifts and cramped hangar, *Illustrious* did not survive for long post-war.

Summary of service

05.04.39 Launched by Lady Henderson, wife of Controller of Navy who inspired design
00.05.40 Acceptance and sea trials; work-up off Bermuda with 806 (Fulmar) and 815 and 819 (Swordfish) NAS embarked
22.08.40 Left Scapa Flow for MF flying flag of RA Aircraft Carriers (Mediterranean), escorted to Sicilian Narrows by Force H
02.09.40 Joined up with MF; Fulmars shot down three Italian aircraft and Swordfish struck at Rhodes
05.09.40 Arrived in Alexandria
17.09.40 Nine aircraft of 815 NAS sank Italian destroyer and two merchant ships in Benghazi by dive-bombing; six aircraft of 819 NAS laid minefield which sank destroyer and two merchant ships and damaged a third
00.09.40 Two Malta convoys covered; strike carried out on Leros during latter (to 00.10.40)
00.10.40 Damaged by accidental hangar fire (but aircraft ashore at RNAS Dekhalia)
11.11.40 Operation 'Judgement': strike on Italian Fleet at Taranto by aircraft of 813, 815, 819 and 824 (Swordfish) NAS (813 and 824 were from damaged *Eagle*, which was unable to participate); for loss of 2 Swordfish and expenditure of 11 torpedoes and a number of bombs, battleship *Conte di Cavour* was sunk and 2 others put out of action for many months; 806 NAS proved very successful in keeping shadowers at bay
26.11.40 Leros attacked
12.12.40 Strikes on German Army positions near Bardia in support of 8th Army offensive
17.12.40 Airfields bombed on Rhodes and Stampalia
21.12.40 Merchant ships sunk off Kerkeneh Island
22.12.40 Tripoli attacked
07.01.41 Sailed to cover fast convoy to Malta
10.01.41 Severely damaged by German air attack 75 miles east of Malta; arrived in Malta under own power in evening
23.01.41 Sailed from Malta after emergency repairs
25.01.41 Arrived in Alexandria for further emergency repairs
10.03.41 Sailed for Durban via Suez Canal; docked at Durban to assess underwater damage
12.05.41 Arrived in Norfolk, Va, for full repairs and modifications, including reduction of the after round-down to give 50ft more available flight deck
28.11.41 Repairs and modifications complete
02.12.41 Sailed in company with *Formidable*
16.12.41 Collided with *Formidable* in heavy seas, resulting in damage to spaces port side

HMS *Illustrious* operating as a trials and training carrier in 1947. The aircraft on deck aft is a Sea Fury, and a late-model Seafire is parked on an outrigger forward of the island. (FAA Museum)

	forward; repairs carried out in Birkenhead after initial hooked Spitfire deck landing trials
00.03.42	Work-up started with 881 and 882 (Martlet) and 810 and 829 (Swordfish) NAS embarked
23.03.42	Sailed for Operation 'Ironclad' (landings on Madagascar); en route hangar suffered another fire (repaired in Freetown) which destroyed 11 aircraft
05.05.42	Vichy French submarine and AMC sunk during strikes on Diego Suarez
06.05.42	Vichy French Submarine *Le Héros* sunk near British transport anchorage by Swordfish
07.05.42	Diego Suarez taken (air combats had destroyed 7 French aircraft for loss of one Martlet)
Sum. 42	Two sweeps carried out with EF
24.08.42	Only carrier with EF
00.09.42	Covered occupation of southern Madagascar, followed by a short refit in Durban, after which operations constrained by lack of escorts
13.01.43	Sailed from Mombasa to UK for refit
07.06.43	Sailed from Birkenhead after further increase in size of usable flight deck (which allowed deck park) and improved light gun armament and fire-control radar; worked up with HF and carried out trials with new aircraft
26.07.43	Sweep off Norwegian coast
05.08.43	Escorted *Queen Mary* (which was carrying Winston Churchill to USA) until she was beyond range of German aircraft; on completion, replaced damaged *Indomitable* in Force H; deck park allowed ship to carry 50 aircraft—878 and 890 (Martlet), 894 (Seafire) and 810 (Barracuda) NAS
09.09.43	Provided heavy cover for Salerno landings together with *Formidable*
29.10.43	Arrived in Birkenhead for further modifications, round-down being cut back still further to give 740ft usable flight deck (compared with 620ft as built), thus allowing even bigger deck park
28.11.43	Arrived in Clyde to begin work-up with new air group: 21 TBR Wing (810 and 847 NAS with Barracudas) and 15 Naval Fighter Wing (1830, 1833 and 1837 NAS with Corsairs)
00.01.44	Sailed to join EIF
31.01.44	Arrived in Trincomalee; continued to work up in Eastern waters
08.03.44	Sweep against Japanese cruisers
16.04.44	Sailed from Trincomalee in company with USS *Saratoga* and 26 other ships for strike operations against Sabang, Sumatra

21.04.44 Returned to Trincomalee and disembarked 21 TBR Wing, replacing them with 832 and 851 NAS (Avenger)

17.05.44 Struck at oil refineries at Soerabaya, Java, in company with *Saratoga* after replenishment in Exmouth Gulf, Australia

21.06.44 Attacked Port Blair in Andaman Islands, Avengers having disembarked and Barracudas re-embarked (on this day ship had 57 aircraft embarked, 51 of which were airborne at one stage)

00.07.44 Worked up with *Victorious* and *Indomitable*

25.07.44 Carrier squadron struck at Sabang (aircraft of 15 Fighter Wing destroyed 4 Japanese fighters for no loss and spotted for battleship gunfire); on completion, ship sailed for Durban with only 810 NAS embarked for AS protection

14.08.44 Refit in Durban

10.10.44 Refit completed

00.11.44 854 NAS (Avenger) replaced Barracuda Wing, 1837 NAS absorbed into other two Corsair NAS; allocated to 1 ACS, BPF

20.12.44 Strike on Belawan Deli when weather proved unsuitable for primary attack on Pangkalon Brandan, Sumatra

16.01.45 Sailed from Trincomalee with 1830 and 1833 (Corsair) and 854 (Avenger) NAS embarked

24.01.45 BPF struck at Pladjoe Refinery near Palembang with 43 Avengers (carrying 172 x 500lb bombs), 12 Fireflies and 50 escorting fighters from carriers *Illustrious*, *Indomitable* (flagship of Rear-Admiral Sir Philip Vian), *Victorious* and *Indefatigable*; result highly successful

29.01.45 Attack on Soengi Gerong Refinery, also in Palembang complex, even more successful: 16 aircraft from carriers lost but over 30 Japanese aircraft shot down and 38 more destroyed on ground (Palembang strikes were largest carried out by RN in WW2 and achieved strategic results with the output of oil being reduced to mere fraction of pre-attack amount; Japanese had relied on Palembang for supply of aviation fuel but could no longer do so); *Illustrious* slightly damaged by two 5.25in shells fired wildly at attacking Japanese 'Lily' bombers by battleship *King George V* (casualties in island and on flight deck)

10.02.45 Arrived in Sydney (new main base of BPF); docked to investigate defects in centre propeller shaft (legacy of January 1941 damage); rather than reduce strength of 1 ACS, shaft was removed, reducing ship's maximum speed to 24 knots; on completion of work, joined Squadron at Manus Island, forward operating base

26.03.45 Operation 'Iceberg' (strikes against Sakashima Gunto islands in support of US landings on Okinawa): 2-day attack/2-day replenishment cycle to prevent enemy aircraft staging through from Formosa to reinforce Okinawa; BPF formed Task Force 57 and USPF Task Force 58

06.04.45 Narrowly missed by Kamikaze which crashed close alongside (explosion caused extensive damage to underwater plating and internal frames)

11.04.45 Strikes at Kamikaze bases in northern Formosa (since start of 'Iceberg', ship's air group had flown 643 sorties on 9 strike days for loss of 5 aircraft in operations and 7 in accidents)

13.04.45 Task Force 57 withdrew to San Pedro Bay, Leyte, for week's rest and recuperation; during this period *Formidable* replaced *Illustrious* in 1 ACS

01.05.45 Sailed from Leyte after repairs; landed air group and underwent further minor repairs in Sydney

24.05.45 Sailed from Sydney for UK

27.06.45 Arrived in Rosyth for refit (originally planned to last 4 months but extended on cessation of hostilities

00.06.46 Completed refit with improved flight deck, radio and radar; commissioned for use as trials and training carrier

00.00.47 Reduced to reserve due to shortage of trained manpower

00.09.48 Recommissioned; carried out trials with all first-generation jet and turboprop aircraft (most pilots trained between 1949 and 1954 carried out their first deck landings on *Illustrious*)

00.11.51 Ferried troops to Cyprus during Suez Canal Zone crisis

00.09.52 Exercise 'Mainbrace': largest NATO maritime exercise to date with 860 Dutch NAS (Sea Fury) and 824 NAS (Firefly) embarked

Aut. 54 Last cruise

00.12.54 Laid up in reserve in Gareloch

03.11.56 Sold to British Iron and Steel Corp.

00.00.57 Broken up

Illustrious (1982) (R06) Invincible *Class Light Fleet Carrier*

Laid down: 7 October 1976
Launched: 1 December 1978
Completed: 18 June 1982

Builder: Swan Hunter, Wallsend-on-Tyne
Machinery: 2 shafts (each with a reversible gearbox); 4 Rolls-Royce TBM3 Olympus gas turbines; 112,000shp = 28 knots (94,000 max continuous shp)
Displacement: 16,000 tons standard; 20,000 tons deep load
Dimensions: 677ft 9in overall x 104ft 6in max beam x 29ft max draught
Missile/gun armament: Single GWS.30 Sea Dart SAM (2); 3 x 30mm Goalkeeper CIWS (3)
Fuel: 3,000 tons diesel
Endurance: 5,000miles @ 18 knots
Complement: 1,400
Protection: None
Flight deck: 600ft x 65ft steel
Arrester wires: None
Hangar: 500ft (including lift wells) x 74ft max/40ft min x 20ft
Catapults: None
Ski-jump: 12-degree
Lifts: *Fwd* 54ft 8in long x 31ft 8in wide; *aft* 54ft 8in long x 31ft 8in wide
Aircraft: Up to 26
Aircraft fuel: 250,000 gallons AVCAT
Air weapons: AMRAAM; Sidewinder AAM; Sea Eagle ASM; Stingray homing torpedoes; 1,000lb LGB; BL.755 cluster bombs; Mk 11 depth charges; 30mm cannon ammunition; 7.62mm GMPG ammunition; flares and pyrotechnics

Notes: Completion was brought forward from target date in November 1982 to get her ready for service in the Falklands War but, in the event, she did not leave the builder's yard until two days after the Argentine surrender. As built *Illustrious* incorporated several improvements over *Invincible*, including a more capable command and control system. Operations off the Falkland Islands showed the need for improved close-range air defence and before completion she was fitted with 2 Vulcan Phalanx mountings, one on forecastle and one on starboard side of flight deck aft. Details are given for the ship after her 1991–94 modernisation, during which the deck park forward of the island was enlarged, a new 100-seat aircrew briefing room was installed and workshops were modified to support the new Sea Harrier F/A.2 and its weapons. A new mainmast was stepped to take improved communications and sensors and Goalkeeper CIWS replaced the Vulcan Phalanx.

Summary of service

11.01.82	Contractor's sea trials off Tyne
18.06.82	Sailed from Swan Hunter's Walker yard for trials
20.06.82	Commissioned at sea (first ship in RN to do so)
02.08.82	Sailed for South Atlantic after OST at Portland
00.08.82	Relieved *Invincible* off Falklands; air group comprised 809 (Sea Harrier) and 814 (Sea King HAS) NAS and 824D (Sea King AEW 2) Flight (world's first helicopter AEW unit, which was soon to re-form as 849 NAS)
21.10.82	Transferred responsibility for air defence of Falkland Islands Protection Zone to RAF fighters based ashore; sailed for UK in company with *Amazon* and *Brambleleaf*
05.11.82	Visited Puerto Rico
12.11.82	Visited Fort Lauderdale
22.11.82	Visited Philadelphia
06.12.82	809 NAS disembarked to RNAS Yeovilton to disband
07.12.82	Returned to Portsmouth, having disembarked 824D Flight and 814 NAS to RNAS Culdrose (143 days had been spent at sea, 43,560 miles covered and 7,127 deck landings carried out since sailing)
00.01.83	Work carried out to complete areas unfinished when ship left builders
11.03.83	OST at Portland
30.03.83	Rededication ceremony in Portsmouth with HRH Princess Margaret
00.04.83	Carried out her previously incomplete trials programme for missile and electronic equipment (1 Wessex of 845 NAS embarked for HDS)
05.05.83	Visited Newcastle with aircraft of 899 (Sea Harrier) and 846 (Sea King Commando) NAS embarked
09.05.83	Air defence training in North Sea with RAF fighters and radar units ashore
16.05.83	Sea Dart firings off Aberporth
20.05.83	Embarked 801 (Sea Harrier) and 820 (Sea King) NAS from *Invincible* off Plymouth
23.05.83	Air group work-up in SWAPS

31.05.83 Visited Lisbon
07.06.83 Exercise 'Ocean Safari' in company with *Hermes*, USS *John F. Kennedy* and FNS *Foch* (during this exercise a Sea Harrier which was uncertain of its position and low on fuel landed on the 2,500-ton Spanish freighter *Alraigo*, incurring some damage and much publicity; it was subsequently removed and repaired)
17.06.83 Visited Brest
24.06.83 Returned to Portsmouth for AMP
24.08.83 In Portsmouth for Navy Days
31.08.83 Sailed for air group work-up with 800 (Sea Harrier) and 814 (Sea King) NAS embarked (this group came from *Hermes* and was intended to remain with *Illustrious*)
06.09.83 In Portsmouth
17.09.83 Deployed to Mediterranean in company with *Glamorgan*, *Leander*, *Charybdis* and *Opossum*
24.09.83 Exercise 'Display Determination'
04.10.83 After lift broke down (repairs in Taranto)
14.10.83 Visited Athens
24.10.83 Visited Genoa
29.10.83 In Gibraltar
03.11.83 Arrived in Devonport
07.11.83 Exercise 'Ready Rob' in SWAPS
24.11.83 Visited Hamburg
01.12.83 Returned to Portsmouth for AMP including work on after lift
19.01.84 Sailed for WESTLANT deployment in company with *Broadsword*, *Avenger* and *Bayleaf*
03.02.84 Visited New York
10.02.84 Visited Norfolk, Va
16.02.84 Exercise 'United Effort'
06.03.84 Exercise 'Teamwork', during which ship crossed to Eastern Atlantic and embarked aircraft of 899 (Sea Harrier) and 810 (Sea King HAS) NAS to bring number of aircraft on board to 22; Sea Harriers flew 4-hour CAP sorties with AAR from USS *Independence*'s aircraft
24.03.84 Visited Bergen
30.03.84 In Portsmouth for SMP
25.04.84 Sailed for Exercise 'Open Gate' off Gibraltar
07.05.84 Exercise 'Distant Hammer' (on completion, 800 and 814 NAS jointly awarded Australia Shield for their intensive, professional operations in 1983–84)
19.05.84 Visited Palma
27.05.84 Live Sidewinder firings
30.05.84 In Portsmouth
27.06.84 JMC.842 off northern Scotland
29.06.84 Visited Copenhagen
06.07.84 Visited Amsterdam
12.07.84 Embarked 1 instrumented Sea Harrier from A&AEE off Plymouth for Sea Eagle missile trials
16.07.84 Old destroyer *Devonshire* sunk by Sea Eagle missile
20.07.84 Exercise 'Remount', during which 819 (Sea King ASW) and 845 and 846 (Sea King Commando) NAS were embarked for amphibious operations
20.08.84 Returned to Portsmouth for BAMP
17.09.84 Sailed for shakedown with normal air group embarked
08.10.84 Exercise 'Autumn Train'
20.10.84 In Gibraltar
25.10.84 Visited Lisbon
01.11.84 In Rosyth
05.11.84 JMC 843
21.11.84 Returned to Portsmouth and disembarked 814 NAS
25.11.84 Exercise 'High Tide' with 800 (Sea Harrier), 846 (Sea King Commando) NAS, COMAW and 1 ACG RNLMC embarked
06.12.84 Visited Hamburg
11.12.84 Disembarked air group and amphibious forces; returned to Portsmouth for DAMP
23.04.85 Sailed for shakedown with air group embarked
09.05.85 In Portsmouth
14.05.85 BOST at Portland
25.05.85 Sidewinder/Sea Dart high sea firings
01.06.85 Air group work-up with *Churchill* as target for Sea Kings
04.06.85 ORI
20.06.85 VIP Sea Day off Portsmouth
31.07.85 Exercise 'Pilgrim's Progress'
14.08.85 In Philadelphia
21.08.85 In Norfolk, Va
23.08.85 Exercise 'Ocean Safari' with COMASWSTRIKFOR embarked
21.09.85 Visited Bergen
25.09.85 In Portsmouth
11.10.85 Exercise 'Autumn Train'
16.10.85 Sea King XV672 ditched and successfully recovered on board by crane
24.10.85 In Gibraltar
31.10.85 In Rosyth
19.11.85 JMC.853 with FOF1 embarked
27.11.85 Visited Newcastle
04.12.85 Returned to Portsmouth
27.1.86 Sailed for Devonport

HMS *Illustrious* (foreground) relieving HMS *Invincible* in South Atlantic waters in August 1982. (FAA Museum)

04.02.86	JMC 861
13.02.86	Exercise 'Western Change'
19.02.86	In Portsmouth for DAMP
02.04.86	Embarked air group whilst alongside, then sailed in company with *Exeter*
03.04.86	Serious fire in forward starboard gear room; air group disembarked; ship returned to Portsmouth for repairs.
14.07.86	Sea machinery trials after repairs
21.07.86	Sailed for Deployment 'Global 86' to Far East in company with *Beaver*, *Amazon*, *Manchester*, *Olmeda* and *Fort Grange*
04.08.86	Passed through Suez Canal after exercises with Greek Navy
06.08.86	Fire in port outer Olympus gas turbine, which necessitated its replacement
18.08.86	Arrived in Singapore
[illegible].10.86	Visited Fremantle
30.10.86	Sailed to rendezvous with other 'Global' ships
10.11.86	Exercises with IN
14.11.86	Visited Bombay
24.11.86	Exercise 'Saif Sarees' off Masirah
07.12.86	Passed through Suez Canal
12.12.86	In Gibraltar
18.12.86	Returned to Portsmouth for DAMP and further repairs to port gearbox
27.04.87	Shakedown with enhanced air group comprising 800 (Sea Harrier), 814 (Sea King ASW) and 849A (Sea King AEW) NAS
06.05.87	OST at Portland
01.06.87	Aviation work-up
10.06.87	ORI
15.06.87	Visited Amsterdam
26.06.87	In Portsmouth
25.08.87	Exercise 'Ocean Safari'
22.09.87	Visited Devonport
25.09.87	Returned to Portsmouth for SMP
08.10.87	Visited Hamburg
19.10.87	Exercise 'Offshore Remount'
30.10.87	Prepared for LPH role in Portsmouth
03.11.87	Embarked 845 and 846 HAS (Sea King

Commando) and 40 RM Cdo
04.11.87 Exercise 'Purple Warrior'
23.12.87 Returned to Portsmouth for BAMP
19.01.88 Shakedown with air group embarked
01.02.88 'ASWEX 1/88' in Iceland–Faeroes Gap
18.02.88 In Rosyth
24.02.88 Visited Newcastle
01.03.88 PASSEX with *Ark Royal*
04.03.88 In Portsmouth for SMP
07.04.88 Sailed for Mediterranean
08.04.88 Exercises with Spanish Navy
24.04.88 Crossdeck operations with Italian carrier *Garibaldi*
27.04.88 Visited Naples
02.05.88 Exercise 'Dragon Hammer'
13.05.88 In Gibraltar
19.05.88 Returned to Portsmouth
23.05.88 Staff College Sea Days off Portsmouth
07.06.88 Sailed for Rosyth
11.06.88 Rosyth Navy Days
13.06.88 JMC.882
25.06.88 Returned to Portsmouth for BAMP
26.08.88 Portsmouth Navy Days
31.08.88 Exercise 'Teamwork'
23.09.88 Returned to Portsmouth
03.10.88 Sailed for WESTLANT deployment
18.10.88 Visited Mayport
23.10.88 Autec Range for Trial 'Baste 88'
01.11.88 Visited Charleston, SC
07.11.88 'Fleetex 1/88'
21.11.88 Visited Fort Lauderdale
01.12.88 Sailed for UK
16.01.89 Exercise 'Water Baby'
03.02.89 In Rosyth
07.02.89 JMC 891
18.02.89 Visited Amsterdam
23.02.89 Returned to Portsmouth
28.02.89 Exercise 'North Star'
17.03.89 Visited Hamburg
22.03.89 Transferred air group to *Invincible* (recently emerged from major modernisation)
23.03.89 DAMP in Portsmouth
26.06.89 Moved into No 3 Basin, Portsmouth
30.06.89 Paid off into reserve for 2 years' 'preservation by operation'
00.00.91 Taken in hand in Devonport for major modernisation
00.05.94 Modernisation completed
06.06.94 Participated in Review of Ships in Solent to commemorate 50th anniversary of the D-Day landings
00.03.95 Deployed to Adriatic to relieve *Invincible* with 801 (Sea Harrier F/ A.2), 820 (Sea King ASW) and 849B (Sea King AEW) NAS embarked

Implacable (R86) *Modified* Illustrious *Class Fleet Carrier*

Laid down: 21 February 1939
Launched: 10 December 1942
Completed: 28 August 1944

Builder: Fairfield Shipbuilding & Engineering Co., Clydeside
Machinery: 4-shaft Parsons geared turbines; 8 Admiralty 3-drum boilers; 148,000shp = 32 knots
Displacement: 23,450 tons; 32,110 tons deep load
Dimensions: 766ft 2in overall x 131ft 3in max beam x 29ft 4in max
Gun armament: 8 twin 4.5in QF Mk III HA (16); 5 octuple 2pdr pompom (40); 3 quadruple 2pdr pompom (12); 21 twin 20mm Oerlikon (42); 19 single 20mm Oerlikon (19)
Fuel: 4,690 tons FFO
Endurance: 12,000 miles @ 10 knots
Complement: 2,300 in 1945
Protection: 3in flight deck; 4.5in waterline belt; 2in hangar; 2in–3in hangar bulkheads; 4.5in magazine sides; 3in magazine crowns
Flight deck: 760ft x 90ft armoured steel
Arrester wires: *9 aft* 20,000lb @ 60 knots; *3 fwd* 20,000lb @ 60 knots; 3 barriers
Hangar: *Upper* 456ft x 62ft x 14ft; *lower* 208ft x 62ft x 14ft
Catapults: 1 x BH3 (twin-track); 20,000lb @ 56 knots (tail-down method only)
Lifts: *Fwd* 45ft long x 33ft wide (served upper hangar only); *aft* 45ft long x 22ft wide (served both hangars); both 20,000lb
Aircraft: 81 in 1945
Aircraft fuel: 94,650 gallons AVGAS
Air weapons: 18in torpedoes; 1,000lb MC bombs; 500lb SAP bombs; 500lb GP bombs; 3in RP; Mk 11 depth charges; 20mm cannon ammunition; .5in gun

A bow view of HMS *Implacable* in August 1944. (FAA Museum)

ammunition; .303in gun ammunition; flares and pyrotechnics

Notes: Work was stopped during 1940 when higher priority was given to destroyers and escorts. The opportunity was taken to modify the design to fit in a second hangar under the first to increase aircraft storage. To compensate for the extra topweight, the thickness of hangar and flight deck armour was reduced. The extra hangar was not all positive gain, however, since a fourth machinery unit had to be worked in to achieve the designed speed with the increased weight. To reduce topweight, the height of the hangars was limited to 14 feet. As a result of this, the requirement to strike down floatplanes on their floats into the hangar was deleted for the first time in a British carrier design. The low hangar height damned *Implacable* and her sister-ship *Indefatigable* for the remainder of their short lives. They could not strike down USN-supplied fighters such as the Corsair in 1945, and after the war, the cost of modernisation—including increasing hangar height—was prohibitive. Moreover, the machinery required additional manpower who had to be put into messdecks made out of space originally intended for the lower hangar. It is easy to be wise after the event but it is hard to escape the conclusion that a repeat of the *Indomitable* design would have been preferable. The rapid disappearance of *Implacable* and *Indefatigable* from the post-war fleet reflected this flaw in their design and the high cost of running the two ships.

Summary of service

23.05.44 Commissioned in Fairfield's yard, followed by sea trials which showed up number of defects

16.06.44 Docked in Rosyth for defect rectification

28.08.44 Accepted for service and commenced work-up in Clyde area with 2 TBR Wing, comprising 828 and 841 NAS (Barracuda) embarked (no fighters available)
22.09.44 1771 NAS (Firefly) joined air group (Seafire Wing intended for *Implacable* still re-equipping and training replacement aircrew ashore after service in *Furious*)
07.10.44 Work-up completed in Scapa Flow; joined HF
16.10.44 First mission was to relocate *Tirpitz* which had moved from Kaafjord to Tromsø; ship sighted and photographed by pair of Fireflies off Haakøy Island but request to launch Barracuda strike firmly refused by Admiralty owing to the lack of escort fighters; armed sweep by 7 Fireflies damaged 4,700-ton merchant ship at Mosjoen and 3 aircraft at Sorreisen
26.10.44 Embarked 24 Naval Fighter Wing comprising 887 and 894 NAS (Seafire) for Operation 'Athletic' (strikes on Rørvik, Bodø and Lødings) during which 40 Barracuda sorties dropped 27 tons bombs
28.10.44 Barracudas carried out last airborne torpedo attack in anger by RN; during this operation 6 merchant ships sunk (one of 2,693 tons) and 7 others damaged; *U1060* driven on to reef and became total loss (only one aircraft lost)
30.10.44 Disembarked 24 Naval Fighter Wing on return to Scapa Flow
08.11.44 Sailed and embarked 38 Naval Fighter Wing comprising 801 and 880 NAS (Seafire); acted as cover for escort carriers carrying out minelaying operations off Norway
27.11.44 Strikes off Alster Island when Barracudas and Fireflies sank two ships and damaged four others out of convoy; escorts also damaged by cannon-fire
28.11.44 Damaged forward by heavy seas and returned to Scapa Flow
04.12.44 Sailed as cover for another HF minelaying operation
08.12.44 Fireflies of 1771 NAS with Wildcats from *Trumpeter* sank inshore minesweeper
15.12.44 Entered Rosyth Dockyard for refit
10.03.45 Completed refit and embarked revised air group (828 NAS re-equipped with 21 Avengers and 38 Fighter Wing increased to 48 Seafires)
16.03.45 Sailed from Scapa Flow to join 1 ACS, BPF
00.04.45 Worked up off Ceylon
00.05.45 Arrived in Sydney
00.06.45 Joined rest of 1 ACS at forward operating base at Manus as they returned from operations off Okinawa
16.06.45 Carried out strikes on by-passed Japanese base of Truk as final work-up (*Ruler* acted as spare deck)
04.07.45 Worked up off Manus with *Victorious* and *Formidable*
06.07.45 Sailed with BPF to form Task Force 37
16.07.45 Rendezvoused with USN Task Force 38 off Honshu
17.07.45 Struck against targets on Tokyo plain (in the next 25 days, only 8 days of strikes were possible owing to bad weather and replenishment cycles; ship's aircraft flew 1,000 sorties and hit airfields, shipyards, shipping, factories and railway installations)
10.08.45 Launched 70 offensive sorties against Honshu
11.08.45 Replenished and left for Manus and Sydney with *Victorious* and *Formidable*
24.08.45 Arrived in Sydney and disembarked air group; from then on, used to repatriate Allied former POWs to Australia and Canada from Japan
18.10.45 Sailed from Vancouver to repatriate Dutch personnel to Balikpapan, Borneo, after which ship ferried Australian Army personnel home from New Guinea
00.12.45 Repairs carried out in Sydney, on completion of which ship embarked 801 (Seafire), 828 (Avenger) and 1790 (Firefly) NAS for cruise in Australian and New Zealand waters
00.03.46 Refit in Sydney
05.05.46 Sailed for UK
03.06.46 Arrived in Portsmouth; NAS disembarked and disbanded; ship subsequently allocated to HF as DLT carrier
00.02.47 Exercised with *Ocean* in Western Mediterranean but had no air group of her own
00.04.47 Refitted for further operational service
00.10.47 Refit completed; used as trials carrier since air group not yet ready owing to problems with new aircraft types
00.10.48 Refitted at Rosyth to be HF flagship
00.12.48 Refit completed
00.04.49 1 CAG finally embarked with 801 (Sea Hornet) and 813 (Firebrand) NAS

29.04.49 Became Flagship HF; took part in all major exercises in European waters; carried 702 NAS (Sea Vampire) for autumn 1949 cruise but 1 CAG remained small because of shortage of aircrew and aircraft (702 NAS was jet fighter evaluation unit and operated very successfully)
Sum. 50 815 NAS (Barracuda) added to ship's air group
13.09.50 Ceased to fly flag of CinC HF and paid off into reserve; low-key work done to provide accommodation and classrooms in hangars
00.01.52 Recommissioned as flagship HFTS
10.10.53 Ferried battalion of Argyll and Sutherland Highlanders from Plymouth to Trinidad to deal with crisis ashore in British Guiana
19.08.54 Flag of HFTS transferred to battleship *Vanguard*
01.09.54 Paid off into reserve and placed on disposal list
27.10.55 Towed away to be broken up
03.11.55 Arrived in Inverkeithing for scrapping

Indefatigable (R10) *Modified* Illustrious *Class Fleet Carrier*

Laid down: 3 November 1939
Launched: 8 December 1942
Completed: 3 May 1944

Builder: John Brown & Co., Clydebank
Machinery: 4-shaft Parsons geared turbines; 8 Admiralty 3-drum boilers; 150,000shp = 32 knots
Displacement: 23,450 tons standard; 32,110 tons deep load
Dimensions: 766ft 2in overall x 131ft 4in max beam x 29ft 4in max

HMS *Indefatigable* as completed. (FAA Museum)

Gun armament: 8 twin 4.5in QF Mk III HA (16); 5 octuple 2pdr pompom (40); 1 quadruple 2pdr pompom (4); 19 twin 20mm Oerlikon (38); 17 single 20mm Oerlikon (17)
Fuel: 4,180 tons FFO
Endurance: 6,900 miles @ 20 knots
Complement: 2,300 in 1945
Protection: 3in flight deck; 2.5in lower hangar deck; 4.5in waterline belt; 2in hangar; 2in hangar bulkheads; 4.5in magazine sides; 3in magazine crowns; underwater protection against 750lb torpedo
Flight deck: 760ft x 90ft armoured steel
Arrester wires: *9 aft* 20,000lb @ 60 knots; *2 fwd* 20,000lb @ 60 knots; 3 barriers
Hangar: *Upper* 456ft x 62ft x 14ft; *lower* 208ft x 62ft x 14ft
Catapults: 1 x BH3 (twin-track); 20,000lb @ 56 knots (tail-down method only)
Lifts: Fwd 45ft long x 33ft wide (served upper hangar only); *aft* 45ft long x 22ft wide (served both hangars); both 20,000lb
Aircraft: 73 in January 1945
Aircraft fuel: 94,650 gallons AVGAS
Air weapons: 18in torpedoes; 500lb SAP bombs; 500lb GP bombs; 250lb MC bombs; 3in RP; Mk 11 depth charges; 20mm cannon ammunition; .5in gun ammunition; .303in gun ammunition; flares and pyrotechnics

Notes: *Indefatigable* suffered from the same design shortcomings as *Implacable*. She saw little active service and proved too expensive to modernise in the 1950s. Post-war, plans were drawn up to convert the two hangars into a single one 20ft high with new accommodation over it, but lack of money prevented their implementation. It is sad to reflect that this ship saw only 18 months' operational service.

Summary of service

03.05.44 Commissioned in Clydebank; allocated to WAC

00.07.44 Joined HF at Scapa Flow; embarked 894 (Seafire) and 1770 (Firefly) NAS and 9 TBR Wing comprising 820 and 826 NAS (Barracuda)

17.07.44 Operation 'Mascot' (strike on *Tirpitz* in Kaafjord): smoke screen up to 800ft made attack ineffective

02.08.44 Operation 'Turbine' (sweep through Norwegian Leads during which fighters had some success)

09.08.44 Sailed for Operation 'Offspring', acting as support for minelaying aircraft from *Nabob* and *Trumpeter*

22.08.44 Further strikes on *Tirpitz*

19.09.44 Operation 'Divan' north of Lofoten Islands (bad weather prevented flying)

00.11.44 Allocated to BPF

19.11.44 Sailed from Portsmouth for Far East with 24 Naval Fighter Wing comprising 887 and 894 (Seafire), 1770 Firefly) and 820 (Avenger) NAS embarked

10.12.44 Arrived in Colombo; joined 1 ACS, BPF

04.01.45 Operation 'Lentil' (strike by *Victorious* and *Indefatigable* on refineries at Pangkalan Brandan, Sumatra)

24.01.45 Strike on Pladjoe (first of Palembang group of oil refineries) with 1 ACS (24 Wing provided most of CAP over Fleet and strike itself was extremely successful in denying aviation fuel to Japanese)

29.01.45 Strike on Soengi Gerong (second refinery in Palembang group): 24 Wing shared destruction of 5 'Lily' bombers (out of raid on force by 7) with Corsair from *Victorious* and Hellcat from *Indomitable* (January strikes at refineries by BPF were largest ever mounted by FAA and its greatest strategic contribution to victory over Japanese)

10.02.45 Arrived in Sydney with main body of BPF

15.03.45 BPF arrived at Manus, forming Task Force 57 for Operation 'Iceberg' (to support US landings on Okinawa by preventing Japanese aircraft reinforcements from staging through airfields on Sakashimo Gunto islands)

23.03.45 Sailed from Ulithi in Caroline Islands (forward operating base) hampered by fact that only 27 out of planned 69 ships of the fleet train were in position to support TF.57)

01.04.45 Hit by Kamikaze aircraft at base of island, killing 21 and injuring 27 (flight deck out of action for an hour but 'reasonably operational' later same day)

07.06.45 Returned to Sydney for operational turn-round; machinery defects delayed departure and ship sailed later than remainder of 1 ACS

12.07.45 Sailed from Sydney to join BPF which now formed TF.37 (USN fast carriers were TF.38); improvements to Seafires of 24 Wing enabled them to carry out escort for Avenger strikes as well as interdiction missions of their own armed with bombs

17.07.45 Strike operations commenced over mainland of Japan

09.08.45 Sweeps over enemy airfields resulted in destruction of over 50 Japanese aircraft for loss of 7 RN aircraft and 5 pilots

10.08.45 Last planned day of operations while details of Japanese surrender were worked out

11.08.45 Shortage of fuel in the fleet train led to main strength of BPF having to withdraw to Australia; token force comprising *Indefatigable*, *King George V*, 2 cruisers and

HMS *Indefatigable* at the quayside in Wellington, New Zealand, in 1945. (FAA Museum)

	10 destroyers remained under direct command of Admiral McCain USN as part of TF.38
13.08.45	Strikes in Tokyo area, after which carriers withdrew to refuel
15.08.45	In absence of notification about ceasefire, dawn strikes launched; *Indefatigable*'s Avengers intercepted by 12 Zero fighters and, in last air combat of WW2, Seafires of 24 Wing shot down 8 Zeros for loss of 1 Seafire; an Avenger turret gunner destroyed a ninth Zero during raid (on chemical factory); further operations halted at 0700 but several Kamikazes attacked Fleet, one near-missing *Indefatigable*
27.08.45	Joined TG.38.3 with US carriers *Essex*, *Wasp* and *Randolph* and carried out CAP and tactical reconnaissance sorties looking for Allied POW camps; on completion, anchored in Sagami Bay near Tokyo
02.09.45	Surrender signed on quarterdeck of USS *Missouri* in Tokyo Bay
00.00.45	Ship used to repatriate Commonwealth former POWs and troops to Australia, then carried out trooping runs between Far East and UK (to 00.00.46)
00.12.46	Reduced to reserve in Portsmouth
00.00.49	Taken in hand for conversion to training ship with accommodation and classrooms built into former hangars
00.00.50	Commissioned for service in HFTS
00.02.52	Moored at Dover to act as saluting ship to members of foreign royal families arriving in England for funeral of HM King George VI
00.08.54	Relieved in HFTS by *Ocean* and *Theseus*
00.09.54	Reduced to reserve in Rosyth
00.06.55	Towed to Gareloch
00.09.56	Sold to British Iron and Steel Corp. for scrapping

Indomitable (R92) Illustrious *Class Fleet Carrier*

Laid down: 10 November 1937
Launched: 26 March 1940
Completed: 10 October 1941

Builder: Vickers-Armstrong, Barrow-in-Furness
Machinery: 3-shaft Parsons geared turbines; 6 Admiralty 3-drum boilers; 111,000shp = 30.5 knots
Displacement: 23,000 tons standard; 29,730 tons deep load
Dimensions: 754ft overall x 116ft 3in max beam x 29ft 5in max
Gun armament: 8 twin 4.5in QF Mk III HA (16); 6 octuple 2pdr pompom (48); 2 quadruple 40mm Bofors (8); 2 twin 40mm Bofors (4); 21 twin 20mm Oerlikon (42); 18 single 20mm Oerlikon (18)
Fuel: 4,500 tons FFO
Endurance: 9,000 miles @ 18 knots
Complement: 2,100 in 1945

HMS *Indomitable* shortly after completion. (FAA Museum)

Protection: 3in flight deck; 4.5in side belt; 1.5in hangar sides; 1.5in–3in hangar bulkheads; 2.5in magazine crowns; 1.5in magazine bulkheads
Flight deck: 745ft x 95ft (extended from 680ft in 1943) armoured steel
Arrester wires: *7 aft* 11,000lb @ 55 knots; *2 fwd* 11,000lb @ 55 knots; 3 barriers
Hangar: *Upper* 416ft x 62ft x 14ft; *lower* 168ft x 62ft x 16ft
Catapults: 1 x BH3; 14,000lb @ 66 knots (tail-down method only)
Lifts: Fwd 45ft long x 33ft wide (served upper hangar only); *aft* 45ft long x 22ft wide (served both hangars); both 14,000lb
Aircraft: 56 in 1945
Aircraft fuel: 75,110 gallons AVGAS
Air weapons: 18in torpedoes; 1,000lb MC bombs; 500lb SAP bombs; 500lb GP bombs; 250lb bombs; B bombs; 3in RP; Mk 11 depth charges; 20mm cannon ammunition; .5in gun ammunition; .303in gun ammunition; flares and pyrotechnics

Notes: Most successful design of the *Illustrious* group. Shortly after she was laid down, the design was modified to incorporate a lower hangar in order to increase aircraft storage to 48. Topweight was saved by lowering the upper hangar height to 14ft and reducing the hangar side armour to 1.5in. The other improvement was the enlarged forward lift, which enabled non-folding Sea Hurricanes to be struck down into the upper hangar position obliquely and moved fore and aft on special trolleys. The extra aircraft complement was further increased during the war by use of a deck park, and air weapon storage was increased to 50 per cent more than that of *Illustrious*. Aviation fuel was increased at the expense of FFO and the degree of protection afforded to AVGAS by the RN may be judged from the fact that the extra 25,000 gallons (89 tons) of AVGAS was stowed at the expense of 350 tons of FFO. She was the only carrier of the BPF to operate Hellcat fighters since Corsairs could not be stored in the upper hangar owing to their height when folded. The success of *Indomitable*'s basic design led to her being the only fleet carrier of the *Illustrious* group (apart from the rebuilt *Victorious*) to see extensive operational service after WW2.

Summary of service

10.10.41 Commissioned in Barrow and sailed for West Indies to work up with 800 (Fulmar), 880 (Sea Hurricane), 827 and 831 (Albacore) NAS embarked

00.10.41 Damaged by grounding off Kingston, Jamaica, and had to proceed to Norfolk, Va, where new bow section was fabricated and fitted in only 10 days

22.11.41 Work-up originally due to complete

29.11.41 Admiralty War Diary shows that *Indomitable* was due in Gibraltar after planned work-up (this was the day after *Prince of Wales* and *Repulse* met in Colombo en route to Singapore, and Diary reveals that *Indomitable* was never ordered to join them and that her programme would have made it impossible for her to do so)

10.12.41 In Cape Town

00.02.42 Disembarked half air group at Aden and ferried 50 RAF Hurricane fighters to Singapore

27.02.42 RAF aircraft flown off in two ranges to Batavia

00.03.42 Returned to Aden for another 50 RAF Hurricanes, which were delivered to Ceylon; on completion, ship re-embarked full air group from Aden and joined EF under Admiral Sir James Somerville at Addu Atoll (*Formidable* and *Hermes* also formed part of fleet)

01.04.42 EF concentrated to counter carrier strikes by Japanese against Ceylon but were not brought to action

05.04.42 Japanese struck at Colombo

05.05.42 Operation 'Ironclad' (occupation of Diego Saurez) in company with *Illustrious*; 4 aircraft of 806 NAS (Fulmar) added to air group

00.07.42 Deployed to Mediterranean

09.08.42 Operation 'Pedestal' (most heavily defended convoy to Malta) in company with *Victorious* (flag of Rear-Admiral Aircraft Carriers, Rear-Admiral A. L. St G. Lyster), *Eagle* and *Furious*, which was to fly off 38 RAF Spitfires to Malta; *Indomitable*'s air group comprised 800 and 880 (Sea Hurricane), 806 (Wildcat) and 827 and 831 (Albacore) NAS (30 enemy aircraft shot down, 5 of them by Lt R. J. Cork DSC RN of 880 NAS)

11.08.42 Damaged by two armour-piercing bombs which penetrated flight deck fore and aft and near-miss that blew 30ft hole under water; repairs in US took rest of 1942

00.07.43 Joined Force H in Mediterranean in company with *Formidable* to provide heavy cover for landings in Sicily (Operation 'Husky'); air group comprised 807, 880 and 899 (Seafire) and 817 (Albacore) NAS

HMS *Indomitable* as flagship of the Home Fleet in 1951 with Sea Furies on deck. (Author)

16.07.43 Torpedoed on port side by single Ju 88 whilst 90 miles north-east of Malta (port boiler room extensively damaged); again, proceeded to Norfolk, Va, for repairs
00.04.44 Arrived in Clyde
00.05.44 Sailed to join EIF with 5 Naval Fighter Wing, comprising 1839 and 1844 (Hellcat) NAS and 12 TBR Wing (815 and 817 NAS with Barracudas); based at Trincomalee
29.08.44 Struck at Emmahaven and Indaroeng in company with *Victorious*
18.09.44 Struck at Sigli in company with *Victorious*
17.10.44 Struck at Nicobar Islands in company with *Victorious* (Operation 'Millet')
00.12.44 Became flagship of Rear-Admiral Sir Philip Vian, 1 ACS; 857 NAS (Avenger) replaced the two Barracuda NAS
20.12.44 Struck at Belawan Deli in company with *Illustrious* (bad weather obscured Pangkalan Brandon, primary target)
01.01.45 1 ACS became striking force of newly formed BPF
04.01.45 Struck at refineries at Pangkalon Brandon, considerably reducing their output by causing heavy damage with accurate weapon delivery
16.01.45 Sailed with BPF for Australia
24.01.45 1 ACS, including *Indomitable*, *Illustrious*,

Victorious and *Indefatigable*, struck at Pladjoe refineries in Palembang group

29.01.45 Struck at Soengi Gerong, remaining refinery in Palembang group (strikes were largest mounted by RN in WW2 and achieved strategic results, reducing Japanese aviation fuel supplies to a mere 35 per cent of 1944 normal level: the 3 refinery strikes of January 1945 were probably BPF's greatest contribution to ultimate Allied victory)

10.02.45 Arrived in Sydney

15.03.45 Arrived in Manus with TF.57

23.03.45 Sailed from Ulithi, forward operating base for Operation 'Iceberg' (strike operations against islands in Sakashima Gunto to prevent their being used by Japanese to oppose US landings on Okinawa); BPF carried out two-day strike cycles, alternating with US carriers *Santee*, *Suwanee*, *Chenango* and *Steamer Bay* (with their smaller aircraft complements, USN carriers were less efficient)

20.04.45 Left operational area for San Pedro Bay, Leyte, after 32 days at sea, for period of rest and re-storing (fleet train, still far short of number of ships needed, had run out of fuel, stores, ammunition and replacement aircraft)

01.05.45 Sailed for further strikes against airfields in Sakashima Gunto

04.05.45 Strikes resumed against Ishigaki and Miyako islands (whilst battleships *King George V* and *Howe* were away bombarding Miyako,a force of 20 Kamikaze aircraft attacked fleet; 8 splashed by CAP but 2 broke through, one of which hit *Indomitable* glancing blow on flight deck aft before going over side)

25.04.45 Left operational area for Sydney

07.06.45 Arrived in Sydney for refit (*Formidable* became flagship 1 ACS)

00.08.45 On completion of refit, became flagship of 11 ACS, flying flag of Rear-Admiral C. H. J. Harcourt with light fleet carriers *Vengeance*, *Colossus*, *Glory* and *Venerable*

31.08.45 With *Venerable*, bombed and strafed Japanese suicide boats sailing for last attack off Hong Kong and destroyed others hidden in bays on north side of Hong Kong

30.11.45 Arrived in Portsmouth

00.00.46 Used for trooping duties to and from Far East

00.00.47 Extensive refit and modernisation in Portsmouth Dockyard (to 00.00.50)

00.00.51 Became flagship HF, Admiral Sir Philip Vian; air group comprised 802 (Sea Fury), 820 (Firefly), 801 and 809 (Sea Hornet) and 813 (Firebrand) NAS; ship was one of first RN carriers to operate helicopter (Sikorsky S-51 for SAR duties)

00.05.52 Battleship *Vanguard* became flagship HF; *Indomitable* became flagship, Heavy Squadron, HF, until relieved by *Eagle* in 1953

03.02.53 During combined HF/MF exercise in Mediterranean, explosion caused serious damage below island on starboard side, killing 8 men and wounding 32 (it was thought that vapour leaking from a defective fuel valve was detonated by a cigarette); 10 gallantry awards, including two George Medals, were made to those who fought fire and rescued survivors; damaged compartment, and hole in ship's side, were filled with cement

15.06.53 Present at HM Queen Elizabeth II's Coronation Review at Spithead

05.10.53 Towed from Portsmouth to Clyde and placed in unmaintained reserve; ship's company reallocated to provide nucleus crews for the new carriers *Ark Royal* and *Bulwark*

21.09.55 Sold for scrapping and broken up at Faslane

The first ever launch by a Sea Harrier from a ski-jump at sea during HMS *Invincible*'s 'First of Class' Flying Trials in 1980. (British Aerospace)

Invincible **(R05)** Invincible *Class Anti-Submarine Carrier*

Laid down: 20 July 1973
Launched: 3 May 1977
Completed: 11 June 1980

Builder: Vickers Shipbuilding, Barrow-in-Furness
Machinery: 2 shafts (each with reversible gearbox); 4 Rolls-Royce TBM3 Olympus gas turbines; 112,000shp = 28 knots (94,000 max continuous shp)
Displacement: 16,000 tons standard; 19,500 tons deep load
Dimensions: 677ft 9in overall x 104ft 6in max beam x 29ft max draught
Missile/gun armament: Single GWS.30 Sea Dart SAM (2)
Fuel: 3,000 tons diesel
Endurance: 5,000 miles @ 18 knots
Complement: 1,100
Protection: None
Flight deck: 550ft x 65ft steel
Arrester wires: None
Hangar: 500ft (including lift wells) x 74ft max/40ft min x 20ft
Catapults: None
Ski-jump: 7-degree
Lifts: *Fwd* 54ft 8in long x 31ft 8in wide; *aft* 54ft 8in long x 31ft 8in wide; both 35,000lb
Aircraft: Up to 20
Aircraft fuel: 250,000 gallons AVCAT
Air weapons: Tactical nuclear bombs; nuclear depth bombs; Sidewinder AAM; Mk 46 homing torpedoes; 1,000lb MC bombs; BL.755 cluster bombs; 2in RP; Mk 11 depth charges; 30mm cannon ammunition; 7.62mm GMPG ammunition; flares and pyrotechnics

Notes: Designed as a light carrier intended to act as a command ship for an anti-submarine task force, specifically to operate Sea King helicopters although it was always intended that she should be capable of operating STOVL fighters for the air defence role (it would have been a waste of a ship of this size had she not had such a capability). The resultant ship has proved rather better at operating Sea Harriers than helicopters but has suffered from poor design features, such as the long inboard island, which prevent her from reaching her true potential as a carrier. After the Nott Defence Review in 1981 it was announced that she would be sold to Australia for £175 million. In the event, after her service in the Falklands War, the sale was not proceeded with and she was retained in service in the RN. Both the ship and aircraft fuel can be used to fuel either if necessary. Details are for the ship as completed.

Summary of service

19.03.80	Accepted into RN at Portsmouth
28.04.80	Trials off Spithead
03.05.80	In Devonport
07.05.80	Trials in Plymouth and Portsmouth area
21.05.80	SAT 'Air' and wind-flow trials in North Sea
29.05.80	In Portsmouth
09.06.80	OST at Portland
23.06.80	Visited Lisbon
30.06.80	Trials off Portland
11.07.80	Commissioned by HM Queen Elizabeth II at Portsmouth
01.09.80	Sea Dart firings in Bristol Channel
15.09.80	Trials in Clyde area
28.09.80	Embarked 800 NAS (Sea Harrier)
29.09.80	Visited Brest
06.10.80	In Gibraltar
27.10.80	Embarked trial Sea Harrier and equipment for FOCFT from A&AEE off Portsmouth
29.10.80	FOCFT; first-ever ski-jump launch at sea
12.11.80	Returned to Portsmouth for docking
04.02.81	At sea with 800 (Sea Harrier) and 820 (Sea King) NAS embarked
07.02.81	CASEX with *Sovereign*
12.02.81	In Portsmouth
06.03.81	Sailed with air group embarked
13.03.81	Visited Toulon
23.03.81	In Gibraltar
30.03.81	Returned to Portsmouth
21.05.81	Sailed for trials in Portsmouth area
09.06.81	Returned to Portsmouth
15.06.81	ODMA inspection
19.06.81	Declared operational
24.06.81	Embarked designated air group, 801 (Sea Harrier) and 820 (Sea King) NAS for BOST at Portland
23.07.81	In Portsmouth
27.07.81	Sailed for Norfolk, Va
05.08.81	Flight deck 'street party' to celebrate Prince of Wales's wedding
08.08.81	Visited Norfolk, Va
20.08.81	Exercise 'Ocean Venture' as flagship of FOF3/COMASGRUTWO
02.09.81	Visited Bergen for 'wash-up'
04.09.81	Exercise 'Ocean Safari'
19.09.81	Visited Ferrol

24.09.81 Returned to Portsmouth for AMP
16.11.81 Embarked air group for shakedown
20.11.81 PASSEX with French warships
23.11.81 Sea Dart firings off Aberporth
27.11.81 In Plymouth
02.12.81 Embarked 40 RM Cdo for amphibious trials
11.12.81 Returned to Portsmouth
05.04.82 Sailed with air group enhanced by part of 899 NAS (Sea Harrier) in company with Falklands Task Force
01.05.82 Entered British-declared Total Exclusion Zone around Falkland Islands
04.05.82 820 NAS assisted in evacuating the ship's company from HMS *Sheffield* after she was hit by Exocet missile; during the war, further Sea Harriers of 809 NAS were added to air group (Sea Kings flew 3,099 missions, mainly ASW; fighters flew 599 combat missions, claiming 7 enemy aircraft shot down and 3 probables; *Invincible* spent 160 days at sea)
17.09.82 Welcomed home to Portsmouth by HM Queen Elizabeth II (whose son, HRH Prince Andrew, had served as pilot in 820 NAS)
18.09.82 Commenced short refit, during which Vulcan Phalanx CIWS were fitted
00.02.83 Exercises in Caribbean and Eastern US sea areas
01.09.83 Sailed from Portsmouth for 'Orient Express' deployment to Far East in company with *Achilles*, *Aurora*, *Rothesay*, *Olmeda*, *Appleleaf* and *Regent*
09.09.83 Exercise 'Jolly Roger'
12.09.83 In Gibraltar
22.09.83 Passed through Suez Canal
10.10.83 Visited Bombay
23.10.83 Visited Penang
25.10.83 Visited Singapore
04.11.83 Exercise 'Valiant Usher'
05.11.83 Visited Fremantle
13.11.83 Exercise 'Transitex' with HMAS *Torrens*, *Hobart* and *Canberra*
17.11.83 WASEX with RAN and RAAF
19.11.83 Anchored in Jervis Bay
25.11.83 Visited Wellington in company with HMNZS *Canterbury*
28.11.83 Exercises with RNZN
30.11.83 Visited Auckland
08.12.83 Visited Sydney
09.01.84 In Singapore for docking to repair vibrating propeller shafts
14.02.84 Visited Penang
00.03.84 Returned to Portsmouth early for major work to cure propeller shaft problems
00.03.85 Visited Hamburg
00.04.85 Exercise 'Cold Winter' with 42 RM Cdo embarked
00.05.85 Exercise 'Hardy Crab' (DLT for No 1 Squadron RAF (Harrier)
00.09.85 Exercise 'Rolling Deep' with 42 RM Cdo embarked
00.10.85 Exercise 'Autumn Turn' (ASWEX 2/85)
00.11.85 Exercise 'Iles d'Or' with French and US Navies in Mediterranean
04.12.85 Air group disembarked for last time and transferred to *Ark Royal*
Spr. 86 Deployed to West Indies as Dartmouth Training Ship with 3 Wessex of 845 NAS embarked and 240 young officers and 80 artificer apprentices
00.05.86 Entered Devonport Dockyard for major refit and modernisation
18.05.89 Recommissioned by HM Queen Elizabeth II in Portsmouth
00.06.89 Visited by General Yazov, Soviet Minister of Defence
00.08.89 ORI with new air group comprising 800 (Sea Harrier), 814 (Sea King AS) and 849A (Sea King AEW) NAS, all of which had previously served in *Illustrious*
16.10.89 Sailed for WESTLANT deployment, carrying out ASW training on passage
02.11.89 Visited Wilmington, NC
00.11.89 Trial 'Punish' on Autec Range with 814 NAS embarked (800 and 849A NAS disembarked to US NAS Cecil Field for air combat exercise with USN)
20.11.89 Visited Fort Lauderdale
24.11.89 Operational training in AFWR
08.12.89 Visited Mayport
15.01.90 Visited Norfolk, Va
00.01.90 Exercise 'Fleetex 1/90'
08.02.90 Visited Barbados
23.02.90 Returned to Portsmouth to prepare for LPH role
05.03.90 Exercise 'Cold Winter' with 845 and 846 (Sea King Commando) NAS, COMAW and 42 RM Cdo embarked
Sum. 90 Exercise 'Dragon Hammer' with 4 other Allied carriers in Mediterranean; Sea Harriers cross-decked with the Spanish *Príncipe de Asturias* and Italian *Garibaldi*
00.11.90 814 NAS replaced Sea King HAS.5s with HAS.6s
29.08.91 Sailed from Portsmouth with air group embarked

01.09.91 Exercise 'Vendetta'
10.09.91 Exercise 'North Star'
25.09.91 High seas firings
27.09.91 Visited Lisbon
07.10.91 Exercise 'Display Determination'
17.10.91 Visited Alexandria with FOF3 embarked
18.10.91 Exercise 'Nilex 91'
20.10.91 Egyptian Navy Days
28.10.91 Visited Istanbul with CinC Fleet embarked
31.10.91 Salvaged MV *The Ark*
02.11.91 Visited Palermo
11.11.91 In Gibraltar
18.11.91 Returned to Portsmouth
00.00.92 OST at Portland
12.05.92 Sailed from Portsmouth to Far East for Deployment 'Orient 92' flying flag of Rear-Admiral Brigstocke, Commander UK Task Group, in company with *Newcastle*, *Norfolk*, *Boxer*, *Olwen* and *Fort Austin*
00.05.92 Exercise 'Dragon Hammer' in Eastern Mediterranean
00.06.92 Visited Piraeus
14.06.92 'Crossing the Line' ceremony
00.06.92 Visited Mombasa
00.07.92 Exercise 'Sea Copra', covering landing by 40 RM Cdo on Diego Garcia
09.07.92 Arrived in Sembawang Dockyard, Singapore
13.07.92 Sailed into South China Sea
23.07.92 Visited Yokosuka
28.07.92 Sailed for exercises with Japanese Maritime Self-Defence Force, with Rear-Admiral Nitta JMSDF embarked
01.08.92 Arrived in Pusan, South Korea, to host British Defence Trade Sales Exhibition
00.08.92 Arrived in Hong Kong for SMP and leave
00.09.92 Exercise 'Starfish' off Singapore, followed by Integrated Air Defence Exercise '92-4' involving air group and RAF Tornados, RAAF F/A-18s, RNZAF A-4s and RMAF F-5s
00.09.92 Banyan on Pulau Tioman Island
00.10.92 Visited Penang while *Boxer* visited Australia; later arrived in Persian Gulf and took several senior officers of United Arab Emirates armed forces to sea for briefings; present at British Defence Day in Abu Dhabi
04.11.92 Arrived in Port Suez prior to transiting Canal
00.11.92 Visited Haifa; air defence exercise held off Cyprus on completion with 2 Italian Navy TAV-8Bs and Sea King embarked
27.11.92 Returned to Portsmouth for DAMP
27.03.93 Shakedown period with CAG embarked
00.04.93 COST at Portland
00.05.93 JMC.932 off Scotland
22.07.93 Sailed from Portsmouth for Adriatic to relieve *Ark Royal* in Operation 'Grapple', enforcing 'No Fly Zone' over Bosnia and supporting British forces operating with UN in former Yugoslavia
00.01.94 Relieved in turn by *Ark Royal* in Adriatic and returned to Portsmouth for DAMP and leave
00.08.94 Sailed to relieve *Ark Royal* in Adriatic with 800 (Sea Harrier FRS.1), Flight of 899 (Sea Harrier F/A.2), 814 (Sea King HAS.6) and 849A (Sea King AEW.2) NAS embarked
00.00.95 Continuing in operational service

Khedive (D62) Ruler *Class Assault Escort Carrier*

Laid down: 22 September 1942
Launched: 30 January 1943
Completed: 23 August 1943

Builder: Seattle-Tacoma Shipbuilding Corp., Seattle; completed by Willamette Valley Ironworks
Machinery: 1-shaft Allis-Chalmers geared turbine; 2 Foster Wheeler boilers 8,500shp – 18.5 knots
Displacement: 11,400 tons standard; 15,400 tons deep load
Dimensions: 492ft overall x 108ft 6in max beam x 25ft 5in max draught
Gun armament: 2 single 5in US Mk 12 (2); 8 twin 40mm Bofors (16); 8 twin 20mm Oerlikon (16); 15 single 20mm Oerlikon (15)
Fuel: 3,160 tons FFO
Endurance: 27,500 miles @ 11 knots
Complement: 646
Protection: Splinter protection for bomb room
Flight deck: 450ft x 80ft wood-covered steel
Arrester wires: 9 x 19,800lb @ 55 knots; 3 barriers
Hangar: 260ft x 62ft x 18ft

Catapults: 1 x H4C; 16,000lb @ 74 knots (tail-down method only)
Lifts: *Fwd* 42ft long x 34ft wide; *aft* 34ft long x 42ft wide; both 14,000lb
Aircraft: Up to 30 could be operated; up to 90 could be ferried
Aircraft fuel: 36,000 gallons AVGAS
Air weapons: 500lb SAP bombs; 250lb bombs; Mk 11 depth charges; .5in gun ammunition; .303in gun ammunition; flares and pyrotechnics

Notes: Built from the outset as an aircraft carrier of the USN *Prince William* class, 23 units of which served in the RN with only the name-ship retained by the USN. Launched as USS *Cordova* (CVE-39). Transferred to the RN under Lend/Lease arrangements.

Summary of service

25.08.43 Transferred to RN at Vancouver and taken in hand for modification to RN standards
24.09.43 Sailed for Norfolk, Va
01.11.43 Sailed for UK with 849 (Avenger) and 1834 (Corsair) NAS embarked for passage
16.11.43 Arrived in Liverpool; aircraft disembarked to Speke
21.11.43 Allocated to WAC; taken in hand in Rosyth for modification to assault carrier
22.03.44 Collided with *Stuart Queen*
27.04.44 Clyde for defect rectification and repairs
15.05.44 Work-up based on Scapa Flow with 899 NAS (Seafire) embarked
15.07.44 Sailed for Malta with 899 NAS
15.08.44 Operation 'Dragoon' (invasion of southern France); formed part of TG.88.1 with *Attacker*, *Emperor*, *Pursuer* and *Searcher*
02.09.44 Arrived in Alexandria to prepare for strike operations in Aegean
08.09.44 Collided with *Ocean Messenger*
09.09.44 Operations 'Outing', 'Cablegram', 'Manna' and 'Contempt' (all strikes in Aegean) in company with *Attacker*, *Hunter*, *Emperor*, *Searcher* and *Pursuer*; 4 Naval Fighter Wing (Seafire NAS) embarked in *Khedive*, *Attacker* and *Hunter*, with 7 Naval Fighter Wing (Hellcat and Wildcat NAS) in *Emperor*, *Pursuer* and *Searcher* (they flew over 1,500 sorties against shipping and island garrisons for negligible losses)
08.10.44 Arrived in Gibraltar
12.10.44 Arrived in Belfast
23.10.44 London for refit and rectification of machinery defects
11.01.45 Allocated to 21 ACS, EIF; sailed for East Indies with 808 NAS (Hellcat) embarked
24.01.45 Arrived in Suez
03.02.45 Arrived in Cochin
11.02.45 In Trincomalee; used as aircraft ferry between India and Ceylon
11.04.45 Operation 'Sunfish' (photographic reconnaissance of Port Swettenham area) with 808 NAS embarked in company with *Emperor*
30.04.45 Operation 'Dracula' (strikes on Rangoon and Tenasserim coastal areas) by 21 ACS, *Emperor*, *Khedive* and *Stalker*, under Rear-Admiral A. W. La T. Bisset in cruiser *Royalist*; 1 Walrus of 1700 NAS embarked for SAR duties.
10.05.45 Operations to intercept Japanese cruiser *Haguro*
18.06.45 Operation 'Balsam' (photographic reconnaissance of southern Malaya and strikes against Sumatran airfields) in company with *Ameer* and *Stalker*
10.08.45 Sailed from Trincomalee for reoccupation of Penang
08.09.45 Operation 'Zipper' (reoccupation of Malaya and Singapore)
10.09.45 Entered Singapore with *Emperor*, *Hunter* and *Stalker*
13.09.45 Sailed for Durban via Trincomalee
17.10.45 Arrived in Durban
12.11.45 In Colombo

HMS *Khedive* in 1945. (FAA Museum)

13.11.45	Sailed for UK with 808 NAS embarked
05.12.45	808 NAS disembarked to disband
08.12.45	In Clyde for de-storing; allocated to Rosyth Command
04.01.46	Sailed for Halifax
15.01.46	Sailed for Norfolk, Va
26.01.46	Returned to USN at Norfolk
23.01.47	Sold as mercantile *Rempang*
00.00.68	Renamed *Daphne*
20.01.76	Arrived at Gandria to be broken up

Leviathan (R97) Majestic *Class Light Fleet Carrier*

Laid down: 18 October 1943
Launched: 7 June 1945

Builder: Swan Hunter & Wigham Richardson, Wallsend-on-Tyne
Machinery: 2-shaft Parsons geared turbines; 4 Admiralty 3-drum boilers; 40,000shp = 24.5 knots
Displacement: 14,000 tons standard; 18,590 tons deep load
Dimensions: 694ft overall x 112ft 6in max beam x 25ft max draught
Gun armament: (Designed but never fitted) 6 twin 40mm Bofors (12); 20 single 40mm Bofors (20)
Fuel: 3,196 tons FFO
Endurance: 8,300 miles @ 20 knots
Complement: 1,300 designed
Protection: Armoured mantlets for 32 torpedo warheads

Flight deck: 690ft x 80ft steel
Arrester wires: (Designed but never fitted) 8 x 20,000lb @ 87 knots; 2 barriers
Hangar: 275ft (plus 57ft extension aft of aft lift) x 52ft x 17ft 6in
Catapults: (Designed but never fitted) 1 x BH3; 20,000lb @ 66 knots
Lifts: *Fwd* 54ft long x 34ft wide; *aft* 54ft long x 34ft wide; both 24,000lb
Aircraft: 42 as designed
Aircraft fuel: 98,600 gallons AVGAS
Air weapons: Magazines never fitted out (design similar to *Magnificent* and *Sydney*)

HMS *Leviathan* laid up incomplete in Fareham Creek in March 1966. (I. L. Buxton)

Notes: One of six units of the *Majestic* class, externally similar to the *Colossus* class but with the flight deck and larger lifts strengthened to operate aircraft up to 24,000lb. The gun armament was all-Bofors and messing and accommodation arrangements were improved. Engine and boiler rooms were arranged *en echelon* to give a measure of survivability against torpedo attack, the starboard shaft being longer than the port. Fore and aft watertight subdivision was minimised so that if damaged below the waterline the ship would settle on an even keel rather than list. Both *Colossus* and *Majestic* classes were built to Lloyd's specifications up to the hangar deck to speed construction and enable yards unused to warship construction to build them. It was not, as has sometimes mistakenly been supposed, intended to enable them to be converted into merchant ships after the war. Many schemes were put forward to complete her as a commando carrier or a missile cruiser or to sell her abroad but none came to fruition. In 1966 her boilers and turbines were removed by Portsmouth Dockyard and sold to the Dutch shipyard that refitted *Karel Doorman* (ex *Venerable*) for service in Argentina. Rumours that the ship was not completed because her keel was bent on launch are untrue. The truth of the matter is that there was a surplus of carrier hulls in the post-war world; no foreign navy bought her and the RN had no immediate use for her. She was improperly preserved whilst used as an accommodation ship and her material state declined during the 1950s.

Summary of service

00.05.46 Work on ship suspended; laid up structurally 80 per cent complete

00.07.46 Towed to Portsmouth for preservation; used for many years as accommodation ship for dockyard personnel

00.00.66 Docked to have boilers and turbines removed

00.05.68 Towed to Faslane for scrapping

Magnificent (CVL-21) Majestic *Class Light Fleet Carrier*

Laid down: 29 July 1943
Launched: 16 November 1944
Completed: 21 May 1948

Builder: Harland & Wolff, Belfast
Machinery: 2-shaft Parsons single reduction geared turbines; 4 Admiralty 3-drum boilers; 40,000shp = 24.5 knots
Displacement: 15,700 tons standard; 19,550 tons deep load
Dimensions: 698ft overall x 112ft 6in max beam x 25ft max draught
Gun armament: 8 twin 40mm Bofors (16); 14 single 40mm Bofors (14)
Fuel: 3,196 tons FFO
Endurance: 8,300 miles @ 20 knots
Complement: 1,350
Protection: Armoured mantlets for 32 torpedo warheads
Flight deck: 690ft x 106ft steel
Arrester wires: 9 x 20,000lb @ 87 knots; 2 barriers
Hangar: 275ft (plus 57ft extension aft of aft lift) x 52ft x 17ft 6in
Catapults: 1 x BH5 twin-track; 20,000lb @ 56 knots
Lifts: *Fwd* 54ft long x 34ft wide; *aft* 54ft long x 34ft wide; both 20,000lb
Aircraft: 37
Aircraft fuel: 70,000 gallons AVGAS
Air weapons: Mk 43 homing torpedoes; 1,000lb MC bombs; 500lb SAP bombs; 5in RP; 3in RP; depth charges; 20m cannon ammunition; flares and pyrotechnics

Notes: Originally allocated pennant number R36 by the RN. The ship was completed to virtually the original *Majestic* class design except for the reduced close-range armament. She was loaned to Canada pending the completion of HMCS *Bonaventure* and returned to the RN in 1957. However, she never recommissioned into the RN.

Summary of service

16.11.44 Launched by Lady Hyacinth Needham, daughter of Earl of Kilmorey, hereditary Vice-Admiral of Ireland

00.03.48 Large contingent from HMCS *Warrior* transferred to *Magnificent*

17.04.48 Commissioned in Belfast; commanded by Commodore H. G. de Wolf CBE DSO DSC RCN, formerly of *Warrior*

15.05.48 Sailed for acceptance trials

00.05.48 Flying trials off Isle of Wight, followed by embarkation of stores in Portsmouth; late in May she secured alongside RNAY Sydenham to hoist on board 19th CAG comprising 803 (Seafire) and 825 (Firefly) CNAS plus 806 (Vampire, Sea Hornet, Sea Fury) NAS which took passage for North America to give season of air displays

24.05.48 Visited by 5th Sea Lord, Vice-Admiral Sir Philip Vian KCB KBE DSO**

25.05.48 Sailed for Canada

01.06.48 Arrived in Halifax; disembarked aircraft and stores, after which ship carried out brief shakedown cruise

HMCS *Magnificent* with Sea Furies of 19 CAG on deck. (Author)

10.08.48 Worked up with 19 CAG, embarked in St Lawrence area (171 deck landings carried out with loss of 2 aircraft)

02.09.48 At sea for further flying operations, including simulated strikes on Magdalen Islands

11.09.48 Disembarked aircraft to RCNAS Shearwater; proceeded to St John, New Brunswick, for docking

00.10.48 Cruise to Quebec, Seven Islands, Charlottetown and Sydney; joined HMC ships *Nootka*, *Haida* and *Swansea* as TG.211.2 for intensive sea drills ending in November

00.02.49 Ferried Firefly 4 aircraft to UK and returned to Canada with Firefly 5 and Seafires and number of other stores

25.02.49 Secured in Halifax after some storm damage on passage

05.03.49 Sailed with *Nootka* and *Haida* as TG.215.8; carried out exercises in Caribbean with ships of RN America and West Indies Station, during which HMS *Jamaica* was located by aircraft at 210 miles and 'attacked' at 162 miles

07.04.49 CAG disembarked

08.04.49 Returned to Halifax

00.05.49 Flying operations in Halifax area

04.06.49 Grounded in Port Mouton, Nova Scotia; refloated after 4 hours with aid of destroyers

14.06.49 Docked stern-first at St John for repairs

00.10.49 Repairs and refit complete

17.11.49 Flying operations off Nova Scotia with *Haida* and *Swansea*; detached to search for missing US B-29 bomber (crew found on 19 May)

24.11.49 Visited Guantanamo, Cuba, and San Juan, Puerto Rico

06.12.49 Returned to Halifax

13.01.50 Sailed for Bermuda with 18 CAG, comprising 825 and 826 (Firefly) CNAS, embarked as wholly ASW force

13.02.50 Participated in Canadian Fleet's spring cruise (including intensive sea exercises and visit to Charleston, SC, after which 18 CAG put up 18-aircraft fly-past)

00.03.50 Visited Havana, Cuba

11.03.50 Sailed from Cuba for Exercise 'Caribex 50' with RN and USN warships

16.03.50 Successfully 'struck' at USN force comprising carrier *Philippine Sea*, battleship *Missouri*, cruisers and destroyers

31.03.50 'Endex': ship put up fly-past for CinC A&WI in cruiser *Glasgow*

00.04.50 Visited New York (secured on north side of Pier 26)

14.04.50 Returned to Halifax

22.08.50 Sailed with 19 CAG comprising 803 and 883 (Sea Fury) CNAS together with HMC ships *Micmac* and *Huron* (cruise intended to visit and strengthen ties with NATO allies)

00.08.50 Visited Londonderry and exercised with JASS

00.09.50 Visited Rosyth, on completion of which 'strikes' were flown against HMAS *Sydney* in Moray Firth; then visited Oslo

00.10.50 Visited Gothenburg, Sweden (longest ship ever to do so); on completion, visited Rotterdam, secured between 2 buoys

12.10.50 Rammed by barge *Shell 25* which hit on port side and crushed captain's barge and a motor boat

16.10.50 Sailed for Cherbourg

17.10.50 Disembarked 6 Sea Furies and 4 Fireflies to RNAS Lee-on-Solent

24.10.50 Arrived in Cherbourg

28.10.50 Sailed and re-embarked aircraft

01.11.50 Visited Lisbon

06.11.50 Arrived in Gibraltar and berthed at south mole astern of *Vengeance* and battleship *Vanguard* of HF

09.11.50 Exercise 'Maple Leaf' with HF in Gibraltar area; on completion, sailed for Canada via Bermuda

25.11.50 Located and 'attacked' by recently acquired Avengers of 826 CNAS which had carried out most sustained search in history of RCN; 19 CAG disembarked to RCNAS Shearwater

27.11.50 Returned to Halifax

00.12.50 Docked at St John

06.02.51 Sailed for Quonset Point where 18 CAG, now comprising 883 (Sea Fury) and 825 (Avenger) CNAS, embarked

00.03.51 Returned to Halifax

23.03.51 Flying operations off Bermuda

00.04.51 Salvaged small diesel passenger ship *Gilbert* off Trinidad, together with HMCS *Micmac*

06.04.51 Visited Port of Spain, Trinidad (largest ship ever to do so); further visits made to Barbados and Boston

01.05.51 RCN squadrons reorganised: 18 CAG became 30 CAG, 883 CNAS renumbered 871 CNAS and 826 CNAS renumbered 881

CNAS, 19 CAG became 31 Support Air Group, 803 CNAS became 870 CNAS and 825 CNAS became 880 CNAS

00.08.51 Sailed for cruise in Mediterranean

24.08.51 Intensive training period off Malta, ship anchoring at night in Marsaxlokk Bay

24.09.51 Sailed for Naples and Saint Raphael

04.10.51 NATO Exercise 'Symphonie Deux' with large number of ships, including *Ocean*

14.10.51 Sailed for Canada

29.10.51 Embarked personnel of 410 Squadron RCAF and proceeded to Norfolk, Va, where 48 Sabre jets were loaded as cargo for delivery to Glasgow; on return voyage, loaded with Sea Furies for RCN

00.12.51 Long refit carried out by Halifax Shipyards

12.04.52 Sailed for post-refit trials

00.05.52 Shakedown cruise with 30 CAG embarked (unusually, cruiser *Quebec* acted as planeguard and landings included USN blimp)

02.06.52 Cruise to European waters, starting with visit to Plymouth

17.06.52 Exercise 'Castanets' with *Indomitable* flying flag of Rear-Admiral Caspar John, FO Heavy Squadron, HF; on completion, sailed for Malta and Greece, where ship joined MF Regatta at Navarino

25.07.52 Visited Istanbul with *Glory* (visit cut short when RN ships sailed at short notice because of deteriorating situation in Egypt when King Farouk abdicated on 23 July and was replaced by military government under General Naguib; *Magnificent* proceeded to Malta a few hours after British ships)

11.08.52 Intensive work-up off Malta

18.08.52 Sailed for Belfast

00.09.52 Work-up with JASS followed by Exercise'Mainbrace' (largest NATO exercise held to date, with over 160 warships involved; *Magnificent* formed part of carrier support group with *Theseus*, USS *Mindoro*, RNZN cruiser *Bellona* and 8 US destroyers); on completion, ship fuelled and stored in Clyde

01.10.52 Sailed from Londonderry to New York as part of convoy support Exericse 'Emigrant'

09.10.52 Returned to Halifax

12.01.53 Refitted by Halifax Shipyards

00.04.53 Work-up in Halifax area

00.05.53 Sailed for Coronation Review with cruisers *Quebec* and *Ontario* and 3 destroyers

29.05.53 Arrived in Portsmouth with CAG disembarked to RNAS Lee-on-Solent

08.06.53 Participated in Coronation Fleet Review of HM Queen Elizabeth II at Spithead (8 Sea Furies and 8 Avengers tok part in fly-past)

25.06.53 Returned to Halifax

00.07.53 Docking in St John

21.08.53 Autumn cruise to US East Coast

04.09.53 Visited New York

16.09.53 Participated in Exercise 'Mariner', which involved 300 warships, 1,000 aircraft and over 500,000 men from 9 NATO countries (Canadian Squadron formed part of 'Blue Force' which was opposed by 'Orange' submarines, surface raiders and land-based air; *Magnificent* flew sorties round clock as part of Commonwealth Squadron which included *Eagle* and battleship *Vanguard*)

04.10.53 Visited Belfast, Portsmouth and Glasgow, where ship loaded 9 new Sea Furies and an Avenger in addition to CAG for passage to Canada

02.11.53 Disembarked aircraft and arrived in Halifax

00.12.53 Carried out DLT with 31 Support Air Group

09.12.53 Halifax for defect rectification

01.03.54 Sailed for UK without air group

09.03.54 Refit in Portsmouth Dockyard (many of ship's company attended RN courses)

00.06.54 Loaded stores in Belfast

11.06.54 Arrived in Halifax

00.07.54 DLT and carrier qualification

00.08.54 ASW exercises off US East Coast

00.09.54 Participated in NATO Exercise 'New Broom II' in North Atlantic; on completion, headed for Panama

27.09.54 Passed through Panama Canal

11.10.54 Visited San Diego

18.10.54 Visited San Francisco

25.10.54 Arrived in Esquimalt (part of air group disembarked to airport at Patricia Bay)

01.11.54 Visited Vancouver

00.11.54 Passed back through Panama Canal for exercises in Bermuda area

15.12.54 Refit at Halifax Shipyards

17.04.55 Sailed for exercises in West Indies with *Haida* and *Micmac*

09.05.55 Departed from Bermuda for UK for brief visit to Portsmouth

07.06.55 Returned to Halifax

00.06.55 Atlantic Command Regatta in Bedford Basin (*Magnificent* came 9th overall)

HMCS *Magnificent* in Port Said in January 1957 with RCAF Otter aircraft on deck. Note the deck recognition number '21' painted forward and aft rather than the letters used on other Commonwealth carriers. (Canadian Department of National Defence)

03.07.55 Docking in Halifax
08.08.55 DLPs for VC-920 (first RCNR Squadron to embark for training)
15.08.55 Visited New York with *Quebec* and four destroyers for combined US and Canadian Naval Week (total of over 40 warships present)
04.09.55 Sailed with VF-871 (Sea Fury) and VS-880 and VS-881 (Avenger) CNAS embarked (CAG system discontinued and USN-style designator letters added to squadron numbers at this time); spent over 24 days at sea in Exercises 'New Broom IV' and 'Sea Enterprise' (designed to test convoy protection techniques)
14.09.55 Bad weather interrupted second exercise (designed to practise carrier strikes against 'Orange' foe in northern Norway)
27.09.55 Visited Trondheim
07.10.55 Visited Plymouth for boiler cleaning
20.10.55 Visited Rotterdam
28.10.55 Sailed for Gibraltar area and visited Valencia
11.11.55 Visited Genoa
15.11.55 Visited Marseilles
27.11.55 Sailed for Canada
06.12.55 Disembarked CNAS and arrived in Halifax for SMP
27.02.56 Sailed for Exercise 'Spring Tide' with VS-881 (Avenger), HS-50 (Sikorsky HO4S-3) and HU-21 (Sikorsky HO4) CNAS embarked for ASW work-up (target drone

unit also embarked); on completion, visited USN base at Chaguaramus Bay, Trinidad

16.03.56 Arrived in Barbados for visit

25.03.56 Work-up programme off Roosevelt Roads with *Quebec* and 8 destroyers (some of which came from Pacific)

13.04.56 Visited Port au Prince, Haiti, with 3 destroyers and RN submarine *Astute*

19.04.56 Visited Havana, Cuba

01.05.56 NATO Exercise 'New Broom V'

05.05.56 Visited Norfolk, Va

07.05.56 Returned to Halifax (cruise had proved ability of helicopters to work with Fleet)

00.05.56 Sailed for UK with members of National Defence College on board

00.06.56 Returned to Canada

00.07.56 SMP in Halifax

00.08.56 DLT by VC-920

20.08.56 Sailed for ASW exercises with VS-881 and HS-50 embarked

08.09.56 Exercise 'New Broom VI (storms made flying difficult and damaged ship's boats)

25.09.56 Work-up period off Halifax with VS-880 CNAS (Avenger) embarked

10.10.56 Last scheduled deck landing by Avenger

29.10.56 Sailed to carry out deep-water helicopter trials with frigate *Buckingham*, which had been fitted with flight deck aft; on completion, sailed for Belfast to deliver stores for new *Bonaventure*

07.11.56 Called at Glasgow to collect 50 Sabre fighters for RCAF; at 2000, ordered to return to Halifax at best speed to be fitted out as troopship and headquarters vessel for Canadian contingent to be sent to Egypt following Suez crisis

08.11.56 Sailed for Halifax

13.11.56 Arrived in Halifax after stormy passage; once there, ship's company reduced to 600 and accommodation for 500 troops and stores built into hangars (Operation 'Rapid Step'); on completion, ship reverted to 8 hours' notice while UN pondered what best to do with its peacekeeping force

00.12.56 Operation 'Rapid Step II' (ship again modified, this time to act as troop transport)

29.12.56 Sailed for Egypt with 406 Army personnel, 100 tons supplies, 233 vehicles, 4 RCAF Otter aircraft and Ship's Flight helicopter

09.01.57 Arrived in Port Said; stores unloaded by UN and native working parties

19.01.57 Otters flown off

20.01.57 Sailed for Naples

27.01.57 Sailed for Glasgow

01.02.57 Arrived in Glasgow to pick up 59 Sabre aircraft to be returned to Canada from RCAF units in Europe; Ship's Flight helicopter and several crew members transferred to *Bonaventure* in Belfast

00.03.57 De-storing in Halifax

10.04.57 Sailed from Halifax for last time

14.06.57 Reverted to RN in Plymouth (remainder of ship's company took passage back to Canada in *Bonaventure*); laid up in reserve in Plymouth (no further use made of her)

00.00.61 Declared for disposal

12.07.65 Arrived in Faslane for breaking up

Melbourne (R21) Majestic *Class Light Fleet Carrier*

HMAS *Melbourne* with a Gannet landing on. Two further Gannets and a Wessex are parked forward. (RAN Official)

Laid down: 15 April 1943
Launched: 28 February 1945
Completed: 8 November 1955

Builder: Vickers-Armstrong, Barrow-in-Furness
Machinery: 2-shaft Parsons geared turbines; 4 Admiralty 3-drum boilers; 40,000shp = 24.5 knots
Displacement: 16,000 tons standard; 19,996 tons deep load
Dimensions: 701ft 6in overall x 126ft max beam x 25ft max draught
Gun armament: 7 twin 40mm Bofors (14); 11 single 40mm Bofors (11); 4 single 3pdr saluting
Fuel: 3,200 tons FFO/diesel
Endurance: 12,000 miles @ 14 knots
Complement: 1,354
Protection: Armoured mantlets for 32 torpedo warheads
Flight deck: 690ft x 80ft steel
Arrester wires: 6 x 20,000lb @ 104 knots; emergency nylon barriers
Hangar: 275ft (plus 53ft extension aft of aft lift) x 52ft x 17ft 6in
Catapults: 1 x BS4 (103ft stroke); 40,000lb @ 78 knots
Lifts: *Fwd* 54ft long x 34ft wide; *aft* 54ft long x 34ft wide; both 24,000lb, 23-second cycle
Aircraft: 27
Aircraft fuel: 212,000 gallons AVCAT; 5,000 gallons AVGAS
Air weapons: Sidewinder AAM; Mk 30/43/44/46 homing torpedoes; 1,000lb MC bombs; 500lb MC bombs; 5in RP; 3in RP; depth charges; 20mm cannon ammunition; flares and pyrotechnics

Notes: Built as *Majestic*, name-ship of class which followed *Colossus* class and formed a second batch of 1942 light fleet carrier design. Externally identical but had a modified flight deck strengthened to operate heavier aircraft and had larger lifts and improved internal subdivision. The opportunity was taken to improve the living accommodation with separate dining halls and partial air conditioning.

Summary of service

00.00.46 Construction suspended; laid up incomplete at Barrow-in-Furness
00.00.49 Construction resumed after purchase by Australian Government
25.01.55 Sea trials off Belfast
00.08.55 808 (Sea Venom), 816 and 817 (Gannet) ANAS plus Ship's Flight of 2 Sycamore helicopters formed at RNAS Culdrose for service in *Melbourne*
28.10.55 Commissioned in Barrow
14.11.55 In Plymouth for trials
09.01.56 At Spithead for calibration and trials
21.01.56 Visited Le Havre
08.03.56 In Glasgow
12.03.56 Sailed for Australia via Gibraltar, Naples, Malta, Suez, Aden, Colombo, Fremantle and Melbourne
09.05.56 Arrived in Sydney
14.05.56 Flagship of RAN
28.09.56 In Singapore
13.10.56 n Hong Kong
19.10.56 In Manila
01.11.56 In Manus
10.12.56 Returned to Sydney
18.02.57 Visited Dunedin, Wellington, Auckland and carried out exercises with RNZN
15.03.57 In Sydney
18.04.57 In Singapore
14.05.57 In Hong Kong
11.07.57 In Jervis Bay
00.07.57 Montaga Island area
29.11.57 In Brisbane
03.02.58 In Jervis Bay
00.02.58 Sydney for refit
25.03.58 Arrived in Singapore
28.03.58 Exercise 'Festoon'
29.01.59 In Williamstown
08.04.59 In Singapore
28.04.59 In Manila
02.05.59 In Manus
02.06.59 In Port Moresby
11.06.59 In Brisbane
00.11.59 Australian government announced that *Melbourne* would be withdrawn from service in 1963 but in the event she was refitted for further service and this decision was rescinded; air group comprised 805 (Sea Venom) and 816 (Gannet) ANAS
00.01.60 In Darwin
14.04.60 In Singapore
28.04.60 In Manila for Exercise 'Sealion'
13.05.60 Post-exercise 'wash-up' at Singapore
02.06.60 Visited Yokahama

16.06.60 Visited Djakarta
24.06.60 In Fremantle
07.07.60 Returned to Sydney
15.08.60 Hervey Bay area for exercises off Lower Barrier Reef
13.09.60 Exercises in Jervis Bay area
26.01.61 In Sydney
18.02.61 In Fremantle
20.02.61 Sailed for Exercise 'Jet 61'
12.03.61 Post-exercise 'wash-up' in Trincomalee
18.03.61 Visited Bombay
22.03.61 Visited Karachi
17.04.61 Visited USN base at Subic Bay
01.06.61 In Manus
03.06.61 Visited Rabaul
13.07.61 Exercises in Jervis Bay area
15.08.61 Exercise 'Tucker Box' in Hervey Bay area
29.08.61 Exercises with RNZN, followed by visits to Auckland and Wellington
19.09.61 In Sydney
15.01.62 Exercises in Jervis Bay area
09.02.62 Visits to Hobart, Adelaide and Fremantle
02.04.62 Subic Bay for Exercise 'Sea Devil'
12.05.62 Exercises in Japanese waters, followed by visits to Nagasaki, Kobe and Yokohama
09.06.62 In Manus
21.06.62 Returned to Sydney
24.08.62 Exercises in Hervey Bay area
06.09.62 Exercise 'Tucker Box'
17.09.62 In Sydney; refitted as ASW carrier
09.01.63 Exercises in Jervis Bay area; Wessex helicopters replaced Gannets of 817 ANAS; from now on, air group comprised flexible mixture drawn from 805 (Sea Venom), 816 (Gannet) and 817 (Wessex) ANAS
03.03.63 In Sydney
14.03.63 In Manus
22.03.63 Visited Manila
29.03.63 In Hong Kong
20.04.63 Exercise 'Sea Serpent' in South China Sea
25.05.63 In Fremantle
03.06.63 In Melbourne
28.07.63 Visited Fitzroy Island
30.07.63 In Sydney
26.08.63 Exercise 'Carbine' in Sydney area
06.02.64 Exercises in Jervis Bay area
10.02.64 Collided with RAN destroyer *Voyager* during exercises (destroyer sank with loss of 79 lives)
11.02.64 Arrived in Sydney for repairs
11.05.64 Exercises in Jervis Bay area
29.06.64 In Manus
06.07.64 Visited USN base at Subic Bay
24.07.64 Exercise 'FOTEX 64'
21.08.64 Visited Rabaul
22.09.64 Exercise 'Winchester' off east coast of Australia
13.10.64 Exercises in Jervis Bay area
15.10.64 In Sydney
03.03.65 In Manus
09.03.65 Operations off Labuan
15.03.65 Exercise 'FOTEX 65' with *Victorious* and *Eagle* in Singapore area
26.03.65 In Singapore
07.05.65 Exercise 'Sea Horse' in Manila area
22.05.65 Visited Bangkok and Gulf of Thailand
29.05.65 Visited Manila
22.06.65 Returned to Sydney
09.08.65 Exercises in Hervey Bay area
03.09.65 In Sydney
18.09.65 Visited Port Moresby
05.10.65 Returned to Sydney for refit
07.02.66 Work-up in Sydney area
30.03.66 Visited Rabaul
02.04.66 In Manus
19.05.66 In Manila for start of Eercise 'Sea Imp'
09.06.66 Visited Penang
18.06.66 Exercises in Indian Ocean
22.06.66 In Fremantle
01.07.66 Returned to Sydney for SMP
16.09.66 Exercises with RNZN and visited Auckland and Wellington
28.10.66 In Sydney
18.03.67 Exercises in Jervis Bay area
12.04.67 Exercises in Hervey Bay area
09.05.67 Visited Rabaul
11.05.67 In Manus
18.05.67 Visited USN base at Subic Bay
25.05.67 Visited Yokohama
31.05.67 Visited Kure
08.06.67 In Hong Kong
26.06.67 In Singapore
04.07.67 Exercise 'Sea Dog' off Manila
16.08.67 Returned to Sydney for SMP
22.09.67 Sailed for USA without air group in order to collect Skyhawk and Tracker aircraft purchased from USN to re-equip air group
02.10.67 In Pearl Harbor
11.10.67 Visited Vancouver
25.10.67 Visited San Francisco
27.10.67 In San Diego to load 10 Skyhawks and 14 Trackers
10.11.67 Unloaded aircraft in Sydney
22.11.67 Paid off for refit in Sydney during which workshops were modified to support new air group, flight deck was strengthened and

HMAS *Melbourne* with Skyhawks on deck. Note that the RAN had discontinued the use of deck recognition letters by this stage and she has her pennant number, '21', painted on the flight deck forward. (RAN Official)

	new radars fitted (result was a very capable carrier able to operate in a variety of roles)
03.02.69	Worked up in Sydney/Jervis Bay areas with 805 (Skyhawk), 816 (Tracker) and 817 (Wessex) ANAS embarked
11.05.69	In Manus
16.05.69	Exercises with USN off Subic Bay
02.06.69	Collided with USN destroyer *Frank E. Evans* in South China Sea (destroyer cut in half, forward half subsequently sinking; as a result, Exercise 'Sea Spirit' cancelled and *Melbourne* proceeded to Singapore for emergency repairs)
06.06.69	Docked in King George VI drydock in Singapore
27.06.69	Sailed for more detailed repairs in Sydney
09.07.69	Arrived in Sydney for repairs
01.10.69	Work-up in Sydney/Jervis Bay areas
15.03.70	In Manus
22.03.70	Exercises with USN off Subic Bay
13.04.70	In Hong Kong
05.05.70	Visited Osaka
09.05.70	Visited Kobe
21.05.70	In Singapore
25.05.70	Exercise 'Crackshot'
26.06.70	SMP in Singapore
15.07.70	Returned to Sydney for docking and SMP
09.11.70	Exercise 'Swan Lake' off Fremantle
18.12.70	Returned to Sydney for refit
02.08.71	Work-up in Sydney/Jervis Bay areas, after which ship remained in Australian waters for most of year
25.10.71	Exercises with USN off Honolulu
10.12.71	Returned to Sydney
03.02.72	In Manus
10.02.72	Subic Bay
15.03.72	In Singapore for start of Exercise 'Genesis'
05.04.72	Visited Djakarta
14.04.72	Returned to Australian waters
30.08.72	Arrived in Pearl Harbor to collect further batch of Skyhawk aircraft
21.09.72	Exercises with USN in Hawaii area
15.10.72	Visited Manila
24.11.72	Returned to Sydney for refit
29.06.73	Work-up in Jervis Bay area
00.07.77	Represented RAN at HM Queen Elizabeth II's Jubilee Fleet Review at Spithead (air group remained embarked and did not participate in fly-past)
00.00.77	Further batch of Trackers collected from USA to replace aircraft lost in hangar fire at RANAS Nowra
00.00.78	Flight deck extended during major refit
25.02.82	HMS *Invincible* purchased by Australian Government for £175 million, for delivery in 1983, to replace *Melbourne* (in the event, Australian government offered not to hold UK to deal after *Invincible*'s service in Falklands conflict and purchase was cancelled)
30.06.82	ANAS having flown ashore, ship paid off for disposal at Sydney
02.07.82	805 and 816 ANAS disbanded at RANAS Nowra (817 ANAS remained in commission, operating from other ships)
00.00.83	Moored off Garden Island, Sydney, awaiting disposal
00.00.85	Sold for scrap; broken up at Dallan, China

Nabob (D77) Ruler *Class Escort Carrier*

Laid down: 20 October 1942
Launched: 9 March 1943
Completed: 7 September 1943

Builder: Seattle-Tacoma Shipbuilding Corp., Seattle; machinery by Allis-Chalmers
Machinery: 1-shaft Allis-Chalmers geared turbine; 2 Foster Wheeler boilers; 8,500shp = 18 knots
Displacement: 11,400 tons standard; 15,390 tons deep load
Dimensions: 492ft overall x 108ft 6in max beam x 25ft 5in max draught
Gun armament: 2 single 5in US Mk 12 (2); 8 twin 40mm Bofors (16); 14 twin 20m Oerlikon (28); 7 single 20mm Oerlikon (7)
Fuel: 3,160 tons FFO
Endurance: 27,500 miles @ 11 knots
Complement: 646
Protection: Splinter protection for bomb room
Flight deck: 450ft x 80ft wood-covered steel
Arrester wires: 9 x 19,800lb @ 55 knots; 3 barriers
Hangar: 260ft x 62ft x 18ft
Catapults: 1 x H4C; 16,000lb @ 74 knots (tail-down method only)
Lifts: *Fwd* 42ft long x 34ft wide; *aft* 34ft long x 42ft wide; both 14,000lb
Aircraft: Up to 30 could be operated; up to 90 could be ferried
Aircraft fuel: 43,200 gallons AVGAS
Air weapons: 22.4in torpedoes; 500lb SAP bombs; 250lb SAP bombs; 250lb GP bombs; 3in RP; Mk 11 depth charges; .5in gun ammunition; .303in gun ammunition; flares and pyrotechnics

Notes: Built as USS *Edisto* (CVE-41), one of 23 units of the US *Prince William* class transferred to the RN under the Lend/Lease arrangements. Her ship's company, apart from the Air Department, were all provided by the RCN in order for them to gain experience of carrier operations so that a carrier could be included in the post-war Canadian Fleet. She was hit by an acoustic torpedo fired by *U354* which blew a hole 50ft x 40ft below the waterline and bent the shaft. Greatly to the credit of her ship's company, she made Scapa Flow under her own steam and even flew off and recovered a night AS patrol by two Avengers despite being down by the stern. At Scapa Flow the engine room bulkhead was shored up to keep her afloat but there was no industrial capacity to repair her either in the UK or the US.

HMS *Nabob* shortly after being torpedoed on 22 August 1944. Her aircraft have all been parked forward to counter the flooding aft. Her sister-ship HMS *Trumpeter* is visible in the back-ground. (FAA Museum)

Summary of service

07.09.43	Transferred to RN and commissioned in Vancouver
15.10.43	Modifications carried out to bring her up to British standards of protection
24.01.44	Arrived in Esquimalt
25.01.44	Grounded on silt bottom at 17 knots but not damaged
28.01.44	Floated off
08.02.44	Sailed for New York via San Francisco and Panama Canal
19.03.44	Arrived in New York; embarked 852 NAS (Avenger) from Squantum for passage to UK
23.03.44	Sailed with UT.10 to Liverpool
07.04.44	Allocated to WAC; defect repairs in Clyde yard
18.04.44	Liverpool for further repairs
29.06.44	Flying work-up off Belfast with 852 NAS (Avenger/Wildcat) embarked
01.08.44	Loaned to HF; arrived at Scapa Flow
22.08.44	Operation 'Goodwood' (strikes against *Tirpitz*) by HF with *Formidable*, *Furious*, *Indefatigable* and *Trumpeter*); hit by acoustic torpedo fired by *U354*
27.08.44	Arrived in Scapa Flow in badly damaged state
30.09.44	Paid off (laid up, unrepaired, on mud bank on south side of the Firth of Forth); allocated to Rosyth Command in nominal reserve
16.03.45	Returned to USN custody 'as lies' in Firth of Forth
00.03.47	Sold to Dutch shipbuilding firm

HMS *Nairana* working up in the Clyde area in January 1944. (J. D. Brown)

21.09.47 Arrived in Rotterdam for conversion; rebuilt as merchant ship, retaining name *Nabob*
00.00.52 Conversion completed
00.00.68 Renamed *Glory*
06.12.77 Broken up in Taiwan

Nairana (1943) (D05) *Escort Carrier*

Laid down: 6 November 1941
Launched: 20 May 1943
Completed: 12 December 1943

Builder: John Brown & Co., Clydebank
Machinery: 2-shaft Doxford diesels; 10,700shp = 17 knots
Displacement: 13,825 tons standard; 17,210 tons deep load
Dimensions: 524ft overall x 68ft max beam x 25ft 9in max draught
Gun armament: 1 twin 4in QF Mk XVI HA (2); 4 quadruple 2pdr pompom (16); 8 twin 20mm Oerlikon (16)
Fuel: 1,655 tons diesel
Endurance: 13,000 miles @ 16 knots
Complement: 554
Protection: 1in protective plating over magazines; empty oil drums in void spaces to protect against torpedoes
Flight deck: 502ft x 66ft steel
Arrester wires: 8 x 15,500lb @ 60 knots; 2 barriers
Hangar: 231ft x 61ft x 17ft 6in
Catapults: None
Lifts: *Aft* 45ft long x 34ft wide; 15,000lb
Aircraft: 20
Aircraft fuel: 52,000 gallons AVGAS
Air weapons: Mk XXIV mines (homing torpedoes);

18in torpedoes; 250lb GP bombs; 3in RP; Mk 11 depth charges; 20mm cannon ammunition; .303in gun ammunition; flares and pyrotechnics

Notes: The small flight deck precluded a deck park and the lack of a second lift forward made ranging aircraft sufficiently difficult to limit the maximum practical air group to 20. Like her half-sisters *Vindex* and *Campania*, *Nairana* was used on the Russian convoy runs since it was felt that her riveted hull was less susceptible to cracking than the welded hulls of US-built escort carriers.

Summary of service

26.11.43 Commissioned in Clyde
17.12.43 Sailed for work-up in Clyde area
25.01.44 Allocated to WAC with 835 NAS (Swordfish/Sea Hurricane) embarked
29.01.44 Sailed to cover OS.66/KMS.70 and provide distant cover for ON.222/ ONS.28
07.02.44 Covered SL.147/MKS.38
11.02.44 Covered HX.22
13.02.44 Covered CU.13 in Clyde area
24.02.44 Covered OS.59/KMS.43
06.03.44 Arrived in Gibraltar
09.03.44 Sailed with MKF.29 to Clyde; fighters shot down two Ju 290Bs
24.03.44 Sailed from Clyde to support OS.72/ KMS.46
10.04.44 Sailed from Gibraltar with SL.154/ MKS.45
13.05.44 AS sweep off Londonderry
16.05.44 Provided cover for SL.157, MKS.48, SL.158 and MKS.49
03.06.44 Arrived in Clyde
12.06.45 Sailed with KMF.32
27.06.44 Sailed from Gibraltar with MKF.32
04.07.44 Clyde for docking and repairs
24.08.44 Sailed with KMF.34
10.09.44 Left Gibraltar with MKF.34
14.09.44 Clyde for repairs
15.10.44 Loaned to HF, arrived Scapa Flow; 835 NAS augmented with extra Swordfish, bringing air group up to 20
21.10.44 Sailed to cover JW.61 to North Russia
31.10.44 Sailed from Kola with RA.61
09.11.44 Arrived in Clyde for defect rectification
30.11.44 Sailed from Scapa Flow with JW.62
10.12.44 Sailed from Kola with RA.62
20.12.44 Defect rectification in Clyde
27.01.45 Arrived in Scapa Flow.
28.01.45 Sailed in company with *Premier* to cover strike by *Campania* on Vaagsø
30.01.45 Strike on Stadtlandet
03.02.45 Sailed from Scapa Flow with cover for JW.64 (Operation 'Hitbed')
27.02.45 Returned to Scapa Flow
26.03.45 Sailed for night strikes on Trondheim (cancelled)
29.03.45 Arrived in Scapa Flow
31.03.45 Major refit in Belfast
07.08.45 Struck jetty coming out of dock
00.10.45 DLT carrier in Irish Sea areas with no dedicated air group
23.01.46 Clyde for repairs
23.03.46 Loaned to RNethN (its first carrier); renamed *Karel Doorman* (pennant number QH1)
28.05.48 Returned to RN at Devonport and sold immediately as mercantile *Port Victor*
21.07.71 Broken up at Faslane

Ocean (1945) (R68) Colossus *Class Light Fleet Carrier*

Laid down: 8 November 1942
Launched: 8 July 1944
Completed: 8 August 1945

Builder: Alexander Stephen & Sons, Govan
Machinery: 2-shaft Parsons geared turbines; 4 Admiralty 3-drum boilers; 40,000shp = 25 knots
Displacement: 13,190 tons standard; 18,040 tons deep load
Dimensions: 695ft overall x 112ft 6in max beam x 23ft 5in max draught
Gun armament: 6 twin 40mm Bofors (12); 16 single 40mm Bofors (15); 4 single 3pdr saluting (4)
Fuel: 3,196 tons FFO
Endurance: 8,500 miles @ 20 knots
Complement: 1,093
Protection: Armoured mantlets over torpedo warheads in magazine
Flight deck: 690ft x 80ft steel
Arrester wires: 10 x 20,000lb @ 60 knots; 2 barriers
Hangar: 275ft (plus 57ft extension aft of aft lift) x 52ft x 17ft 6in

HMS *Ocean* leaving Grand Harbour, Valletta, Malta with Sea Furies and Fireflies on deck. (FAA Museum)

Catapults: 1 x BH3 (twin-track); 16,000lb @ 66 knots
Lifts: *Fwd* 45ft long x 34ft wide; *aft* 45ft long x 34ft wide; both 15,000lb
Aircraft: Up to 42
Aircraft fuel: 98,600 gallons AVGAS
Air weapons: 1,000lb MC bombs; 500lb GP bombs; 250lb B bombs; 3in RP; Mk 11 depth charges; aircraft mines; 20mm cannon ammunition; flares and pyrotechnics

Notes: Immediately after completion, the ship was taken in hand by Cammell Laird of Birkenhead for conversion to a night fighter carrier. Major changes included installation of the superior, US-supplied, SM-1 radar instead of the British Type 277 on the island, the installation of Type 961 CCA radar and improved direction-finding equipment. A box-like structure was added to the forward part of the island to house the SM-1 'office'.

Sea Vampire LZ551 carrying out deck landing trials aboard *Ocean* in December 1945. (FAA Museum)

Summary of service

08.08.45 Commissioned in Glasgow
13.08.45 Taken in hand for modifications by Cammell Laird
16.11.45 Work completed; allocated to Rosyth Command for flying trials (which included first deck trials of Sea Hornet and last carrier take-off by Swordfish)
03.12.45 Modified Vampire (LZ551) made first pure jet landing on aircraft carrier (flown by Lt-Cdr E. M. Brown RN); total of 15 landings and take-offs were made over 2-day period
00.12.45 Deployed to MF with air group comprising 805 (Seafire) and 816 (Firefly NF) NAS; detachment of 784 NAS (Hellcat NF) temporarily embarked for night fighter trials
00.06.46 Used for ferry and trooping run to Singapore, leaving air group at RNAS Hal Far
00.08.46 805 NAS temporarily exchanged Seafires for Fireflies
00.10.46 Gave medical and fire-fighting assistance to destroyers *Saumarez* and *Volage* when they were mined in Corfu Channel
00.07.47 Visited Istanbul during MF summer cruise
00.05.48 Formed part of task force covering withdrawal of British forces from Palestine (her NAS provided only air cover once RAF bases had been evacuated)
00.08.48 Air group changed to comprise 804 (Seafire) and 812 (Firefly) NAS
00.06.49 Disembarked air group and misemployed to carry troops to Mediterranean and Far East (made total of four runs to the Far East, last two carrying reinforcements and equipment for Commonwealth forces in Korea)
00.01.51 Returned to UK for refit
27.06.51 Recommissioned for MF
25.01.52 Sailed from Malta for Suez Canal (replaced in MF by *Theseus*, which had returned from operations off Korea)
00.05.52 Arrived in Hong Kong to relieve *Glory* on Korean War operations; air group comprised 802 (Sea Fury) and 825 (Firefly) NAS (2 Sikorsky S-51 helicopters, several aircrew and much advice transferred from *Glory*)
06.05.52 Sailed for Sasebo
09.05.52 Arrived in Sasebo
10.05.52 Sailed for first patrol off west coast of Korea
17.05.52 Created new daily operating record for light fleet carriers with 123 sorties, 76 by 802 NAS and 47 by 825 NAS, during which 90 tons of bombs were dropped
20.05.52 Returned to Sasebo to refuel and re-arm
29.05.52 Sailed for second war patrol
06.06.52 Left operational area for Kure in Japan
08.06.52 Arrived in Kure; replacement aircraft received from pool at Iwakuni
13.06.52 Sailed for third patrol
15.06.52 Visited by Field Marshal Lord Alexander of Tunis, UK Minister of Defence, whilst anchored off Inchon, Korea
24.06.52 Joined USN carriers of TF.77 in attacks on North Korean power stations and electrical installations
25.06.52 Arrived in Sasebo
03.07.52 Sailed in company with *Unicorn* and 5 destroyers
11.07.52 Aircraft joined in operation 'Pressure Pump' (combined RN, USN, USMC, USAF and RAAF strike on Pyongyang, North Korean capital, coordinated by US 5th Air Force): *Ocean*'s aircraft contributed 39 to total of 1,254 offensive Allied sorties, ships's target being large railway marshalling yard thought to contain crated MiG-15s (successfully attacked)
13.07.52 Arrived in Sasebo
21.07.52 Sailed for operations off Korean west coast; interdiction targets including bridges attacked
01.08.52 Arrived in Kure; replacement aircraft and aircrew embarked (iincluding first 5 RNVR pilots to be deployed to Korean war zone)
08.08.52 Sailed for sixth patrol
09.08.52 North Korean MiG-15 jet shot down by Lt Carmichael of 802 NAS and his Flight (first jet to be shot down by FAA—or indeed any

British fighter; 2 others damaged for not even a scratch on Sea Furies)

16.08.52 Flying curtailed by passage of Hurricane 'Karen'

19.08.52 Arrived in Kure

26.08.52 Sailed for west coast of Korea

28.08.52 Five bridges destroyed by bombing

29.08.52 Three more bridges destroyed

05.09.52 Arrived in Sasebo

13.09.52 Sailed for war zone (on this typical patrol, ship flew 749 sorties in 9 days, an average of 83 per day)

16.09.52 Last of rail bridges between Pyongyang and Chinnampo destroyed

25.09.52 Arrived in Kure to exchange aircraft with *Unicorn*

03.10.52 Sailed for ninth war patrol off west coast of Korea (targets of trucks and transport remained priority)

13.10.52 Visited by First Sea Lord, Admiral Sir Roderick McGrigor

14.10.52 Arrived in Sasebo

23.10.52 Sailed for operations off Korea

28.10.52 Sea Furies attacked sluice gates at Yonan and more bridges with 1,000lb bombs

30.10.52 Last day of operations off Korea (after last land-on, short service held on flight deck and wreaths dropped overboard for 8 aircrew who had died during Korean operations); 802 and 825 NAS subsequently awarded Boyd Trophy for 1952 for operations in Korean war zone

04.11.52 Rendezvoused with *Glory* for Exercise 'Tai-Pan' (practising air defence of Hong Kong); on completion, *Glory* replaced *Ocean* off Korea

17.05.53 Arrived in Sasebo from Hong Kong with 807 (Sea Fury) and 810 (Firefly) NAS embarked; aircraft and stores embarked from *Glory*, and *Ocean* relieved her as Commonwealth carrier in war zone

19.05.53 Sailed to provide CAS for Commonwealth Division and to interdict enemy communications and troop movements

25.05.53 Spotted for bombardment by USS *New Jersey*

29.05.53 Targets attacked in Haeju area

31.05.53 Arrived in Sasebo

01.06.53 14 Sea Furies used RATOG to take off from *Ocean* whilst in harbour (not done before);

HMS *Ocean* awaiting disposal in the River Tamar in 1961, stripped of most of her equipment. (Author)

	aircraft took part in fly-past to celebrate Coronation of HM Queen Elizabeth II but had not been able to disembark to Iwakuni whilst on passage from Korea due to fog and low cloud
02.06.53	Coronation Day: ships dressed overall and parade held in ship's hangar
08.06.53	Sailed from Sasebo; most sorties CAS as front line stabilised prior to armistice
19.06.53	Arrived in Kure for replenishment
25.06.53	Sailed for next patrol (fog prevented flying at first but more CAS sorties soon became possible)
07.07.53	Arrived in Sasebo
14.07.53	Sailed for war zone
16.07.53	3 Fireflies disembarked to K6 airfield at Pyongtaek to act as night fighters against slow-flying North Korean nuisance raiders (idea proved very successful)
27.07.53	Armistice signed at Panmunjon; ship carried out another 4 patrols off west coast of Korea in case fighting should break out but she was not needed
31.10.53	Sailed for Hong Kong flying paying-off pennant
00.11.53	Relieved as Far East carrier by HMAS *Sydney* in Hong Kong and sailed for UK after foreign service of 2½ years.
00.12.53	Refit in Devonport Dockyard
19.08.54	Relieved *Indefatigable* in HFTS
00.00.55	Used twice to ferry troops and equipment to Cyprus
00.08.56	Carried 16th Parachute Brigade to Cyprus in company with *Theseus* and *Cumberland* as part of build-up of forces during Suez emergency
00.09.56	Taken in hand for rapid conversion to operate helicopters
00.10.56	Carried out commando assault exercises in English Channel with 845 NAS (Whirlwind) embarked in company with *Theseus* (which had been similarly converted)
31.10.56	Arrived in Malta with Joint Service Experimental Helicopter Unit embarked (845 NAS had gone to *Theseus*)
06.11.56	45 RM Cdo landed by helicopter from *Ocean* and *Theseus* (first 'vertical envelopment' in history, with 415 men and 23 tons of stores going ashore in 1½ hours to Port Said
14.12.56	Arrived in Devonport; converted back for training role
17.01.57	Beginning of busy year of training, with visits to Weymouth, Milford Haven, Rothesay, Glasgow, Rosyth and Antwerp
24.03.57	In Plymouth
16.05.57	Sailed for Rosyth, Invergordon, Reykjavik, Hamburg, Penzance and back to Plymouth again
30.08.57	Sailed for Helsinki and Oslo before passing through Plymouth on 5 October en route for Gibraltar and Bilbao
00.11.57	Visited Rosyth, Liverpool and Portsmouth
05.12.57	Arrived in Plymouth; paid off and de-stored into extended reserve
00.03.58	Placed on disposal list
00.05.58	Stripped of useful fittings and equipment
06.05.62	Towed to Faslane by British Iron and Steel Corp. for scrapping (completed by 00.08.62)

Ocean (1997) *Commando Carrier*

Laid down: June 1994
Launched: 11 October 1995
Completion: Due 1997

Builder: Vickers Shipbuilding & Engineering, Barrow-in-Fiurness; hull subcontracted to Kvaerner Govan
Machinery: 2-shaft diesels
Displacement: 20,000 tons deep load
Dimensions: 660ft overall x 107ft max beam x 21ft 4in max draught
Gun armament: CIWS (probably Goalkeeper)
Fuel: Similar to *Invincible* class
Endurance: Greater than *Invincible* class
Complement: 1,200 (inc.squadrons and Commando)
Protection: None
Flight deck: 650ft x 80ft steel
Arrester wires: None
Hangar: Approx. 400ft x 60ft x 20ft
Catapults: None
Lifts: 2 (plus vehicle ramp)
Aircraft: 12 Commando helicopters (Sea Harriers can also be operated)
Aircraft fuel: Similar to *Invincible* class

HMS *Ocean* in the River Clyde shortly after her launch. Many of the defects in the design of the *Invincible* have been set right in this ship, with the island set as far as possible to starboard and the flight deck taken right forward over the cable deck (although why it should be pointed like the pre-war *Eagle* rather than rectangular to allow more parking is difficult to imagine). (MoD Navy).

Air weapons: 7.62mm GPMG ammunition

Notes: Based on *Invincible* design but with diesel propulsion machinery to give better range and endurance. As well as the hangar, there is to be a vehicle deck aft, accessible via a ramp to the flight deck. Although designed to operate commando helicopters, *Ocean* will be capable of operating Sea Harriers (and, indeed, Harrier GR.7s). She is a most important ship and her arrival will fill the gap left when *Hermes* was sold.

Summary of service

11.05.93	Order placed with VSEL
30.05.93	First steel cut
00.06.94	Fabrication commenced
11.10.95	Launched (it is intended that propulsion machinery will be installed and ship will be fitted out on Clydeside)
00.00.96	Move to VSEL at Barrow-in-Furness for installation of naval systems and completion
00.00.97	Planned completion

Patroller (D07) Ruler *Class Ferry Carrier*

Laid down: 27 November 1942
Launched: 6 May 1943
Completed: 25 October 1943

Builder: Seattle-Tacoma Shipbuilding Corp., Seattle; machinery by Allis-Chalmers
Machinery: 1-shaft Allis-Chalmers geared turbine; 2 Foster Wheeler boilers; 8,500shp = 18 knots
Displacement: 11,400 tons standard; 15,390 tons deep load
Dimensions: 492ft overall x 108ft 6in max beam x 25ft 5in max draught
Gun armament: 2 single 5in US Mk 12 (2); 8 twin 40mm Bofors (16); 14 twin 20m Oerlikon (28); 7 single 20mm Oerlikon (7)
Fuel: 3,160 tons FFO
Endurance: 27,500 miles @ 11 knots
Complement: 646
Protection: Splinter protection for bomb room
Flight deck: 450ft x 80ft wood-covered steel
Arrester wires: 9 x 19,800lb @ 55 knots; 3 barriers
Hangar: 260ft x 62ft x 18ft
Catapults: 1 x H4C; 16,000lb @ 74 knots (tail-down method only)
Lifts: *Fwd* 42ft long x 34ft wide; *aft* 34ft long x 42ft wide; both 14,000lb
Aircraft: Up to 90 could be ferried; up to 30 could be operated
Aircraft fuel: 36,000 gallons AVGAS
Air weapons: None

Notes: Laid down as aircraft carrier of the USN *Prince William* class. Built as USS *Keweenam* (CVE-44) but transferred to RN on completion, under Lend/Lease arrangements, along with 23 other ships of the class. The design was based on the US mercantile C3 hull and closely resembled the preceding *Attacker* class.

Summary of service

22.10.43	Transferred and commissioned into RN in Tacoma and renamed *Patroller*
22.11.43	Sailed for San Francisco
03.12.43	Allocated to EF as ferry carrier; sailed for South-West Pacific
22.12.43	Arrived in Melbourne
02.01.44	In Fremantle
22.01.44	In Cochin
23.01.44	In Colombo

HMS *Patroller* in her late-war Admiralty 'Standard' paint scheme. (FAA Museum)

02.02.44 In Fremantle
07.02.44 In Brisbane
14.02.44 In Wellington
07.03.44 In San Francisco
15.03.44 Allocated to US Army as ferry carrier
06.04.44 Sailed for Esquimalt
23.04.44 Arrived in Esquimalt
02.05.44 Reverted to RN control; moved to Vancouver to be fitted out for operational duties
25.07.44 Arrived in San Francisco
10.08.44 Arrived in Norfolk, Va
22.08.44 Allocated to WAC as ferry carrier; sailed for New York
27.08.44 Sailed for Liverpool
07.09.44 Arrived in Liverpool
12.09.44 Sailed for Norfolk, Va
23.09.44 Arrived in Norfolk, Va
09.10.44 Arrived in Clyde for repairs
10.11.44 Sailed for Norfolk, Va
12.12.44 Arrived in Clyde for further repair work
21.12.44 1843 (Corsair) NAS carried out DLT
28.01.45 Loaned to USN for duty as ferry carrier in Pacific
25.02.45 Arrived in San Diego
04.03.45 Sailed for ferry operations with US Pacific Fleet
11.04.45 Returned to San Diego
17.04.45 Sailed for Norfolk, Va
01.05.45 In Norfolk, Va
04.05.45 1852 NAS (Corsair) embarked for Atlantic passage to UK
05.05.45 Sailed for Clyde
21.05.45 Arrived in Clyde
26.05.45 Arrived in Liverpool for refit; allocated to Rosyth Command
15.08.45 Moved to Clyde yard for modifications to equip ship for trooping duties
13.11.45 Arrived in Plymouth
19.11.45 Sailed for Colombo
15.12.45 In Colombo
21.12.45 Sailed for Plymouth
08.01.46 Arrived in Plymouth
29.01.46 Sailed for Colombo
17.02.46 In Colombo
19.02.46 Sailed for Fremantle
28.02.46 Arrived in Fremantle
29.02.46 Sailed for UK
15.05.46 Left UK for round trooping trip to Sydney and return
07.08.46 Left UK for round trooping trip to Hong Kong and return
27.11.46 Left UK for round trooping trip to Bermuda and return
13.12.46 Returned to USN at Norfolk, Va; sold by USN as mercantile *Almkerk*
00.00.68 Renamed *Pacific Alliance*
00.02.74 Broken up in Taiwan

Perseus (R51) *Maintenance Carrier*

Laid down: 1 June 1942
Launched: 26 March 1943
Completed: 10 October 1945

Builder: Vickers-Armstrong, Newcastle-upon-Tyne; machinery by Vickers-Armstrong, Barrow-in-Furness
Machinery: 2-shaft Parsons single-reduction geared turbines; 4 Admiralty 3-drum boilers; 40,000shp = 24 knots
Displacement: 12,265 tons standard; 16,500 tons deep load
Dimensions: 694ft 6in overall x 80ft 4in max beam x 23ft max draught
Gun armament: 6 quadruple 2pdr pompom (24); 19 single 40mm Bofors (19)
Fuel: 3,196 tons FFO
Endurance: 8,500 miles @ 11 knots
Complement: 1,076
Protection: None
Flight deck: Space for helicopter operations
Arrester wires: None
Hangar: 275ft (plus 57ft extension aft of aft lift) x 52ft x 17ft 6in
Catapults: Fitted with original prototype BXS1 steam catapult in 1949 for trials; 40,000lb @ 80 knots
Lifts: *Fwd* 45ft long x 34ft wide; *aft* 45ft long x 34ft wide; both 15,000lb
Aircraft: None operated; up to 60 could be ferried
Aircraft fuel: 98,600 gallons AVGAS
Air weapons: None carried

Notes: Laid down as the *Colossus* class carrier *Edgar*. She was altered into an aircraft maintenance ship and renamed following the recommendation of the Future Building Committee in 1942 that more afloat support for naval aircraft was required with a planned massive increase in the number of carriers; *Mars* was similarly converted and renamed *Pioneer*. Unlike *Unicorn*, they were unable to operate aircraft because deckhouses and cranes were built on to the former flight deck. There was no need for the armament to be fitted clear of the deck and so there were no sponsons, the weapons being mounted on the upper deck. The deckhouse aft carried spare engines, an oxygen producing plant and an oxygen cylinder fitting room. Two 48ft aircraft lighters were stored on the upper deck amidships to move aircraft to other ships or the shore and a second 15-ton crane was mounted on the port side forward. The deckhouse to port of the island contained recreation facilities, including a cinema. Much of the former hangar was used as a

HMS *Perseus* leaving Malta in an early post-war paint scheme with a deck load that includes Seafires, Fireflies, Oxfords, Martinets, vehicles and storage crates. (FAA Museum)

workshop and the original lifts were retained so that aircraft could be taken to the upper deck for engine runs. The BXS1 prototype steam catapult was installed in a structure built on to the upper deck which covered the forward lift. The ship's pennant number changed to A197 when she became a ferry carrier.

Summary of service

00.10.45	Sailed to join BPF as aircraft maintenance ship
00.05.46	Returned to Portsmouth and paid off into reserve
00.00.49	Refitted with prototype steam catapult for trials, which were conducted amid great secrecy off Rosyth and at Belfast
00.00.51	After successful trials with RN aircraft, ship demonstrated steam catapult to USN late 1951 (during all trials, more than 1,000 dead loads and 127 piloted aircraft—RN and USN, both piston-engine and jet—were catapulted)
00.00.52	Refit (during which steam catapult and much workshop equipment, together with several deckhouses removed)
00.06.52	Redesignated as ferry carrier
00.00.53	Ferried Avenger AS.4 aircraft from USA
00.06.53	Present at HM Queen Elizabeth II's Coronation Review of the Fleet at Spithead (upper deck fitted out with seating galleries for VIPs and Press)
21.04.54	Embarked 845 NAS (Whirlwind) for passage from Portsmouth to RNAS Hal Far in Malta for proving trials of AS helicopter concept
Late 54	Ferried stores to Korea; paid off into reserve on return
00.00.55	Towed to Belfast for conversion to submarine depot ship
00.00.57	Work suspended and ship placed on disposal list
06.05.58	Broken up at Port Glasgow by Smith & Houston

HMS *Pioneer* on completion in 1945. Note the massive sheerlegs forward, intended for lifting aircraft on to the deck. (Author)

Pioneer (R76) *Maintenance Carrier*

Laid down: 2 December 1942
Launched: 20 May 1943
Completed: 8 February 1945

Builder: Vickers-Armstrong, Barrow-in-Furness
Machinery: 2-shaft Parsons single-reduction geared turbines; 4 Admiralty 3-drum boilers; 40,000shp = 24.5 knots
Displacement: 12,265 tons standard; 16,500 tons deep load
Dimensions: 695ft overall x 80ft 4in max beam x 23ft max draught
Gun armament: 6 quadruple 2pdr pompom (24); 19 single 40mm Bofors (19)
Fuel: 3,196 tons FFO
Endurance: 8,500 miles @ 11 knots
Complement: 1,076
Protection: None
Flight deck: Space for parking and engine runs on upper deck
Arrester wires: None
Hangar: 275ft (plus 57ft extension aft of aft lift) x 52ft x 17ft 6in
Catapults: None
Lifts: *Fwd* 45ft long x 34ft wide; *aft* 45ft long x 34ft wide; both 15,000lb
Aircraft: Up to 60 could be ferried
Aircraft fuel: 98,600 gallons AVGAS
Air weapons: None carried

Notes: Laid down as a unit of the *Colossus* class, originally to be named *Mars*. The ship was modified, whilst building, into a maintenance carrier identical to *Perseus* following the recommendation of the Future Building Committee in 1942. Her pennant number was changed to A198 when she was redesignated as a ferry carrier.

Summary of service

08.02.45 Commissioned in Barrow; allocated to BPF and sailed for Far East via Suez
00.04.45 Arrived in Sydney flying broad pennant of Commodore Air Train (COMAT); responsible for air logistic support of BPF
21.06.45 Arrived in Admiralty Islands and set up RN forward aircraft pool on island of Pityilu (2,300 miles north of Australia); whilst there, 24 aircraft repaired in 8 weeks and work also included de-preservation of aircraft shipped from Australia
00.07.45 Air train, including *Pioneer*, handled 348 aircraft for supply to 1 ACS
00.00.46 Returned to UK and paid off into reserve
00.06.53 Redesignated as ferry carrier
00.09.54 Sold to T. W. Ward; towed to Inverkeithing to be broken up

Premier (D23) Ruler *Class Escort Carrier*

Laid down: 31 October 1942
Launched: 22 March 1943
Completed: 3 November 1943

Builder: Seattle-Tacoma Shipbuilding Corp., Seattle
Machinery: 1-shaft Allis-Chalmers geared turbine; 2 Foster Wheeler boilers; 8,500shp = 18 knots
Displacement: 11,400 tons standard; 15,390 tons deep load
Dimensions: 492ft overall x 108ft 6in max beam x 25ft 5in max draught
Gun armament: 2 single 5in US Mk 12 (2); 8 twin 40mm Bofors (16); 14 twin 20m Oerlikon (28); 7 single 20mm Oerlikon (7)
Fuel: 3,160 tons FFO
Endurance: 27,500 miles @ 11 knots
Complement: 646
Protection: Splinter protection for bomb room
Flight deck: 450ft x 80ft wood-covered steel
Arrester wires: 9 x 19,800lb @ 55 knots; 3 barriers
Hangar: 260ft x 62ft x 18ft
Catapults: 1 x H4C; 16,000lb @ 74 knots (tail-down method only)
Lifts: *Fwd* 42ft long x 34ft wide; *aft* 34ft long x 42ft wide; both 14,000lb
Aircraft: Up to 30 could be operated; up to 90 could be ferried
Aircraft fuel: 36,000 gallons AVGAS

Air weapons: 22.4in torpedoes; 500lb SAP bombs; 500lb GP bombs; 250lb GP bombs; Mk 11 depth charges; .5in gun ammunition; flares and pyrotechnics

Notes: Laid down as USS *Estero* (CVE-42) of the USN *Prince William* class, all but the name-ship of which were transferred to the RN on completion under Lend/Lease arrangements. Built as a warship but based on the US mercantile C3 hull design.

Summary of service

03.11.43	Commissioned in Tacoma
11.11.43	Taken in hand in Vancouver for conversion to RN standards
09.01.44	Sailed for delivery voyage
17.02.44	Transited Panama Canal
25.02.44	Arrived in Norfolk, Va
06.03.44	Sailed for UK
20.03.44	Arrived in Liverpool
29.03.44	Allocated to WAC as ferry carrier; sailed for Norfolk, Va
11.04.44	Arrived in Norfolk, Va; returned to Liverpool when loaded with aircraft
26.04.44	In Liverpool
02.05.44	In Clyde; sailed for Norfolk, Va
12.05.44	Arrived in Norfolk, Va, loaded with aircraft
31.05.44	Arrived in Liverpool for repairs
12.07.44	Allocated to WAC as operational carrier
05.09.44	Repairs completed in Liverpool
11.09.44	Sailed for flying work-up
13.09.44	Embarked 856 NAS (Avenger)
13.10.44	Flying work-up complete; to Clyde for defect rectification
10.11.44	Allocated to HF; arrived in Scapa Flow
06.12.44	Sailed with 856 (Avenger) and detachment of 846 (Avenger) NAS embarked for strike on Haugsund
09.12.44	Returned to Scapa Flow
12.12.44	Sailed with same air group for operations off Norwegian coast
16.12.44	Returned to Scapa Flow
23.12.44	Clyde for repairs
06.01.45	Returned to Scapa Flow
11.11.45	Sailed to cover cruiser bombardment of Egersund; Wildcats added to Avengers of 856 NAS
14.01.45	Arrived in Scapa Flow
22.01.45	Sailed for strike on Vaagsø
29.01.45	Returned to Scapa Flow
11.02.45	Sailed for minelaying operations off Stavanger with 856 (Avenger) and 881 (Wildcat) NAS embarked
14.02.45	Returned to Scapa Flow
21.02.45	Sailed for minelaying operations in Norwegian Leads
23.02.45	Returned to Scapa Flow
18.03.45	Sailed for shipping strikes off Norway

HMS *Premier* alongside in King George V Dock in Glasgow. (FAA Museum)

22.03.45 To Clyde for repairs
01.04.45 In Scapa Flow
17.04.45 Sailed with covering forces for JW.66 to North Russia (Operation 'Roundel')
25.04.45 Arrived in Kola
29.04.45 Sailed with RA.66 to UK
05.05.45 In Scapa Flow
21.05.45 Allocated to Rosyth Command as DLT carrier; sailed to Clyde for repairs
24.07.45 Clyde area for DLT
27.09.45 To Clyde for refit
00.11.45 Rosyth de-storing
12.04.46 Returned to USN at Norfolk, Va
00.00.47 Sold by USN as mercantile *Rhodesia Star*
00.00.67 Renamed *Hong Kong Knight*
10.02.74 Arrived in Taiwan for breaking up

Pretoria Castle (F61) *Trials/Training Carrier*

Laid down: ?
Launched: 12 October 1938 (as passenger liner)
Completed: 9 April 1943

Builder: Harland & Wolff, Belfast; converted to carrier by Swan Hunter & Wigham Richardson, Wallsend-on-Tyne
Machinery: 2-shaft Burmeister & Wain diesels; 16,000shp = 18 knots
Displacement: 19,650 tons standard; 23,450 tons deep load
Dimensions: 592ft overall x 76ft 4in max beam x 29ft 10in max draught
Gun armament: 2 twin 4in QF Mk XVI HA (4); 10 twin 20mm Oerlikon (20); 2 quadruple pompom (8)
Fuel: 2,430 tons FFO
Endurance: 16,000 miles @ 16 knots
Complement: 580
Protection: 1in plating over bomb room, magazines and steering gear
Flight deck: 550ft x 76ft steel
Arrester wires: 6 x 15,000lb @ 60 knots; 2 barriers
Hangar: 354ft x 46ft x 17ft
Catapults: 1 x CII; 14,000lb @ 66 knots
Lifts: *Fwd* 45ft long x 39ft wide (prototype of lift used in light fleet carriers)
Aircraft: 21
Aircraft fuel: 74,000 gallons

HMS *Pretoria Castle* on completion of her conversion in August 1943. (Author)

Air weapons: 18in torpedoes; 500lb MC bombs; 250lb GP bombs; 3in RP; Mk 11 depth charges; 20mm cannon ammunition; .303in gun ammunition; flares and pyrotechnics

Notes: Completed pre-war as Union Castle Line passenger liner, requisitioned by the Admiralty on outbreak of war for use as an armed merchant cruiser and subsequently converted to a carrier by Swan Hunter. Her superstructure was stripped down to 'C' deck, which was strengthened before a hangar and flight deck were built on to it. She needed 2,500 tons of ballast to compensate for the extra topweight before completion as a carrier. The catapult was powered by cordite. As with some other escort carriers, many of the technical members of the ship's company were Merchant Navy personnel serving under T124X articles.

Summary of service

28.11.39 Commissioned in Belfast as armed merchant cruiser
21.12.39 Sailed for South Atlantic Station for convoy escort duty based on Freetown with periodic refits in Belfast
30.06.42 Arrived in Tyne for conversion to carrier
16.07.42 Purchased outright by Admiralty
29.07.43 Commissioned on Tyne
09.08.43 Completed conversion
12.08.43 Arrived in Rosyth for trials
16.08.43 Joined WAC as a trials carrier based on Clyde
27.10.43 Used operationally with 825 NAS (Swordfish/Sea Hurricane) embarked to cover DS.46 to Iceland
29.10.43 Arrived in Iceland
30.10.43 Sailed to cover SD.46 to Clyde
29.11.43 Collided with *Ravager* in Clyde
14.02.44 Repairs completed
29.04.44 In Clyde shipyard hands for alterations and additions
14.07.44 Collided with *Edith* in Clyde, necessitating repairs in Rosyth
01.10.44 Returned to Clyde for trial work
19.12.44 Machinery refits and repairs at first in Belfast, then in Clyde
03.04.45 Tail-down catapult launch trials
11.08.45 Conducted landing trials with hooked Meteor aircraft
11.09.45 Allocated to Portsmouth Command; commenced refit in Portsmouth
26.01.46 Sold to Union Castle Line
04.02.46 De-stored in Portsmouth
21.03.46 Paid off and handed over at Belfast; reconverted to merchant use, renamed *Warwick Castle*
00.09.62 Broken up in Spain

Puncher (D79) Attacker *Class Escort Carrier*

Laid down: 21 May 1943
Launched: 8 November 1943
Completed: 5 February 1944

Builder: Seattle-Tacoma Shipbuilding Corp., Seattle; machinery by Allis-Chalmers
Machinery: 1-shaft Allis-Chalmers geared turbine; 2 Foster Wheeler boilers; 8,500shp = 18.5 knots
Displacement: 11,400 tons standard; 15,390 tons deep load
Dimensions: 492ft x 108ft 6in max beam x 25ft 5in max draught
Gun armament: 2 single 4in US Mk 9 (2); 8 twin 40mm Bofors (16); 14 twin 20mm Oerlikon (28); 7 single 20mm Oerlikon (7)
Fuel: 3,160 tons FFO
Endurance: 27,300 miles @ 11 knots
Complement: 646

Protection: Splinter protection for bomb room
Flight deck: 450ft x 80ft wood-covered steel
Arrester wires: 9 x 19,800lb @ 55 knots; 3 barriers
Hangar: 260ft x 62ft x 18ft
Catapults: 1 x H4C hydraulic; 6,000lb @ 74 knots (tail-down method only)
Lifts: *Fwd* 42ft long x 34ft wide; *aft* 34ft long x 42ft wide; both 14,000lb
Aircraft: Up to 30 could be operated; up to 90 could be ferried
Aircraft fuel: 36,000 gallons AVGAS
Air weapons: 18in torpedoes; 500lb SAP bombs; 250lb GP bombs; Mk 11 depth charges; aircraft mines; 20mm gun ammunition; .5in gun ammunition; flares and pyrotechnics

Notes: Laid down as an aircraft carrier but hull based on the US C3 mercantile design. Built as USS *Willapa*

HMS *Puncher* in April 1945 with a Wildcat on deck. (Author)

(CVE-53) of the *Prince William* class, 23 units of which were transferred to the RN on completion. Manned by the RCN, except for the air department, to give them experience of carrier operations prior to the purchase of a light fleet carrier. The terms of the Lend/Lease agreement precluded her becoming a Canadian warship.

Summary of service

05.02.44 Transferred to RN and commissioned in Tacoma
15.03.44 Arrived in Vancouver for alterations to RN standards
09.06.44 Sailed for New York
08.07.44 Arrived in New York
11.07.44 In Norfolk, Va, for defect rectification
22.07.44 Returned to New York; allocated to WAC as ferry carrier; sailed for Casablanca in UGF.12 with cargo of US aircraft
08.08.44 Arrived in Casablanca
12.08.44 Sailed with GUF.13 for Norfolk, Va
27.08.44 Arrived in Norfolk, Va
30.08.44 Embarked 1845 NAS (Corsair) for work-up
08.09.44 Sailed to join CU.38 for passage to UK
15.09.44 Arrived in Clyde
18.09.44 Disembarked 1845 NAS to RNAS Eglinton
19.09.44 Sailed for New York
30.09.44 Arrived in New York
06.10.44 Sailed with CU.42 for Liverpool
21.10.44 Repairs in Clyde
12.11.44 Torpedo-bomber trials with 821 NAS (Barracuda) in Clyde area
27.11.44 Main gearing failure; refitted in Clyde with equipment taken from *Nabob*
01.02.45 Allocated to HF; arrived in Scapa Flow; air group comprised 881 (Wildcat) and 821 (Barracuda) NAS
11.02.45 Sailed for strike operations off Norway
13.02.45 Returned to Scapa Flow
21.02.45 Sailed for strike operations off Norway
23.02.45 Returned to Scapa Flow
24.02.45 Dragged anchor and ran aground
24.03.45 Sailed for strike on Trondheim
29.03.45 Returned to Scapa Flow
06.04.45 Sailed for Norwegian coastal operations (cancelled); 825 Flight (Wildcat) added to normal air group
21.04.45 Clyde shipyard for defect rectification
13.05.45 Allocated to Rosyth Command; operated in Belfast area for DLT with 1790 (Firefly) and 1791 (Firefly NF) NAS
25.06.45 Sailed for Halifax on trooping duties
02.07.45 In Halifax
16.07.45 Arrived in Norfolk, Va, for defect rectification
30.07.45 Sailed for New York
03.08.45 Sailed from New York for Clyde
11.08.45 Arrived in Clyde
29.08.45 Sailed for Halifax
04.09.45 Arrived in Halifax
18.09.45 Sailed for Clyde via New York
25.09.45 Arrived in Clyde
08.10.45 Sailed for Halifax
14.10.45 Arrived in Halifax
26.10.45 Sailed for Belfast via New York
02.11.45 In Belfast; sailed for Clyde
11.11.45 Sailed from Clyde for New York
17.11.45 Sailed from New York for Halifax
18.11.45 Arrived in Halifax
24.11.45 Sailed for New York
26.11.45 In New York
28.11.45 Sailed for Clyde
09.12.45 Arrived in Clyde
14.12.45 Sailed for Halifax
23.12.45 Arrived in Halifax
06.01.46 Sailed for Norfolk, Va
16.01.46 Returned to USN at Norfolk, Va, and sold for mercantile service
00.00.54 Renamed *Bardic*
00.00.59 Renamed *Ben Nevis*
11.06.73 Broken up in Taiwan

Pursuer (D73) Attacker *Class Escort Carrier*

Laid down: 31 July 1941
Launched: 18 July 1942
Completed: 14 June 1943

Builder: Ingalls Shipbuilding Corp, Pascagoula
Machinery: 1-shaft Westinghouse geared turbine; 2 Foster Wheeler boilers; 8,500shp = 18.5 knots
Displacement: 10,200 tons standard; 14,170 tons deep load
Dimensions: 492ft x 102ft max beam x 24ft 8in max draught
Gun armament: 2 single 4in US Mk 9 (2); 4 twin

HMS *Pursuer* in July 1945 after her refit in Durban. Note the improvements made to the bridge. (FAA Museum)

40mm Bofors (8); 6 twin 20mm Oerlikon (12); 10 single 20mm Oerlikon (10)
Fuel: 3,160 tons FFO
Endurance: 27,300 miles @ 11 knots
Complement: 646
Protection: Splinter protection for bomb room
Flight deck: 442ft x 102ft wood-covered steel
Arrester wires: 9 x 19,800lb @ 55 knots; 3 barriers
Hangar: 260ft x 62ft x 18ft
Catapults: 1 x H2; 7,000lb @ 61 knots (tail-down method only)
Lifts: *Fwd* 42ft long x 34ft wide; *aft* 34ft long x 42ft wide; both 14,000lb
Aircraft: Up to 24 could be operated; up to 90 could be ferried
Aircraft fuel: 44,000 gallons AVGAS
Air weapons: 18in torpedoes; 500lb SAP bombs; 250lb GP bombs; Mk 11 depth charges; .5in gun ammunition; flares and pyrotechnics

Notes: Laid down as the mercantile *Mormacland*. Acquired before launch by USN for conversion to an escort carrier. Completed as USS *St George* (CVE-17) and transferred to the RN under Lend/Lease arrangements.

Summary of service

14.06.43 Transferred to RN and commissioned in Pascagoula
28.06.43 Arrived in Norfolk, Va, for modifications
30.07.43 Sailed with HX.250 for passage to UK
11.08.43 Arrived in Liverpool; allocated to WAC but taken in hand for modification to assault carrier
16.11.43 Sailed for Clyde
25.11.43 Sailed for Belfast for further defect rectification
19.12.43 Sailed for work-up in Irish Sea with 881 and 896 NAS (Wildcat) embarked
05.02.44 Provided cover for OS.67 and KMS.41
06.03.44 Returned to Clyde
17.03.44 Loaned to HF; arrived in Scapa Flow with same air group
30.03.44 Sailed for operations off Norwegian coast
03.04.44 Operation 'Tungsten' (successful strike on German battleship *Tirpitz* in Kaafjord in company with *Victorious*, *Furious*, *Emperor*, *Searcher* and *Fencer*)
06.04.44 Returned to Scapa Flow
21.04.44 Sailed for air strike on Bodø
28.04.44 Returned to Scapa Flow after suffering storm damage
01.05.44 Arrived in Liverpool for repairs
01.06.44 Sailed with same air group as part of forces securing English Channel in support of Operation 'Neptune' (D-Day landings)
19.06.44 Operations in Irish Sea, on completion of which 896 NAS disembarked to disband
15.07.44 Allocated to MF
25.07.44 Sailed from Clyde for Malta with 881 NAS (Wildcat) embarked
12.08.44 Sailed from Malta for Operation 'Dragoon' (invasion of southern France) as part of Task Group 88.1 under Rear-Admiral Troubridge (who flew his flag in cruiser *Royalist*); other carriers in group were *Attacker*, *Khedive*, *Emperor* and *Searcher*
02.09.44 Arrived in Alexandria with *Attacker*, *Hunter*, *Stalker*, *Khedive*, *Emperor* and *Searcher* to prepare for operations in Aegean, striking at German garrisons and shipping; 881 NAS part of 7 Naval Fighter Wing with 800 NAS (Hellcat) in *Emperor* and 882 NAS (Wildcat) in *Searcher*
09.09.44 Operation 'Outing' (strike in Aegean)
01.10.44 Arrived in Alexandria
08.10.44 Arrived in Gibraltar
12.10.44 Arrived in Clyde
28.10.44 Returned to HF in Scapa Flow with 881 NAS (Wildcat) embarked
12.11.44 Sailed for strike on Narvik
16.11.44 Returned to Scapa Flow
29.11.44 Arrived in Clyde for defect repairs
12.12.44 Sailed with UC.48B
24.12.44 Repairs in Norfolk, Va
04.02.45 Embarked 1831 NAS (Corsair) for passage and sailed for Belfast

15.02.45 Arrived in Belfast
17.02.45 Arrived in Clyde for repairs
31.03.45 Allocated to 21 ACS, EIF, and sailed with KMF.42 to Gibraltar; 898 NAS (Hellcat) embarked
09.04.45 Sailed from Gibraltar for East Indies via Freetown and Cape Town
03.05.45 Arrived in Durban for refit
07.07.45 Sailed for Colombo
25.07.45 In Colombo
01.08.45 In Trincomalee
04.09.45 Sailed for re-occupation of Port Swettenham
06.10.45 Returned to Trincomalee and employed on trooping duties
20.11.45 Sailed from Colombo for UK
12.12.45 Arrived in Clyde; allocated to Rosyth Command and commenced de-storing
12.01.46 Sailed for Portsmouth
16.01.46 Sailed from Portsmouth for Norfolk, Va
12.02.46 Returned to USN at Norfolk, Va
14.05.46 Sold by USN for scrap

HMS *Queen*. (FAA Museum)

Queen (D19) Ruler *Class Escort Carrier*

Laid down: 12 March 1943
Launched: 2 August 1943
Completed: 7 December 1943

Builder: Seattle-Tacoma Shipbuilding Corp., Seattle
Machinery: 1-shaft Allis-Chalmers geared turbine; 2 Foster Wheeler boilers; 8,500shp = 18 knots
Displacement: 11,400 tons standard; 15,390 tons deep load
Dimensions: 492ft overall x 108ft 6in max beam x 25ft 5in max draught
Gun armament: 2 single 5in US Mk 12 (2); 8 twin 40mm Bofors (16); 14 twin 20m Oerlikon (28); 7 single 20mm Oerlikon (7)
Fuel: 3,290 tons FFO
Endurance: 27,500 miles @ 11 knots
Complement: 646
Protection: Splinter protection for bomb room
Flight deck: 450ft x 80ft wood-covered steel
Arrester wires: 9 x 19,800lb @ 55 knots; 3 barriers
Hangar: 260ft x 62ft x 18ft
Catapults: 1 x H4C; 16,000lb @ 74 knots (tail-down method only)
Lifts: *Fwd* 42ft long x 34ft wide; *aft* 34ft long x 42ft wide; both 14,000lb
Aircraft: Up to 30 could be operated; up to 90 could be ferried
Aircraft fuel: 36,000 gallons AVGAS
Air weapons: 22.4in torpedoes; Mk XXIV mines (homing torpedoes); 500lb SAP bombs; Mk 11 depth charges; .5in gun ammunition; flares and pyrotechnics

Notes: Laid down as an aircraft carrier by the USN but based on the mercantile C3 hull design. Built as USS *St Andrews* (CVE-49) of the *Prince William* class, 23 units of which were transferred to the RN under Lend/Lease arrangements on completion.

Summary of service
07.12.43 Transferred to RN and commissioned in Tacoma
17.12.43 Arrived in Vancouver for modifications to RN standards
26.02.44 Grounded during sea trials; returned to Vancouver for repairs
22.03.44 Sailed for Norfolk, Va
15.04.44 Passed through Panama Canal
24.04.44 Arrived in Norfolk, Va
06.05.44 Sailed for New York with 855 NAS (Avenger) embarked for passage to UK
08.05.44 Arrived in New York; sailed for Clyde
23.05.44 Arrived in Clyde; allocated to WAC as ferry carrier
28.05.44 Sailed for New York
09.06.44 Arrived in New York
13.06.44 Sailed with cargo of aircraft
27.06.44 In Casablanca
02.07.44 Sailed for Freetown
12.07.44 Arrived in Freetown
17.07.44 Sailed for Gibraltar
24.07.44 Arrived in Gibraltar
04.08.44 Sailed with MKF.33 for Clyde
10.08.44 Arrived in Clyde for defect rectification
31.08.44 Arrived in Dundee for refit
23.12.44 Sailed for Rosyth
27.12.44 Arrived in Rosyth
23.01.45 Allocated to HF; worked up in Clyde area with 853 NAS (Avenger/ Wildcat) embarked
02.03.45 Arrived in Scapa Flow

19.03.45 Sailed with cover for JW.66
21.03.45 Returned to Scapa Flow
23.03.45 Sailed for shipping strikes off Norway
29.03.45 Returned to Scapa Flow
03.04.45 Sailed
12.04.45 Returned to Scapa Flow
19.04.45 Sailed for minelaying operations in Norwegian Leads
29.04.45 Returned to Scapa Flow
30.04.45 Sailed for operations off Norwegian coast
04.05.45 Avenger aircraft sank *U711*
10.05.45 Returned to Scapa Flow
14.05.45 Sailed with covering force for JW.67 to North Russia (Operation 'Timeless')
20.05.45 Arrived in Kola Inlet
23.05.45 Sailed with RA.67
30.05.45 Arrived in Scapa Flow
07.06.45 Allocated to Rosyth Command; sailed to Clyde for refit
18.09.45 Sailed for Barrow for further refit
18.11.45 Sailed for Portsmouth
24.11.45 Sailed for trooping duties
14.12.45 Arrived in Colombo
15.12.45 Sailed for Fremantle
27.12.45 Arrived in Fremantle
28.12.45 Sailed for Sydney
10.01.46 Sailed for Fremantle
17.01.46 Sailed for Colombo
25.01.46 Arrived in Colombo
27.01.46 Sailed for UK
15.02.46 Arrived in Devonport
20.09.46 Damaged by storm in Atlantic
31.10.46 Returned to USN at Norfolk, Va
29.07.47 Sold by USN as mercantile *Roebiah*
00.00.67 Renamed *President Marcos*
00.00.72 Re-named *Lucky One* for voyage to breakers' yard
28.07.72 Broken up in Taiwan

Rajah (D10) Ruler *Class Ferry Carrier*

Laid down: 17 December 1942
Launched: 18 May 1943
Completed: 17 January 1944

Builder: Seattle-Tacoma Shipbuilding Corp., Seattle; completed by Willamette Iron & Steel Corp.
Machinery: 1-shaft Allis-Chalmers geared turbine; 2 Foster Wheeler boilers; 8,500shp = 18 knots
Displacement: 11,400 tons standard; 15,390 tons deep load
Dimensions: 492ft overall x 108ft 6in max beam x 25ft 5in max draught
Gun armament: 2 single 5in US Mk 12 (2); 8 twin 40mm Bofors (16); 27 single 20mm Oerlikon (27)

Fuel: 3,160 tons FFO
Endurance: 27,500 miles @ 11 knots
Complement: 646
Protection: Splinter protection for bomb room
Flight deck: 450ft x 80ft wood-covered steel
Arrester wires: 9 x 19,800lb @ 55 knots; 3 barriers
Hangar: 260ft x 62ft x 18ft
Catapults: 1 x H4C; 16,000lb @ 74 knots (tail-down method only)
Lifts: *Fwd* 42ft long x 34ft wide; *aft* 34ft long x 42ft wide; both 14,000lb
Aircraft: Up to 90 could be ferried; up to 30 could be operated
Aircraft fuel: 36,000 gallons AVGAS
Air weapons: None carried

Notes: Built from the outset as an aircraft carrier of the US *Prince William* class but based on the C3 mercantile design. Laid down as USS *Prince* but renamed USS *McClure* (CVE-45) in 1942. She was one of 23 ships of her class transferred to the RN under Lend/Lease arrangements.

Summary of service

17.10.43	Transferred to the RN whilst building
17.01.44	Commissioned in Tacoma
31.01.44	Sailed for Vancouver for modifications to RN standards
05.03.44	Turbine gearing damaged, requiring repairs in Vancouver
26.05.44	Allocated to WAC as ferry carrier; sailed for New York
29.06.44	In New York; embarked 1842 (Corsair) and 857 (Avenger) NAS for passage to UK
30.06.44	Sailed for Liverpool
12.07.44	Arrived in Liverpool
13.07.44	Disembarked aircraft; on completion, sailed for refit in Clyde
03.08.44	DLT by 768 Training NAS
11.08.44	DLT by 769 Training NAS
12.08.44	DLT by 767 Training NAS
10.09.44	Sailed from Clyde to Belfast to embark 849 (Avenger), 857 (Avenger) and 888 (Hellcat) NAS for passage to East Indies via Alexandria and Aden

HMS *Rajah*. (FAA Museum)

09.10.44 Disembarked 849 NAS at RNAS Cochin
11.10.44 Disembarked 857 NAS to RNAS Coimatore and 888 NAS to RNAS China Bay
19.10.44 Embarked personnel of 822 NAS (but no aircraft) for passage to UK via Port Said and Gibraltar
10.11.44 Arrived in Clyde for defect rectification
20.12.44 Allocated to USN as ferry carrier
15.01.45 Arrived in San Diego (ship operated for some months ferrying US aircraft between San Diego and Pearl Harbor)
07.07.45 Sailed for New York
28.07.45 Sailed for Clyde
05.08.45 Arrived in Clyde; refitted for trooping
22.11.45 Sailed for Colombo
14.12.45 Arrived in Colombo
17.12.45 Sailed for Plymouth via Bombay
11.01.46 Arrived in Plymouth; after unloading, sailed for Colombo
23.02.46 In Colombo
23.04.46 Returned to Chatham for repairs
10.08.46 Allocated to Rosyth Command for use as troopship
13.12.46 Returned to USN at Norfolk, Va
07.07.47 Sold by USN as mercantile *Drenthe*
00.00.66 Renamed *Lambros*
00.00.69 Renamed *Ulisse*
23.06.75 Arrived at Savona for scrapping

Ranee (D03) Ruler *Class Ferry Carrier*

Laid down: 5 January 1943
Launched: 2 June 1943
Completed: 8 November 1943

Builder: Seattle-Tacoma Shipbuilding Corp., Seattle
Machinery: 1-shaft Allis-Chalmers geared turbine; 2 Foster Wheeler boilers; 8,500shp = 18 knots
Displacement: 11,400 tons standard; 15,390 tons deep load
Dimensions: 492ft overall x 108ft 6in max beam x 25ft 5in max draught
Gun armament: 2 single 5in US Mk 12 (2); 8 twin 40mm Bofors (16); 14 twin 20mm Oerlikon (28); 7 single 20mm Oerlikon (7)
Fuel: 3,160 tons FFO
Endurance: 27,500 miles @ 11 knots
Complement: 646
Protection: Splinter protection for bomb room
Flight deck: 450ft x 80ft wood-covered steel
Arrester wires: 9 x 19,800lb @ 55 knots; 3 barriers
Hangar: 260ft x 62ft x 18ft
Catapults: 1 x H4C; 16,000lb @ 74 knots (tail-down method only)
Lifts: *Fwd* 42ft long x 34ft wide; *aft* 34ft long x 42ft wide; both 14,000lb
Aircraft: Up to 90 could be ferried; up to 30 could be operated
Aircraft fuel: 36,000 gallons AVGAS
Air weapons: None carried

Notes: Built from the outset as an aircraft carrier of the USN *Prince William* class based on the C3 mercantile hull design; 23 other units of the class were transferred to the RN under Lend/Lease arrangements. Laid down as USS *Niantic* (CVE-46).

Summary of service
08.11.43 Transferred to RN and commissioned in Tacoma
00.11.43 Moved to Vancouver for modification to RN standards
04.02.44 Loaned to USN as ferry carrier; sailed for San Francisco
08.02.44 Sailed for Wellington
25.02.44 Arrived in Wellington
26.02.44 Sailed for Fremantle
08.03.44 In Fremantle
18.03.44 Arrived in Cochin
31.03.44 Sailed for Vancouver via Port Philip
15.05.44 Refit in Vancouver
28.06.44 Sailed for San Francisco
11.07.44 In Cristobal; sailed for Norfolk, Va
17.08.44 Arrived in Norfolk
05.09.44 Sailed for Cape Town
23.09.44 In Cape Town; sailed for New York
18.10.44 Embarked 1846 (Corsair) NAS for passage to UK; allocated to WAC
02.11.44 Disembarked aircraft to Belfast; on completion, sailed for Norfolk, Va
18.11.44 Embarked 1848 NAS (Corsair) NAS for passage to UK
03.12.44 Disembarked aircraft to RNAS Machrihanish and then sailed for Norfolk, Va

HMS *Ranee*. (IWM FXL.7481)

27.12.44	Entered Rosyth for refit
04.01.45	DLT carrier in Clyde
21.01.45	Sailed for San Diego; loaned to USN for ferry duties in Pacific
02.05.45	Sailed from San Diego for New York
24.05.45	Sailed for Clyde
04.06.45	Refitted in Rosyth; allocated to Rosyth Command as troopship
12.09.45	Refitted on Tyne for trooping duties
08.11.45	Sailed for Portsmouth
05.12.45	Sailed for Colombo
27.12.45	Arrived in Colombo
29.12.45	Sailed for Sydney.
20.01.46	Sailed from Sydney for Fremantle
27.01.46	Sailed from Fremantle for UK via Colombo
25.02.46	Arrived in Plymouth
26.02.46	Sailed for refit in Portsmouth prior to further trooping duties
08.11.46	Returned to USN at Norfolk, Va; sold by USN as mercantile *Friesland*
00.00.67	Renamed *Pacific Breeze*
11.05.74	Arrived in Taiwan for scrapping

Ravager (D70) Attacker *Class Training/Ferry Carrier*

Laid down: 30 April 1942
Launched: 16 July 1942
Completed: 26 April 1943

Builder: Seattle-Tacoma Shipbuilding Corp., Seattle; completed by Willamette Iron & Steel Corp.
Machinery: 1-shaft Allis-Chalmers geared turbine; 2 Foster Wheeler boilers; 8,500shp = 18.5 knots
Displacement: 10,200 tons standard; 14,400 tons deep load
Dimensions: 495ft 9in x 102ft max beam x 26ft max draught
Gun armament: 2 single 4in US Mk 9 (2); 4 twin 40mm Bofors (8); 4 twin 20mm Oerlikon (8); 8 single 20mm Oerlikon (8)
Fuel: 3,160 tons FFO
Endurance: 27,300 miles @ 11 knots
Complement: 646
Protection: Splinter protection for bomb room
Flight deck: 442ft x 102ft wood-covered steel
Arrester wires: 9 x 19,800lb @ 55 knots; 3 barriers
Hangar: 262ft x 62ft x 18ft
Catapults: 1 x H2; 7,000lb @ 61 knots (tail-down method only)

Lifts: *Fwd* 42ft long x 34ft wide; *aft* 34ft long x 42ft wide; both 14,000lb
Aircraft: Up to 90 could be ferried; up to 20 could be operated
Aircraft fuel: 52,800 gallons AVGAS
Air weapons: None carried

Notes: Built from the outset as a carrier for the RN under Lend/Lease. Based on the US C3 merchant hull design. Originally to have been named *Charger*.

Summary of service

25.04.43	Commissioned in Tacoma
25.05.43	Sailed for New York
02.07.43	Embarked 846 NAS (Avenger) off Norfolk, Va, for passage to UK
13.07.43	Arrived in New York
15.07.43	Sailed with HX.248 for passage to UK
27.07.43	Disembarked aircraft to RNAS Machrihanish
28.07.43	Arrived in Greenock; allocated to WAC as DLT carrier; extensive flying, with short detachments from both operational and training NAS, in Irish Sea and North-West Approaches
29.11.43	Collided with *Pretoria Castle*; repairs carried out in Clyde yard
08.12.43	Resumed DLT duties
18.04.44	Fitted out in Clyde as ferry carrier
01.05.44	Resumed DLT duties
20.10.44	Sailed with KMF.35A to Gibraltar loaded with aircraft
25.10.44	In Gibraltar
28.10.44	Sailed for Norfolk, Va, in GUF.15B
26.11.44	Arrived in Belfast, having called at Norfolk, Va, and New York
01.12.44	Repairs in London
19.12.44	Sailed for Rosyth
22.12.44	Arrived in Rosyth; resumed DLT duties
04.01.45	Asdic trials
28.01.45	Collided with *Ben Lomond*
11.02.45	Repairs in Rosyth
27.02.45	Reverted to DLT role
25.04.45	Clyde for repairs
08.11.45	Resumed DLT role
28.12.45	Ceased flying operations
27.02.46	Returned to USN at Norfolk, Va; sold by USN as mercantile *Robin Trent* (subsequently renamed *Trent*)
07.07.73	Arrived in Taiwan for scrapping

HMS *Ravager* with a Wildcat on deck. (FAA Museum)

Reaper (D82) Ruler *Class Ferry Carrier*

Laid down: 5 June 1943
Launched: 22 November 1943
Completed: 21 February 1944

Builder: Seattle-Tacoma Shipbuilding Corp., Seattle
Machinery: 1-shaft Allis-Chalmers geared turbine; 2 Foster Wheeler boilers; 8,500shp = 18 knots
Displacement: 11,400 tons standard; 15,390 tons deep load
Dimensions: 492ft overall x 108ft 6in max beam x 25ft 5in max draught
Gun armament: 2 single 5in US Mk 12 (2); 8 twin 40mm Bofors (16); 14 twin 20mm Oerlikon (28); 7 single 20mm Oerlikon (7)
Fuel: 3,160 tons FFO
Endurance: 27,500 miles @ 11 knots
Complement: 646

Protection: Splinter protection for bomb room
Flight deck: 450ft x 80ft wood-covered steel
Arrester wires: 9 x 19,800lb @ 55 knots; 3 barriers
Hangar: 260ft x 62ft x 18ft
Catapults: 1 x H4C; 16,000lb @ 74 knots (tail-down method only)
Lifts: *Fwd* 42ft long x 34ft wide; *aft* 34ft long x 42ft wide; both 14,000lb
Aircraft: Up to 90 could be ferried; up to 30 could be operated
Aircraft fuel: 36,000 gallons AVGAS
Air weapons: None carried

Notes: One of 23 ships of the USN *Prince William* class transferred to RN under Lend/Lease arrangements and named, in the main, after types of ruler.This ship was built from the outset as a carrier but based on the US C3

HMS *Reaper* ferrying a full deck-load of USN aircraft in April 1945. (FAA Museum)

mercantile design. She was laid down as USS *Winjah* (CVE-34).

Summary of service

18.02.44 Transferred to RN and commissioned in Tacoma
31.03.44 Sailed for Vancouver for modifications to RN standards
24.05.44 Sailed for San Francisco
22.06.44 Sailed for Norfolk, Va
09.07.44 Arrived in Norfolk Va
22.07.44 Sailed for New York
25.07.44 Allocated to WAC as ferry carrier; sailed with HX.301 for Clyde
05.08.44 In Clyde for defect rectification
25.08.44 Sailed with KMF.34 loaded with aircraft
10.09.44 Sailed with MKF.34
27.09.44 Sailed from Clyde to Norfolk, Va
09.10.44 Sailed from Norfolk with UGF.16 loaded with aircraft
25.10.44 In Gibraltar
01.11.44 Sailed with GUF.15B
18.11.44 Sailed from Norfolk, Va, for New York
22.11.44 Embarked 1849 and 1850 NAS (Corsair) for passage to UK
23.11.44 Sailed from New York for Belfast
05.12.44 Arrived in Belfast; disembarked NAS
09.12.44 Damaged in collision with *Tegelburg* in Clyde; repairs subsequently carried out in Clyde yard
05.01.45 Repairs completed; loaned to USN as ferry carrier for duty in Pacific; sailed from Clyde for San Diego via Cristobal
29.01.45 Arrived in San Diego; mainly used to carry aircraft off US West Coast
13.05.45 Arrived in New York
25.05.45 Returned to Clyde
31.05.45 Refit in Rosyth
23.07.45 Allocated to 30 ACS, BPF, and sailed for Pacific via Panama Canal
13.09.45 Arrived in Sydney with load of aircraft
03.10.45 In Manus; embarked 1701 NAS (Sea Otter) from Ponam; sailed for Hong Kong via Manila
11.10.45 In Hong Kong
18.10.45 Sailed for Sydney via Manus
04.11.45 In Sydney
17.11.45 In Auckland
19.11.45 Sailed from Singapore for UK
27.03.46 Arrived in Clyde to de-store; allocated to Rosyth Command
20.05.46 Returned to USN at Norfolk, Va; sold by USN as mercantile *South Africa Star*
25.05.67 Arrived at Nikara, Japan, for scrapping

Ruler (D72) Ruler *Class Escort Carrier*

Laid down: 25 March 1943
Launched: 21 August 1943
Completed: 22 December 1943

Builder: Seattle-Tacoma Shipbuilding Corp., Seattle; completed by Willamette Iron & Steel Corp.
Machinery: 1-shaft Allis-Chalmers geared turbine; 2 Foster Wheeler boilers; 8,500shp = 18 knots
Displacement: 11,400 tons standard; 15,390 tons deep load
Dimensions: 492ft overall x 108ft 6in max beam x 25ft 5in max draught
Gun armament: 2 single 5in US Mk 12 (2); 8 twin 40mm Bofors (16); 14 twin 20mm Oerlikon (28); 7 single 20mm Oerlikon (7)
Fuel: 3,160 tons FFO
Endurance: 27,500 miles @ 11 knots
Complement: 646
Protection: Splinter protection for bomb room
Flight deck: 450ft x 80ft wood-covered steel
Arrester wires: 9 x 19,800lb @ 55 knots; 3 barriers
Hangar: 260ft x 62ft x 18ft
Catapults: 1 x H4C; 16,000lb @ 74 knots (tail-down method only)
Lifts: *Fwd* 42ft long x 34ft wide; *aft* 34ft long x 42ft wide; both 14,000lb
Aircraft: Up to 30 could be operated; up to 90 could be ferried
Aircraft fuel: 36,000 gallons AVGAS
Air weapons: 22.4in torpedoes; 500lb MC bombs; Mk 11 depth charges; .5in gun ammunition; flares and pyrotechnics

Notes: One of 23 units of US *Prince William* class transferred to RN under Lend/Lease arrangements. Built from the outset as an aircraft carrier but with a hull based on the US mercantile C3 design. Laid down as USS *St Joseph* (CVE-50) and renamed on transfer.

Summary of service

22.12.43 Transferred to RN and commissioned in Seattle
31.12.43 Sailed for Vancouver to be modified for RN
20.03.44 Sailed for Norfolk, Va
08.04.44 Arrived in Norfolk, Va
21.04.44 Allocated to WAC as ferry carrier; sailed for Liverpool via New York with load of aircraft
06.05.44 Arrived in Liverpool
09.05.44 Sailed for New York
23.05.44 Arrived in New York
26.05.44 Sailed for Liverpool with load of aircraft
11.06.44 Arrived in Liverpool
24.06.44 Refit in Liverpool
18.09.44 In Clyde
30.09.44 Sailed for New York
16.10.44 Arrived in Norfolk, Va
31.10.44 Sailed for New York
01.11.44 Sailed for Clyde with a load of aircraft
18.11.44 Arrived in Clyde; defect repairs carried out once ship unloaded
30.12.44 Operational work-up with 885 NAS (Hellcat) embarked
28.01.45 Allocated to BPF as replenishment carrier; sailed for Far East via Gibraltar, Alexandria and Colombo with 885 NAS embarked and also 1772 NAS (Firefly) for passage to Australia
16.03.45 Arrived in Sydney
00.04.45 Sailed for Leyte
03.05.45 Sailed from Leyte for replenishment operations off Okinawa; 885 expanded to composite Hellcat/Avenger NAS to provide air cover for fleet and replenishment ships whilst replenishment operations under way
06.05.45 Replenishment operations for TF.57
10.05.45 Replenishment operations for TF.57
14.05.45 Replenishment operations for TF.57
18.05.45 Replenishment operations for TF.57

HMS ***Ruler*** **being overflown by Hellcats of 885 NAS in BPF markings. (FAA Museum)**

20.05.45 Sailed for Leyte with destroyer *Quilliam*
27.05.45 Arrived in Leyte
05.06.45 Arrived in Sydney
12.06.45 Sailed with same NAS for replenishment operations off Japan in support of TF.37
31.08.45 Arrived in Tokyo Bay
13.09.45 Sailed for Sydney
27.09.45 Arrived in Sydney
22.10.45 Sailed for Clyde
03.12.45 Arrived in Clyde; de-stored
04.01.46 Sailed for Norfolk, Va
29.01.46 Returned to USN at Norfolk, Va
31.05.46 Sold by USN and broken up

Searcher (D40) Attacker *Class Escort Carrier*

Laid down: 20 February 1942
Launched: 20 June 1942
Completed: 8 April 1943

Builder: Seattle-Tacoma Shipbuilding Corp., Seattle; completed by Willamette Iron & Steel Corp.

Machinery: 1-shaft Allis-Chalmers geared turbine; 2 Foster Wheeler boilers; 8,500shp = 18.5 knots
Displacement: 10,200 tons standard; 14,400 tons deep load
Dimensions: 495ft 9in x 102ft max beam x 26ft max draught

Gun armament: 2 single 4in US Mk 9 (2); 8 twin 40mm Bofors (16); 10 twin 20mm Oerlikon (20); 15 single 20mm Oerlikon (15)
Fuel: 3,270 tons FFO
Endurance: 27,300 miles @ 11 knots
Complement: 646
Protection: Splinter protection for bomb room
Flight deck: 442ft x 88ft wood-covered steel
Arrester wires: 9 x 19,800lb @ 55 knots; 3 barriers
Hangar: 262ft x 62ft x 18ft
Catapults: 1 x H2; 7,000lb @ 61 knots (tail-down method only)
Lifts: *Fwd* 42ft long x 34ft wide; *aft* 34ft long x 42ft wide; both 14,000lb
Aircraft: 28 could be operated (1944); up to 90 could be ferried
Aircraft fuel: 41,000 gallons AVGAS
Air weapons: 500lb SAP bombs; 250lb SAP bombs; .5in gun ammunition; flares and pyrotechnics

Notes: Laid down as a merchant ship of the US C3 design but converted into a carrier of the US *Bogue* class before launch and transferred to the RN under Lend/Lease arrangements. Because the hull was less complete than was the case with earlier escort carrier conversions, a more refined ship resulted. Eleven of this class served with the RN and ten with the USN. *Searcher* was allocated the number CVE-22 by the USN but was never named by them.

Summary of service

07.04.43 Commissioned in Tacoma
02.05.43 Sailed for Seattle for modifications
13.05.43 Sailed for Norfolk, Va
02.06.43 Arrived in Norfolk, Va, for further modifications
28.06.43 Sailed for Liverpool
30.06.43 Joined HX.246 for passage
13.07.43 Arrived in Liverpool; taken in hand for modifications to RN standards
06.10.43 Commenced work-up in Clyde area with 882 and 898 NAS (Wildcat) embarked; allocated to WAC
22.10.43 Sailed to cover ON.207
28.10.43 Covered HX.262
05.11.43 Covered HX.264
12.11.43 Arrived in Argentia
00.11.43 Sailed for Clyde
19.12.43 Sailed for New York
05.01.44 Docked for repairs in New York
07.02.44 Repairs completed
10.02.44 Sailed for Liverpool
22.02.44 Arrived in Liverpool; sailed immediately for work-up in Clyde area with 882 and 898 NAS (Wildcat) embarked
18.03.44 Arrived in Scapa Flow; loaned to HF
03.04.44 Formed part of covering force for Operation 'Tungsten' (carrier-based strike on German battleship *Tirpitz* as she lay in Kaafjord) in company with *Victorious*, *Furious*, *Emperor*, *Pursuer* and *Fencer*
21.04.44 Sailed from Scapa Flow for air strikes on Bodø
03.05.44 Sailed from Scapa Flow for air strikes on Kristiansund
13.05.44 Reverted to WAC and carried out defect repairs in Rosyth
31.05.44 Sailed from Rosyth to Clyde
12.06.44 Covered KMS.54
22.06.44 Covered MKS.52
01.07.44 Returned to Clyde
05.07.44 882 and 898 NAS amalgamated to form single, enlarged 882 NAS (Wildcat)
15.07.44 Allocated to Force H for Operation 'Dragoon' (invasion of southern France)
25.07.44 Arrived in Malta; ship formed part of covering Task Force 88 under Rear-Admiral Sir Thomas Troubridge (in company with *Attacker*, *Khedive*, *Emperor*, *Pursuer*, *Hunter*, *Stalker* and US escort carriers *Tulagi* and *Kasaan Bay*)
02.08.44 Task Force 88 work-up off Malta
15.08.44 Operations off southern France (RN carriers flew 1,673 operational sorties of which 552 were CAP and remainder offensive strikes overland against German troops, railways, aircraft and coastal defences; 21 RN and 14 USN aircraft lost to enemy action and total of 60 to deck-landing accidents)
02.09.44 Arrived in Alexandria; started strike operations against German shipping and island garrisons in Aegean in company with *Attacker*, *Hunter*, *Stalker*, *Khedive*, *Emperor* and *Pursuer* (NAS in *Emperor*, *Pursuer* and *Searcher* formed 7 Naval Fighter Wing)
21.09.44 Returned to Alexandria
01.10.44 Sailed for Gibraltar
08.10.44 Sailed for Belfast
12.10.44 Disembarked 882 NAS to Ballyhalbert
13.10.44 Sailed from Belfast to Clyde for refit
29.01.45 Refit completed; allocated to HF and sailed to work up with 882 NAS embarked
04.03.45 Arrived in Scapa Flow; 746A NAS (Firefly NF) added to air group

19.03.45 Sailed for anti-shipping operations off Norwegian coast
24.03.45 Strike operations off Norwegian coast
01.05.45 Further strike operations off Norwegian coast
06.05.45 Formed part of HF covering force that liberated Copenhagen
10.05.45 Returned to Scapa Flow
15.05.45 Arrived in Clyde for refit
01.07.45 Allocated to 21 ACS, EIF; sailed for East Indies via Cochin, Colombo and Trincomalee with 882 NAS (Wildcat) embarked
19.09.45 Sailed from Ceylon for UK
09.10.45 Arrived in Clyde; 882 NAS disembarked to disband; de-stored
14.11.45 Sailed for USA
29.11.45 Returned to USN at Norfolk, Va; sold by USN as mercantile *Captain Theo*
00.00.64 Renamed *Oriental Banker*
21.04.76 Broken up in Taiwan

Shah (D21) Ruler *Class Escort Carrier*

Laid down: 13 November 1942
Launched: 21 April 1943
Completed: 27 September 1943

Builder: Seattle-Tacoma Shipbuilding Corp., Seattle
Machinery: 1-shaft Allis-Chalmers geared turbine; 2 Foster Wheeler boilers; 8,500shp = 18 knots
Displacement: 11,400 tons standard; 15,390 tons deep load
Dimensions: 492ft overall x 108ft 6in max beam x 25ft 5in max draught
Gun armament: 2 single 5in US Mk 12 (2); 8 twin 40mm Bofors (16); 14 twin 20mm Oerlikon (28); 7 single 20mm Oerlikon (7)
Fuel: 3,160 tons FFO
Endurance: 27,500 miles @ 11 knots
Complement: 646
Protection: Splinter protection for bomb room
Flight deck: 450ft x 80ft wood-covered steel
Arrester wires: 9 x 19,800lb @ 55 knots; 3 barriers
Hangar: 260ft x 62ft x 18ft
Catapults: 1 x H4C; 16,000lb @ 74 knots (tail-down method only)
Lifts: *Fwd* 42ft long x 34ft wide; *aft* 34ft long x 42ft wide; both 14,000lb
Aircraft: Up to 30 could be operated; up to 90 could be ferried
Aircraft fuel: 36,000 gallons AVGAS
Air weapons: Mk 24 mines (homing torpedoes); 22.4in torpedoes; 1,000lb MC bombs; 500lb SAP bombs; Mk 11 depth charges; .5in gun ammunition; flares and pyrotechnics

Notes: Laid down from the outset as an aicraft carrier of the US *Prince William* class but based on the C3 mercantile design. Built as USS *Jamaica* (CVE-43). Only the name-ship of the class was retained by the USN, the remaining 23 ships being transferred to the RN under Lend/Lease arrangements

Summary of service
27.09.43 Transferred to RN and commissioned in Tacoma
18.10.43 Arrived in Vancouver for modification to RN standards
02.01.44 Allocated to 1 ACS, EF; sailed from Seattle for San Francisco
07.01.44 Arrived in San Francisco and embarked 851 NAS (Avenger) which had flown to West Coast from Norfolk, Va

HMS *Searcher* with Wildcats of 882 NAS on deck. (Author)

15.01.44	Sailed for Melbourne
08.02.44	Sailed for Colombo via Fremantle and Cochin
19.03.44	Arrived in Colombo
26.04.44	Sailed for Bombay on aircraft ferrying duties
30.04.44	In Bombay
09.05.44	Sailed for Colombo
12.05.44	In Colombo
13.05.44	Wildcat Flight added to 851 NAS
16.05.44	Arrived in Trincomalee
17.06.44	Sailed for AS patrol off Trincomalee
05.07.44	Trade protection between Colombo and Cochin
30.07.44	Formed part of Task Force 66 (trade protection group in northern Indian Ocean)
18.08.44	In Kilindini
27.08.44	Supported convoy between Kilindini and Aden
15.09.44	Sailed from Aden to Kilindini
21.09.44	Sailed for Cochin
16.10.44	Allocated to 1st Division, EF
00.10.44	AS hunt in Indian Ocean
26.11.44	Arrived in Colombo
10.01.45	Sailed for Trincomalee
08.02.45	Trade protection operations between Trincomalee and Diego Suarez
23.02.45	Arrived in Durban for refit
08.04.45	Sailed for Kilindini
15.04.45	Sailed for Trincomalee via Colombo
27.04.45	Sailed from Trincomalee with 851 (Avenger) and 809 (Seafire) NAS and a Flight of 804 (Hellcat) NAS, in company with *Empress* for Operation 'Bishop' (strikes on Nicobar and Andaman Islands and Burma coast)
10.05.45	Sailed from Trincomalee in company with *Emperor* for operations against Japanese heavy cruiser *Haguro* (unfortunately, *Shah*'s catapult went u/s and her Avengers had to be transferred to *Emperor*, which, as an assault carrier, did not have facilities to brief and arm a TBR strike)
21.05.45	In Trincomalee
24.05.45	Arrived in Bombay
09.06.45	Sailed for Trincomalee
26.08.45	Sailed from Trincomalee for trade protection operations, ending in Colombo
12.09.45	Sailed with aircrew of 845 and 851 NAS (their Avenger aircraft were left behind and destroyed under terms of Lend/Lease agreement)
07.10.45	Arrived in Clyde and de-stored
16.11.45	Sailed from UK for USA
26.11.45	Arrived in Norfolk, Va
06.12.45	Returned to USN at Norfolk, Va
20.06.47	Sold by USN as mercantile *Salta*
00.06.66	Broken up at Buenos Aires

HMS *Shah* with Avengers of 851 NAS on deck. (FAA Museum)

Slinger **(D26)** Ruler *Class Ferry/Replenishment Carrier*

Laid down: 25 May 1942
Launched: 15 December 1942
Completed: 11 August 1943

Builder: Seattle-Tacoma Shipbuilding Corp., Seattle
Machinery: 1-shaft Allis-Chalmers geared turbine; 2 Foster Wheeler boilers; 8,500shp = 18 knots
Displacement: 11,400 tons standard; 15,390 tons deep load
Dimensions: 492ft overall x 108ft 6in max beam x 25ft 5in max draught
Gun armament: 2 single 5in US Mk 12 (2); 8 twin 40mm Bofors (16); 14 twin 20mm Oerlikon (28); 7 single 20mm Oerlikon (7)
Fuel: 3,160 tons FFO
Endurance: 27,500 miles @ 11 knots

Complement: 646
Protection: Splinter protection for bomb room
Flight deck: 450ft x 80ft wood-covered steel
Arrester wires: 9 x 19,800lb @ 55 knots; 3 barriers
Hangar: 260ft x 62ft x 18ft
Catapults: 1 x H4C; 16,000lb @ 74 knots (tail-down method only)
Lifts: *Fwd* 42ft long x 34ft wide; *aft* 34ft long x 42ft wide; both 14,000lb
Aircraft: Up to 90 could be ferried; up to 30 could be operated
Aircraft fuel: 50,480 gallons AVGAS
Air weapons: None carried

Notes: One of 23 units of the USN *Prince William* class transferred to the RN under Lend/Lease arrangements.

HMS *Slinger* turning into wind to launch two Seafires of 768 NAS during November 1944. Both have started, and, with the steam jet forward showing that the wind is down the deck, the launch is imminent. (FAA Museum)

Laid down from the outset as an aircraft carrier but to a design based on the US C3 mercantile hull. Built as USS *Chatham* (CVE-32) and renamed on transfer.

Summary of service

11.08.43 Transferred to RN and commissioned in Tacoma
29.09.43 Passed through Panama Canal
06.10.43 Arrived in Norfolk, Va; allocated to WAC as ferry carrier
09.10.43 Embarked 1830 NAS (Corsair) for passage to UK
15.10.43 Sailed for UK via New York
31.10.43 Arrived in Belfast and disembarked 1830 NAS
20.11.43 Sailed for refit in Chatham
05.02.44 Mined in Medway on leaving Chatham; returned to Chatham and was, at first, cannibalised to provide spare parts for other carriers in refit (forward lift transferred to *Stalker* and later replaced by another)
12.02.44 Repairs carried out in London shipyard
17.10.44 Repairs completed; sailed for Clyde for training and work-up
03.11.44 DLT for 768 NAS from RNAS Abbotsinch
11.01.45 Allocated to BPF as replenishment carrier; sailed from Clyde for Australia with 1845 NAS (Corsair) embarked for passage; called at Gibraltar, Port Said, Aden and Colombo
22.02.45 Arrived in Sydney
11.03.45 Sailed for forward operating base at Manus (standard replenishment complement comprised 10 Corsairs, 7 Hellcats, 3 Seafires,1 Avenger and 1 Firefly); ship formedpart of Task Force 112, BPF fleet train, with *Speaker*, *Ruler*, *Striker* and *Chaser*
19.03.45 Sailed from Manus for Leyte
26.03.45 Arrived in Leyte Gulf
05.04.45 Transferred aircraft to fleet carriers of 1 ACS; on completion ferried damaged and unserviceable aircraft back to main base area in Sydney
09.07.45 In Sydney
00.08.45 Used to repatriate former POWs from Hong Kong to Australia
00.10.45 Defect repairs in Sydney
10.11.45 Sailed for UK via Colombo on trooping duties
24.12.45 Arrived in Plymouth
16.01.46 Sailed for Clyde to de-store
25.01.46 Sailed for USA
27.02.46 Returned to USN at Norfolk, Va; sold by USN as mercantile *Robin Mowbray*
29.01.70 Broken up in Taiwan

Smiter (D55) Ruler *Class Escort Carrier*

Laid down: 10 May 1943
Launched: 27 September 1943
Completed: 20 January 1944

Builder: Seattle-Tacoma Shipbuilding Corp., Seattle; completed by Willamette Iron & Steel Corp.
Machinery: 1-shaft Allis-Chalmers geared turbine; 2 Foster Wheeler boilers; 8,500shp = 18 knots
Displacement: 11,400 tons standard; 15,390 tons deep load
Dimensions: 492ft overall x 108ft 6in max beam x 25ft 5in max draught
Gun armament: 2 single 5in US Mk 12 (2); 8 twin 40mm Bofors (16); 14 twin 20mm Oerlikon (28); 7 single 20mm Oerlikon (7)
Fuel: 3,160 tons FFO
Endurance: 27,500 miles @ 11 knots
Complement: 646

Protection: Splinter protection for bomb room
Flight deck: 450ft x 80ft wood-covered steel
Arrester wires: 9 x 19,800lb @ 55 knots; 3 barriers
Hangar: 260ft x 62ft x 18ft
Catapults: 1 x H4C; 16,000lb @ 74 knots (tail-down method only)
Lifts: *Fwd* 42ft long x 34ft wide; *aft* 34ft long x 42ft wide; both 14,000lb
Aircraft: Up to 30 could be operated; up to 90 could be ferried
Aircraft fuel: 36,000 gallons AVGAS
Air weapons: 22.4in torpedoes; 500lb MC bombs; Mk 11 depth charges; .5in gun ammunition; flares and pyrotechnics

Notes: One of 23 units of the USN *Prince William* class transferred to the RN under Lend/Lease arrangements. The ship was laid down from the outset as an aircraft carrier but to a hull design based on the US mercantile C3. She was originally named USS *Vermillion* (CVE-52).

HMS *Smiter* with three Swordfish parked aft ready to launch. The ship was operating as a DLT carrier in the Clyde at the time this photograph was taken. (Author)

Summary of service

20.01.44	Transferred to RN and commissioned in Tacoma
15.02.44	Sailed for Vancouver for modifications to RN standards
31.03.44	Sailed for San Francisco
08.05.44	Sailed from San Francisco
23.05.44	Arrived in Norfolk, Va, for defect rectification
01.06.44	Embarked 856 NAS (Avenger) for passage to UK
05.06.44	Sailed for UK via New York; embarked 1841 NAS (Corsair) for passage
20.06.44	Arrived in Liverpool; disembarked 856 NAS to RNAS Machrihanish and 1841 NAS to RNAS Ayr; allocated to WAC as ferry carrier
24.06.44	Sailed for New York
07.07.44	Sailed from New York for Clyde
21.07.44	Arrived in Clyde; taken in hand for defect repairs
14.09.44	Sailed for Newport for electrical repairs
02.12.44	Sailed for Clyde; used as DLT carrier in Clyde area
15.01.45	Arrived in Rosyth for refit
26.05.45	Modified in Clyde shipyard for use as general-purpose carrier
07.07.45	Allocated to EIF; sailed for Colombo with no air group
01.09.45	In Trincomalee
02.09.45	Sailed for Singapore
11.09.45	Sailed from Singapore for Hong Kong
26.09.45	Returned to Singapore; used to ferry former POWs between Singapore and Colombo
21.11.45	In Trincomalee
16.12.45	Embarked 888 NAS (Hellcat) for passage
27.12.45	Disembarked 888 NAS to RNAS Sembawang, Singapore
28.12.45	Sailed for UK via Trincomalee and Suez Canal
11.02.46	Arrived in Clyde for de-storing
06.04.46	Returned to USN at Norfolk, Va; sold by USN as mercantile *Artillero*
00.00.65	Renamed *Presidente Garcia*
24.11.67	Broken up in Hamburg

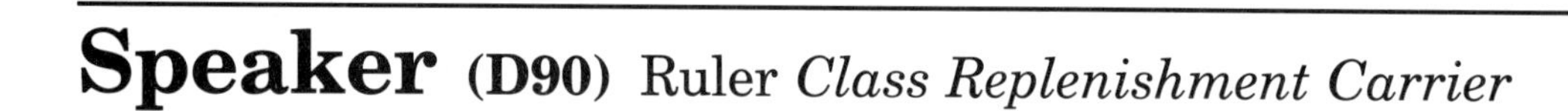

Speaker (D90) Ruler *Class Replenishment Carrier*

Laid down: 9 October 1942
Launched: 20 February 1943
Completed: 20 November 1943

Builder: Seattle-Tacoma Shipbuilding Corp., Seattle; completed by Willamette Iron & Steel Corp.
Machinery: 1-shaft Allis-Chalmers geared turbine; 2 Foster Wheeler boilers; 8,500shp = 18 knots
Displacement: 11,400 tons standard; 15,390 tons deep load
Dimensions: 492ft overall x 108ft 6in max beam x 25ft 5in max draught
Gun armament: 2 single 5in US Mk 12 (2); 8 twin 40mm Bofors (16); 14 twin 20mm Oerlikon (28); 7 single 20mm Oerlikon (7)
Fuel: 3,160 tons FFO
Endurance: 27,500 miles @ 11 knots
Complement: 646
Protection: Splinter protection for bomb room
Flight deck: 450ft x 80ft wood-covered steel
Arrester wires: 9 x 19,800lb @ 55 knots; 3 barriers
Hangar: 260ft x 62ft x 18ft
Catapults: 1 x H4C; 16,000lb @ 74 knots (tail-down method only)
Lifts: *Fwd* 42ft long x 34ft wide; *aft* 34ft long x 42ft wide; both 14,000lb

HMS *Speaker* at anchor. (FAA Museum)

Aircraft: Up to 90 could be ferried; up to 30 could be operated
Aircraft fuel: 36,000 gallons AVGAS
Air weapons: .5in gun ammunition; flares and pyrotechnics

Notes: One of 23 units of the USN *Prince William* class transferred to the RN under Lend/Lease arrangements. Laid down from the outset as an aircraft carrier but with a hull based on the US mercantile C3 design. Built as USS *Delgada* (CVE-40) and renamed on transfer.

Summary of service

20.11.43	Transferred to RN and commissioned in Tacoma
08.12.43	Sailed for Vancouver for modifications to RN standards
25.01.44	Sailed for Norfolk, Va
07.03.44	Passed through Panama Canal
17.03.44	Arrived in Norfolk, Va
25.03.44	Allocated to WAC as ferry carrier; sailed for Liverpool
08.04.44	Sailed for Norfolk, Va
24.04.44	Sailed for Liverpool via New York
14.05.44	Sailed from Liverpool for refit in Dundee
11.09.44	Sailed for Rosyth for further work
19.09.44	Allocated to WAC as DLT carrier, operating in Clyde area
19.12.44	Operational work-up in Clyde area
11.01.45	Allocated to BPF as replenishment carrier; sailed for Sydney via Gibraltar, Suez and Colombo
23.02.45	Arrived in Sydney
09.03.45	Sailed for forward operating base at Manus with 1840 NAS (Hellcat) embarked
17.03.45	Sailed from Manus for Ulithi Lagoon
25.03.45	Replenished TF.57 of BPF off Philippines: 1840 NAS replaced by typical replenishment load of 9 Seafires, 7 Avengers; 6 Corsairs, 1 Hellcat and 1 Firefly (ship formed part of 30 ACS, Task Force 112)
28.03.45	Replenishment operations off Okinawa during Operation 'Iceberg' (capture of island)
17.04.45	Further replenishment operations off Okinawa
19.04.45	In Leyte
10.05.45	Off Okinawa for replenishment operations
00.07.45	Ferry operations to bring aircraft up to forward area
26.07.45	Replenishment operations in support of TF.37 off Japan
31.07.45	Further replenishment operations off Japan
00.08.45	Ferried aircraft forward from Leyte to Japanese coast
03.09.45	Sailed from Tokyo Bay to Sydney via Manila with nearly 500 released Commonwealth POWs on board (ship's Captain, 'Jimmy' James, realised that ship's company of nearly every British ship in Bay was on deck so he took his ship to sea by 'a most tortuous route' to allow them to pay their respects to former POWs on *Speaker*'s flight deck: the ex POWs were cheered in a send-off that no one who saw it would ever forget)
15.10.45	Arrived in Sydney for repairs
28.12.45	Ferried 721 NAS (Seafire/Vengeance) from Archerfield near Sydney to Kai Tak, Hong Kong
08.01.46	Sailed from Hong Kong to UK via Suez
00.06.46	In Clyde, de-storing
06.07.46	Sailed for USA
00.07.46	Boiler repairs in Bermuda
17.07.46	Returned to USN at Norfolk, Va; sold by USN as mercantile *Lancero*
00.00.65	Renamed *Presidente Osmena*
00.00.71	Renamed *Lucky Three* for voyage to breakers
00.00.72	Broken up in Taiwan

Stalker (D91) Attacker *Class Escort Carrier*

Laid down: 6 October 1941
Launched: 5 March 1942
Completed: 30 December 1942

Builder: Western Pipe & Steel Corp., San Francisco
Machinery: 1-shaft GEC geared turbine; 2 Foster Wheeler boilers; 8,500shp = 18.5 knots
Displacement: 10,200 tons standard; 14,400 tons deep load
Dimensions: 495ft 9in x 102ft max beam x 26ft max draught
Gun armament: 2 single 4in US Mk 9 (2); 4 twin 40mm Bofors (8); 8 twin 20mm Oerlikon (16); 6 single 20mm Oerlikon (6)
Fuel: 3,270 tons FFO
Endurance: 27,300 miles @ 11 knots
Complement: 646
Protection: Splinter protection for bomb room
Flight deck: 442ft x 80ft wood-covered steel
Arrester wires: 9 x 19,800lb @ 55 knots; 3 barriers
Hangar: 262ft x 62ft x 18ft
Catapults: 1 x H2; 7,000lb @ 61 knots (tail-down method only)
Lifts: *Fwd* 42ft long x 34ft wide; *aft* 34ft long x 42ft wide; both 14,000lb
Aircraft: Up to 28 could be operated; up to 90 could be ferried
Aircraft fuel: 44,800 gallons AVGAS
Air weapons: 18in torpedoes; 500lb SAP bombs; 250lb GP bombs; Mk 11 depth charges; .5in gun ammunition; .303in gun ammunition; flares and pyrotechnics

Notes: Laid down as a US C3 type merchant ship and converted to an aircraft carrier of the US *Bogue* class before launch. Eleven of this class were transferred to the RN under Lend/Lease arrangements and ten remained with the USN. Originally to have been named USS *Hamlin* (CVE-15) by the USN. Renamed on transfer.

Summary of service

21.12.42 Transferred to RN and commissioned in San Francisco
30.01.43 Sailed to New York
27.02.43 Arrived in New York
05.03.43 Sailed with load of US aircraft for Casablanca in UGF.6.
16.03.43 Unloaded aircraft in Casablanca and sailed for Gibraltar
20.03.43 Arrived in Gibraltar
28.03.43 Sailed for Clyde in MKF.11
05.04.43 Arrived in Clyde; subsequently allocated to WAC
17.04.43 Arrived in Chatham for modifications to RN standards
26.06.43 Sailed for Clyde to work up for operational service with 833 NAS (Swordfish/Seafire) embarked
19.07.43 Defect rectification in Clyde
03.08.43 Allocated to Force H in Mediterranean in order to cover Allied landings in Sicily (Operation 'Avalanche') and sailed for Gibraltar
09.08.43 Arrived in Gibraltar, embarked 880 NAS (Seafire) and disembarked Swordfish Flight of 833 NAS
01.09.43 Sailed for Malta
09.09.43 Operation 'Avalanche': *Stalker* formed part of Force V under Rear-Admiral Sir Philip Vian aboard cruiser *Euralyus* in company with *Attacker*, *Battler*, *Hunter* and *Unicorn*; *Illustrious* and *Formidable* formed part of covering Force H
12.09.43 Two Seafires flown off to forward airstrip at Paestum when carriers were withdrawn
13.09.43 Arrived in Bizerta
20.09.43 Sailed for Gibraltar; re-embarked Swordfish
30.09.43 Sailed for Clyde in MKF.24
06.10.43 Arrived in Clyde; disembarked 833 and 880 NAS
11.10.43 Arrived in Liverpool for refit
16.12.43 Refit completed; operational work-up in Belfast areas with 809 and 897 NAS (Seafire) embarked
28.02.44 Sailed for Thames for refit
28.04.44 Refit completed.
14.05.44 Sailed with KMS.51 to Gibraltar with 809 NAS (Seafire) embarked
25.05.44 In Gibraltar
03.06.44 In Algiers
02.08.44 Operational work-up off Malta with Task Force 88 under Rear-Admiral Sir Thomas Troubridge in cruiser *Royalist* (force split into two task groups: *Stalker* formed part of TG.88.2 with *Hunter* and USN escort carriers *Tulagi* and *Kasaan Bay*; TG 88.1

HMS *Stalker* in her Admiralty 'Standard' paint scheme. (FAA Museum)

comprised *Attacker*, *Khedive*, *Emperor*, *Pursuer* and *Searcher*)

15.08.44 Operation 'Dragoon' (air group cover for amphibious invasion of southern France)
02.09.44 Arrived in Alexandria
25.09.44 Commenced strike operations in Aegean against German shipping and island garrisons (extremely successful operations carried out with *Attacker*, *Hunter*, *Khedive*, *Emperor*, *Pursuer* and *Searcher*; *Stalker*'s 809 NAS formed part of 4 Naval Fighter Wing with NAS from other ships)
22.10.44 Returned to Alexandria
29.10.44 Sailed for UK via Gibraltar with 809 NAS (Seafire) embarked
10.11.44 Arrived in Devonport
29.11.44 Sailed for Gibraltar with 809 NAS (Seafire) embarked
03.12.44 Arrived in Gibraltar for refit
21.02.45 Refit completed, allocated to 21 ACS, EIF; sailed for Trincomalee via Suez
30.04.45 Operation 'Dracula' (strikes on Rangoon and Tenasserim coast in company with *Emperor*, *Khedive* and *Hunter*)
18.06.45 Operation 'Balsam' (photographic reconnaissance of southern Malaya and strikes on Sumatran airfields in company with *Ameer* and *Khedive*); Walrus of 1700 NAS embarked for SAR duties, together with 809 NAS
05.07.45 Operations and training off Trincomalee
10.09.45 Operation 'Zipper' (reoccupation of Malaya and Singapore); entered Singapore in company with *Khedive*, *Emperor* and *Hunter*
13.09.45 Sailed for Trincomalee
20.09.45 Arrived in Trincomalee; employed on aircraft ferrying duties
28.09.45 In Colombo
02.10.45 Sailed for UK via Suez
22.10.45 Arrived in Clyde and de-stored
28.11.45 De-storing complete
02.12.45 Sailed from Clyde to USA
29.12.45 Returned to USN at Norfolk, Va; sold by USN as mercantile *Riouw*
00.00.68 Re-named *Lobito*
00.09.75 Scrapped in Taiwan

Striker (D12) Attacker *Class Escort Carrier*

Laid down: 15 December 1941
Launched: 7 May 1942
Completed: 29 April 1943

Builder: Western Pipe & Steel Corp., San Francisco
Machinery: 1-shaft GEC geared turbine; 2 Foster Wheeler boilers; 8,500shp = 18.5 knots
Displacement: 10,200 tons standard; 14,170 tons deep load
Dimensions: 492ft x 102ft max beam x 26ft max draught
Gun armament: 2 single 4in US Mk 9 (2); 4 twin 40mm Bofors (8); 6 twin 20mm Oerlikon (12); 4 single 20mm Oerlikon (4)
Fuel: 3,270 tons FFO
Endurance: 27,300 miles @ 11 knots
Complement: 646
Protection: None
Flight deck: 442ft x 80ft wood-covered steel
Arrester wires: 9 x 19,800lb @ 55 knots; 3 barriers
Hangar: 262ft x 62ft x 18ft
Catapults: 1 x H2; 7,000lb @ 61 knots (tail-down method only)
Lifts: *Fwd* 42ft long x 34ft wide; *aft* 34ft long x 42ft wide; both 14,000lb
Aircraft: Up to 28 could be operated; up to 90 could be ferried
Aircraft fuel: 43,176 gallons AVGAS

Air weapons: Mk XXIV mines (homing torpedoes); 18in torpedoes; 500lb SAP bombs; 3in RP; Mk 11 depth charges; Mk 7 depth charges; 20mm cannon ammunition; .5in gun ammunition; .303in gun ammunition; flares and pyrotechnics

Notes: Laid down as merchant ship to US mercantile C3 design. Acquired before launch and converted into an aircraft carrier of USN *Bogue* class. Launched as USS *Prince William* (CVE-19; not to be confused with the subsequent CVE-31, name-ship of class of USN escort carriers). Transferred to the RN under Lend/Lease arrangements.

Summary of service

29.04.43 Transferred to RN, renamed and commissioned in San Francisco
29.05.43 Sailed for Norfolk, Va
20.06.43 Work-up off Norfolk, Va
30.06.43 Sailed for UK via New York with HX.246
13.07.43 Arrived in Liverpool
18.07.43 Arrived in Chatham for modification to RN standards
18.10.43 Work completed, sailed for Clyde; allocated to WAC
21.10.43 Work-up in Irish Sea with 824 NAS (Swordfish/Sea Hurricane) embarked
25.11.43 Clyde for defect repair
16.12.43 Sailed to support OS.62 and KMS.36
28.12.43 Supported SL.143 and MKS.34
01.01.44 Supported OS.63 and KMS.37
07.01.44 Supported SL.144 and MKS.35
17.01.44 Clyde for defect rectification
08.02.44 Sailed to support ON.223
15.02.44 Supported HX.278
19.02.44 Defect rectification in Clyde
04.03.44 Supported KMS.44
23.03.44 Supported MKS.43
02.04.44 Defect rectification in Clyde
18.04.44 Loaned to HF; arrived in Scapa Flow
21.04.44 Provided AS cover for naval air strikes on Bodø with 824 NAS embarked
07.05.44 Sailed from Scapa Flow to provide AS cover for naval air strike on Kristiansund with only 12 Swordfish of 824 NAS embarked
11.05.44 Part of HF force that struck at Rørvik, with 824 (Swordfish) and 898 (Wildcat) NAS embarked
12.06.44 Operations against shipping off Norwegian coast with 824 NAS (Swordfish/Wildcat) embarked
19.06.44 AS sweep off Norwegian coast
27.06.44 Defect rectification in Clyde
10.07.44 AS sweep in North-West Approaches
27.07.44 Arrived in Scapa Flow
16.08.44 Sailed with force covering JW.59 with 824 NAS embarked
25.08.44 Arrived in Kola Inlet
28.08.44 Sailed for Scapa Flow covering RA.59A
16.09.44 Sailed from Scapa Flow with force covering JW.60
23.09.44 Arrived in Kola Inlet
27.09.44 Sailed for Scapa Flow covering RA.60
04.10.44 Arrived in Scapa Flow
06.10.44 Arrived in the Clyde for defect rectification
31.10.44 Allocated to BPF as replenishment carrier in 30 ACS; sailed for Sydney via Suez and Trincomalee
07.01.45 Arrived in Sydney
07.03.45 Sailed for forward bases of Manus and Ulithi
28.03.45 Replenishment operations in support of Task Force 57 off Sakashima Gunto (typical load: 10 Corsairs, 7 Hellcats, 3 Seafires, 1 Avenger and 1 Firefly)
30.04.45 Left Sakashima area for Leyte to pick up new aircraft
06.05.45 Further replenishment operations off Sakashima Gunto and Formosa
15.05.45 At Leyte; carried out ferry operations to move replacement aircraft forward
00.07.45 Became flagship of 30 ACS; formed part of Task Force 112 supporting Task Force 37 for operations against Japanese home islands

HMS *Striker* in 1944. (FAA Museum)

14.07.45 Replenishment operations off Japan (typical aircraft load now 9 Seafires, 7 Avengers, 6 Corsairs, 1 Hellcat and 1 Firefly); other CVEs in fleet train were *Ruler*, *Chaser*, *Speaker* and *Arbiter*
20.07.45 Replenishment operations off Japan
26.07.45 Replenishment operations off Japan; on completion, sailed for Sydney
00.08.45 In Sydney
18.09.45 Arrived in Hong Kong from Sydney; employed on trooping duties
09.10.45 Returned to Sydney from Hong Kong; carried out defect rectification
26.10.45 Sailed for Singapore
24.11.45 Sailed for Clyde via Colombo and Suez
16.12.45 Arrived in Clyde and commenced de-storing
20.01.46 Sailed for USA
12.02.46 Returned to USN at Norfolk, Va
05.06.46 Sold by USN for scrap

Sydney (R17) Majestic *Class Light Fleet Carrier*

Laid down: 19 April 1943
Launched: 30 September 1944
Completed: 5 February 1949

Builder: Devonport Dockyard; machinery by Parsons
Machinery: 2-shaft Parsons single reduction geared turbines; 4 Admiralty 3-drum boilers; 40,000shp = 24.5 knots
Displacement: 15,740 tons standard; 19,550 tons deep load
Dimensions: 695ft overall x 112ft 6in max beam x 25ft max draught
Gun armament: 6 twin 40mm Bofors (12); 18 single 40mm Bofors (18); 4 single 3pdr saluting
Fuel: 3,175 tons FFO
Endurance: 8,300 miles @ 20 knots
Complement: 1,300
Protection: Armoured mantlets for 32 torpedo warheads
Flight deck: 690ft x 106ft steel
Arrester wires: 10 x 20,000lb @ 87 knots; 2 barriers
Hangar: 275ft (plus 57ft extension aft of aft lift) x 52ft x 17ft 6in
Catapults: 1 x BH3 (twin-track); 20,000lb @ 56 knots
Lifts: *Fwd* 54ft long x 34ft wide; *aft* 54ft long x 34ft wide; both 15,000lb
Aircraft: Up to 42
Aircraft fuel: 98,600 gallons AVGAS
Air weapons: 18in torpedoes; 1,000lb MC bombs; 500lb SAP bombs; 3in RP; Mk 11 depth charges; 20mm cannon ammunition; flares and pyrotechnics

Notes: Laid down for the RN as a unit of thc *Majestic* class, to have been named *Terrible*. Work on her was suspended in 1945 but resumed when she was purchased by the Australian Government. Pennant number changed to A214 when she was converted to a fast troop transport in 1961.

Summary of service
16.12.48 Commissioned in Devonport as HMAS *Sydney*; on completion, worked up in UK waters with 20 CAG comprising 805 (Sea Fury) and 816 (Firefly) ANAS (which had formed in UK in August 1948)
00.05.49 Arrived in Jervis Bay to disembark ANAS to RANAS Nowra
25.04.50 Returned to UK to embark 21 CAG comprising 808 (Sea Fury) and 817 (Firefly) ANAS
00.11.50 Returned to Australia and worked up for operations with Commonwealth naval forces off Korea
27.09.51 Aircraft and stores transferred from *Glory* at Sasebo, Japan; for Korean operations ship embarked 805 and 808 (Sea Fury) and 817 (Firefly) ANAS and USN Dragonfly helicopter for SAR duties
05.10.51 Strikes launched against Korean east coast targets (first Dominion carrier to send aircraft into action)
12.10.51 Refuelled and re-armed in Sasebo after first patrol
14.10.51 Sailed to avoid Typhoon 'Ruth'; 6 aircraft in deck park written off by storm damage
18.10.51 Second patrol off Korea, during which 474 sorties were flown, including close air support for Commonwealth Division ashore
04.11.51 Left Kure, Japan, for third patrol flying flag of Rear-Admiral Scott-Moncreiff, FO2 FEF; extensive operations flown against rail targets

18.11.51 Sailed for Operation 'Athenaeum' (coordinated air and surface strikes against Hungnam on east coast) followed by patrol operations
06.12.51 Fifth patrol off west coast
19.12.51 Arrived in Kure; alongside over Christmas
28.12.51 Sixth patrol; operated off west coast and carried out strikes in defence of small islands held by South Koreans
16.01.52 Seventh and last patrol off Korea (at end of tour FO2 FEF described *Sydney*'s work off Korea as being 'quite excellent': ship had flown 2,366 sorties in 43 full operational flying days, an average of 55.2 per day, at a cost of 3 pilots and 15 aircraft)
26.01.52 Arrived in Sasebo, sailing next day
30.01.52 Arrived in Hong Kong; transferred aircraft and stores to *Glory*
09.02.52 Sailed for Australia
00.10.52 Observed British atomic bomb trials at Monte Bello Island
00.06.53 Represented RAN at HM Queen Elizabeth II's Coronation Review of the Fleet at Spithead; 817 ANAS (Firefly) took part in fly-past
01.12.53 Patrolled off Korean coast with UN forces in case fighting should break out once more; air group comprised 805 (Sea Fury) and 816 and 817 (Firefly) ANAS
00.06.54 Returned to Australia and disembarked ANAS (plans to modernise ship to same standard as new *Melbourne* had to be abandoned since Australian Government reduced funds available for naval aviation)
00.00.55 Relieved *Vengeance* as training ship (but retained ability to operate aircraft)
00.00.58 Paid off into reserve
00.00.61 Converted into fast troop transport by removal of all fixed-wing aircraft operating equipment (catapult, arrester wires, etc.); hangar converted into accommodation for troops and flight deck used to stow vehicles (helicopters could still be operated)
1962 on Used to support Australian forces in Vietnam War (task in which ship performed well)
00.00.73 Paid off into reserve
23.12.75 Towed from Sydney to be broken up by Dong Kuk Steel Mill Co., South Korea

HMAS *Sydney* carrying out trials in UK waters shortly after her completion in 1949. The aircraft on deck is an Avenger. (Author)

Thane (D48) Ruler *Class Ferry Carrier*

Laid down: 23 February 1943
Launched: 15 July 1943
Completed: 19 November 1943

Builder: Seattle-Tacoma Shipbuilding Corp., Seattle
Machinery: 1-shaft Allis-Chalmers geared turbine; 2 Foster Wheeler boilers; 8,500shp = 18 knots
Displacement: 11,400 tons standard; 15,390 tons deep load
Dimensions: 492ft overall x 108ft 6in max beam x 25ft 5in max draught
Gun armament: 2 single 5in US Mk 12 (2); 8 twin

HMAS *Sydney* leaving Sydney during her later days as a troop transport. Note the two large cranes installed on either side of the deck forward. (RAN Official)

40mm Bofors (16); 14 twin 20mm Oerlikon (28); 7 single 20mm Oerlikon (7)
Fuel: 3,290 tons FFO
Endurance: 27,500 miles @ 11 knots
Complement: 646
Protection: Splinter protection for bomb room
Flight deck: 450ft x 80ft wood-covered steel
Arrester wires: 9 x 19,800lb @ 55 knots; 3 barriers
Hangar: 260ft x 62ft x 18ft
Catapults: 1 x H4C; 16,000lb @ 74 knots (tail-down method only)
Lifts: *Fwd* 42ft long x 34ft wide; *aft* 34ft long x 42ft wide; both 14,000lb
Aircraft: Up to 90 could be ferried; up to 30 could be operated
Aircraft fuel: 36,000 gallons AVGAS
Air weapons: None carried

Notes: One of the carriers laid down as units of the USN *Prince William* class and one of 23 ships transferred to the RN under Lend/Lease arrangements.The ship was built from the outset as a carrier but was based on the C3 mercantile hull design. Originally named USS *Sunset* (CVE-48).

Summary of service

19.11.43	Transferred to RN, renamed and commissioned in Tacoma
15.04.44	Sailed to Vancouver for modification to RN standards
08.06.44	Sailed to Norfolk, Va, via Panama Canal
30.07.44	Allocated to WAC as ferry carrier; remained in Norfolk for defect rectification
14.08.44	Sailed for Cape Town with load of aircraft
02.09.44	Arrived at Cape Town
15.09.44	Sailed for Norfolk, Va
03.10.44	In Norfolk, Va
05.10.44	Sailed for Clyde
17.10.44	Arrived in Clyde
06.11.44	Sailed with KMF.36 for Gibraltar
15.11.44	In Gibraltar
20.11.44	In Port Said
30.11.44	In Gibraltar
01.12.44	Sailed for Clyde

16.12.44 Sailed from Clyde for Norfolk, Va
28.12.44 Embarked 1851 NAS (Corsair) for passage to UK
31.12.44 Sailed for UK via New York
14.01.45 Disembarked 1851 NAS to Belfast
15.01.45 Torpedoed by *U482* in Clyde approaches; towed to Faslane and reduced to reserve since dockyard capacity could not be spared to repair her
21.07.45 Allocated to RF and laid up in care and maintenance at Faslane
05.12.45 Returned to USN custody 'as lies' at Faslane; sold by USN and subsequently broken up by Metal Industries at Faslane

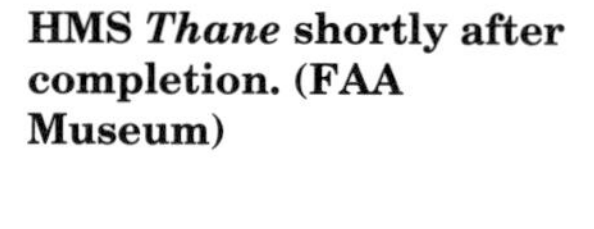

HMS *Thane* shortly after completion. (FAA Museum)

A deck-load of Wildcats being ferried aboard HMS *Thane*. (FAA Museum)

Theseus (R64) Colossus *Class Light Fleet Carrier*

Laid down: 6 January 1943
Launched: 6 July 1944
Completed: 9 February 1946

Builder: Fairfield Shipbuilding & Engineering Co., Govan
Machinery: 2-shaft Parsons geared turbines; 4 Admiralty 3-drum boilers; 40,000shp = 25 knots
Displacement: 13,190 tons standard; 18,040 tons deep load
Dimensions: 695ft overall x 112ft 6in max beam x 23ft 5in max draught
Gun armament: 6 quadruple 2pdr pompoms (24); 16 single 40mm Bofors (16); 4 single 3pdr saluting (4)
Fuel: 3,196 tons FFO
Endurance: 8,300 miles @ 20 knots
Complement: 1,300
Protection: Armoured mantlets over torpedo warheads in magazine
Flight deck: 690ft x 80ft steel
Arrester wires: 10 x 20,000lb @ 60 knots; 2 barriers
Hangar: 275ft (plus 57ft extension aft of aft lift) x 52ft x 17ft 6in
Catapults: 1 x BH3 (twin-track); 16,000lb @ 66 knots
Lifts: *Fwd* 45ft long x 34ft wide; *aft* 45ft long x 34ft wide; both 15,000lb
Aircraft: 35 during Korean operations
Aircraft fuel: 98,600 gallons AVGAS
Air weapons: 1,000lb MC bombs; 500lb GP bombs; 250lb MC bombs; B bombs; 3in RP; Mk 11 depth charges; aircraft mines; 20mm cannon ammunition; flares and pyrotechnics

Notes: The class was designed to mercantile standards below the hangar deck so that they could be built quickly and cheaply in shipyards that did not normally specialise in warship construction.

Summary of service

09.02.46 Commissioned in Glasgow; allocated to Rosyth Command as DLT carrier without assigned air group
01.02.47 Allocated to 1 ACS, BPF, and sailed for Far East via Suez with 804 (Seafire) and 812 (Firefly) NAS embarked
20.12.47 Disembarked 804 and 812 NAS to RNAS Ford; taken in hand for refit in Rosyth
00.00.48 Worked up as flagship of 3 ACS, HF, with 807 (Sea Fury) and 810 (Firefly) NAS
19.06.50 First night landing ever made by jet (Sea Vampire of 703 NAS)
18.08.50 Sailed from Portsmouth for Korea with 17 CAG, comprising 807 (Sea Fury) and 813 (Firefly) NAS, embarked
08.10.50 Sailed from Sasebo for first operational patrol in Yellow Sea off west coast of Korea in company with *Kenya*, *Constance*, *Sioux* and *Cayuga*
09.10.50 Attacks on enemy defences and communications ashore; CAP over Fleet maintained by Sea Furies
10.10.50 Attacks on railway bridges; CAP and AS patrols (latter found minefield north of operating area)
18.10.50 Strikes against coastal shipping, covering sea flank of UN advance into North Korea
21.10.50 Returned to Sasebo for replenishment
27.10.50 Sailed for west coast of Korea (catapult u/s throughout this patrol and aircraft had to 'free take off' without bombs, rockets or drop tanks; sorties consisted mainly of CAP and coastal patrols)
00.11.50 Returned to Sasebo
08.11.50 Sailed for Hong Kong; whilst on passage, catapult re-reeved
13.11.50 Catapult deadweight and flying trials off Hong Kong
01.12.50 Recalled from Hong Kong to join Allied forces attempting to stem communist winter offensive
04.12.50 Arrived at Sasebo to re-join TG 95.1 (Commonwealth force off west coast of Korea)
05.12.50 Strikes launched against bridges, rolling stock, MT and enemy troops (during this third patrol *Theseus* flew 338 sorties in 7 days with 95 per cent serviceability, earning signal of congratulation from Admiral of the Fleet Lord Fraser of North Cape, First Sea Lord)
15.12.50 Returned to Sasebo
16.12.50 Sailed for operational area; at first, bad weather prevented flying
19.12.50 Attacks on troops and transport in Hwangju/Sariwon areas
26.12.50 Returned to Sasebo; in critical month of December, ship spent 23 days at sea and flew 630 sorties, expending 38,000 rounds

	of 20mm ammunition and 1,412 x 3in RP
28.12.50	Moved to Kure to receive replacement aircraft from *Unicorn*
05.01.51	Sailed for operational area
07.01.51	Commenced flying with coastal patrols, CAP and CAS for US 25th Division (bad weather often curtailed flying)
10.01.51	Struck at troops in town of Oryu-Dong
16.01.51	Record number of 60 sorties flown; strikes continued against buildings, railway equipment, trucks and junks
17.01.51	Returned to Sasebo
18.01.51	17th CAG awarded Boyd Trophy for operations off Korea
25.01.51	Sailed for Korean waters with USN helicopter embarked instead of previous Sea Otter
26.01.51	CAS and reconnaissance missions flown from Chinnampo to Haeju
29.01.51	Fireflies spotted for shoot against Nippon Vehicle Factory at Inchon by USS *St Paul*
01.02.51	Attacked dock installations at Haeju and villages and factories south of Suwon
02.02.51	Run of 1,463 accident-free deck landings ended with heavy landing by Sea Fury
03.02.51	Record number of 66 sorties flown, including CAS and attacks on warehouses in Wonum
05.02.51	Entered Kure to take on replacement aircraft from *Unicorn*
13.02.51	Sailed for operational area, giving DLP for new pilots on the way; sorties included coastal patrols as far as Ongju, CAS and attacks on villages and transport near Chowon and Wonju
17.02.51	Sea Furies attacked coastal bridges and gun emplacements between Tungasat and Kwanghwa-do
20.02.51	For remainder of patrol, CAS and armed coastal reconnaissance principal missions
23.02.51	Arrived in Sasebo to take on replacement aircraft from *Unicorn* and spares from *Warrior*
04.03.51	Sailed for west coast of Korea; targets included bridges, rail tunnels and rolling stock, Fireflies using 1,000lb bombs

Whirlwind helicopters of 845 NAS lifting men of 45 RM Commando into action from the deck of HMS *Theseus* during the Suez landings in November 1956. (Author)

HMS *Theseus* entering Sasebo harbour for the last time on 20 April 1951. (Author)

07.03.51 Fireflies spotted for shoot by *Kenya* against bridges in Huhsa-sung estuary
12.03.51 Rocket attack on Ongjin airfield despite heavy, accurate anti-aircraft fire
14.03.51 Returned to Sasebo to take on replacement aircraft from *Unicorn* (during this eighth patrol, *Theseus* had flown 339 sorties of which 226 were offensive)
22.03.51 Sailed for ninth patrol off western Korea; targets included camouflaged vehicles, bridges, roads and rail communications
29.03.51 6 large boats destroyed in Haeju harbour.
01.04.51 Sea Furies attacked hangars at Haeju airfield
02.04.51 Arrived in Sasebo
03.04.51 Embarked USN S-51 Dragonfly from USS *Philippine Sea* for SAR duties
08.04.51 Sailed from Sasebo for last patrol, off east coast of Korea with CTG 95.1, in company with USS *Bataan*, in order to counter possible Red Chinese assault on Formosa
09.04.51 Attacked marshalling yards in Wonsan area; west coast reconnaissance continued by Sea Furies which flew across peninsula
15.04.51 USS *Bataan* left for Sasebo with HMAS *Bataan* as escort; *Theseus* sailed for west coast
17.04.51 Commenced flying operations off west coast for last time (targets included bridges, store dumps and vehicles)
20.04.51 Entered Sasebo for final time with all aircraft ranged on deck and ship's company spelling word 'Theseus'
23.04.51 *Glory* arrived in Sasebo to relieve *Theseus*
25.04.51 Sailed for UK via Hong Kong
29.05.51 Arrived in Portsmouth and presented with Boyd Trophy by First Sea Lord (Admiral of the Fleet Lord Fraser), allocated to 3 ACS, HF
00.01.52 Loaned to MF to relieve *Ocean*
05.06.52 Returned to HF
09.10.52 Loaned to MF to relieve *Glory*
10.12.52 Returned to Portsmouth
00.06.53 Loaned to MF (to October 1953)
19.08.54 Relieved *Implacable* as flagship of HFTS
00.08.56 Left Portsmouth, after hasty modifications, to carry 16 Independent Parachute Brigade Group to Cyprus
00.11.56 Operation 'Musketeer' (Suez landings): acted as commando carrier in company with *Ocean*; helicopters of 845 NAS and JHDU landed 45 RM Cdo at Port Said and evacuated casualties
21.12.56 Returned to Portsmouth and reduced to extended reserve
00.03.58 Approval given for ship to be scrapped
29.11.61 Sold to British Steel Corp. and towed away for scrapping at Inverkeithing

Tracker (D24) Attacker *Class Escort Carrier*

Laid down: 3 November 1941
Launched: 7 March 1942
Completed: 31 January 1943

Builder: Seattle-Tacoma Shipbuilding Corp., Seattle
Machinery: 1-shaft Allis-Chalmers geared turbine; 2 Foster Wheeler boilers; 8,500shp = 18.5 knots
Displacement: 10,200 tons standard; 14,170 tons deep load
Dimensions: 492ft x 102ft max beam x 24ft 8in max draught
Gun armament: 2 single 4in US Mk 9 (2); 4 twin 40mm Bofors (8); 8 twin 20mm Oerlikon (16); 10 single 20mm Oerlikon (10)
Fuel: 3,160 tons FFO
Endurance: 27,300 miles @ 11 knots
Complement: 646
Protection: Splinter protection for bomb room
Flight deck: 442ft x 80ft wood-covered steel
Arrester wires: 9 x 19,800lb @ 55 knots; 3 barriers
Hangar: 262ft x 62ft x 18ft
Catapults: 1 x H2; 7,000lb @ 61 knots (tail-down method only)
Lifts: *Fwd* 42ft long x 34ft wide; *aft* 34ft long x 42ft wide; both 14,000lb
Aircraft: Up to 20 could be operated; up to 90 could be ferried
Aircraft fuel: 44,600 gallons AVGAS
Air weapons: Mk XXIV mines (homing torpedoes); 22.4in torpedoes; 18in torpedoes; 500lb SAP bombs; 250lb MC bombs; Mk 11 depth charges; .5in gun ammunition; .303in gun ammunition; flares and pyrotechnics

Notes: Intended as the sixth unit of the *Avenger* class for the RN (BAVG-6), *Tracker* was laid down as the C3 merchantman *Mormacmail*. She was taken over incomplete and extensively modified to become the lead ship of the later, improved *Attacker* class (known as the *Bogue* class in the USN), 11 units of which were transferred to the RN under Lend/Lease arrangements, the remainder being retained in USN service. Improvements included the distinctive, box like island to starboard, steam turbine rather than diesel propulsion, two lifts rather than a single unit and an enlarged hangar. *Tracker* was equipped as an AS escort carrier.

Summary of service

31.01.43 Commissioned in Tacoma
28.02.43 Moved to Seattle
13.03.43 Sailed for New York
23.03.43 Transited Panama Canal
04.04.43 Arrived in New York
03.05.43 Sailed with UGF.8 with cargo of US aircraft for Casablanca
10.05.43 Arrived in Casablanca
13.05.43 In Gibraltar
30.05.43 Sailed from Gibraltar with MKF.15 to Belfast
04.06.43 Arrived in Belfast; taken in hand for modification to RN standards
15.08.43 Allocated to WAC; commenced work-up in Clyde area with 816 NAS (Swordfish/Seafire) embarked
02.09.43 Operated as DLT carrier in Clyde area, embarking variety of aircraft from 768 NAS while *Argus* was in refit
23.09.43 Re-embarked 816 NAS and sailed to support ON.203
30.09.43 Supported HX.258
05.10.43 Returned to Clyde
19.10.43 Supported ON.207
28.10.43 Supported HX.262
29.10.43 Supported ON.209 and HX.263
05.11.43 Supported HX.264
12.11.43 Arrived in Argentia to carry out machinery defect repairs
23.11.43 Sailed from Argentia for Norfolk, Va
28.11.43 Arrived in Norfolk, Va, for further repair work
05.12.43 Sailed
15.12.43 Supported HX.270
28.12.43 Disembarked 816 NAS to RNAS Donibristle
05.01.44 Embarked 846 NAS (Avenger/Wildcat) and worked up with new aircraft
15.01.44 Repairs in Clyde
13.02.44 Sailed to support KMS.42
02.03.44 Supported MKS.41
12.03.44 Arrived in Clyde for further repairs to machinery
25.03.44 Sailed for Scapa Flow
28.03.44 Sailed from Scapa Flow with escort for JW.58 (during a very successful series of actions to cover this convoy and the returning RA.58 from Kola, *Tracker*'s Avengers shared *U288* with 819 NAS Swordfish, shared *U355* with the destroyer *Beagle* and damaged *U362*, *U673* and *U990*;

Swordfish and Seafires of 816 NAS ranged aft on board HMS *Tracker* in 1943. (J. D. Brown via author)

	Wildcats shot down 3 FW 200Cs, 2 Ju 88s and 1 Bv138C)
15.04.44	Arrived in Belfast for repairs to damage caused when aircraft crashed on deck
29.04.44	Sailed for Scapa Flow
07.05.44	Arrived in Scapa Flow
09.05.44	Arrived in Clyde for refit
03.06.44	Sailed with forces to block English Channel as part of Operation 'Neptune' (Normandy landings)
10.06.44	Collided with *Teme*
11.06.44	Disembarked 846 NAS to Limavady
12.06.44	Arrived in Belfast
19.06.44	Arrived in Liverpool for repairs
20.09.44	Embarked 853 NAS (Avenger/Wildcat) and worked up in Clyde area
05.10.44	Defect rectification in Clyde area
15.10.44	Arrived in Scapa Flow
21.10.44	Sailed as part of escort for JW.61
28.10.44	Arrived in Kola
31.10.44	Sailed with the escort for RAG.1 (although no kills were achieved, neither convoy suffered losses)
07.11.44	In Greenock
10.11.44	Loaned to USN as ferry carrier; sailed from Clyde for New York
01.01.45	Sailed for San Diego
29.01.45	Sailed from Long Beach with cargo of aircraft for USPF forward operating base at Manus (from this point on, *Tracker* continued to be employed by USN to ferry aircraft from US West Coast to forward areas such as Leyte, crossing Pacific via Pearl Harbor)
19.07.45	Sailed from San Pedro for Balboa
22.07.45	Sailed for Norfolk, Va
29.07.45	Sailed for Clyde
09.08.45	De-stored in Clyde and laid up in reserve
10.11.45	Sailed for Portsmouth
14.11.45	Sailed for Norfolk, Va
29.11.45	Returned to USN at Norfolk, Va; sold as mercantile *Corrientes*
24.09.64	Broken up at Antwerp

Triumph (R16) Colossus *Class Light Fleet Carrier*

Laid down: 27 January 1943
Launched: 2 October 1944
Completed: 9 May 1946

Builder: Hawthorn Leslie & Co., Hebburn-on-Tyne
Machinery: 2-shaft Parsons geared turbines; 4 Admiralty 3-drum boilers; 40,000shp = 25 knots
Displacement: 13,350 tons standard; 18,200 tons deep load
Dimensions: 695ft overall x 112ft 6in max beam x 23ft 5in max draught
Gun armament: 6 quadruple 2pdr pompoms (24); 19 single 40mm Bofors (19); 4 single 3pdr saluting (4)
Fuel: 3,196 tons FFO
Endurance: 8,300 miles @ 20 knots
Complement: 1,300
Protection: Armoured mantlets over torpedo warheads in magazine
Flight deck: 690ft x 80ft steel
Arrester wires: 10 x 20,000lb @ 60 knots; 2 barriers
Hangar: 275ft (plus 57ft extension aft of aft lift) x 52ft x 17ft 6in
Catapults: 1 x BH3 (twin-track); 16,000lb @ 66 knots
Lifts: *Fwd* 45ft long x 34ft wide; *aft* 45ft long x 34ft wide; both 15,000lb
Aircraft: 42
Aircraft fuel: 98,600 gallons AVGAS
Air weapons: 18in torpedoes; 1,000lb MC bombs;

500lb GP bombs; 250lb MC bombs; B bombs; 3in RP; Mk 11 depth charges; aircraft mines; 20mm cannon ammunition; flares and pyrotechnics

Notes: Like other units of the *Colossus* and *Majestic* classes, *Triumph* was built to mercantile standards up to the hangar deck. This hastened production and enabled yards that did not normally build warships to participate. She was converted to a heavy repair ship between 1957 and 1964, her pennant number being changed to A108 on completion; in the latter role she looked like her half-sisters *Perseus* and *Pioneer*. With new superstructure on the old flight deck, she lost the ability to operate fixed-wing aircraft but retained a helicopter operating spot forward.

Summary of service:

02.10.44 Launched by Countess Mountbatten of Burma

00.00.46 Commissioned and employed as trials and training carrier

00.07.46 Visited Kronstadt, flying flag of Admiral of the Fleet Lord Fraser, CinC HF.

00.05.47 Escorted battleship *Vanguard* when she returned to UK after HM King George VI's tour of South Africa; 13 CAG, comprising 800 (Seafire) and 827 (Firefly) NAS, embarked

00.06.47 Allocated to MF

00.07.47 Visited Istanbul, flying flag of CinC MF

01.08.47 Embarked HM King Paul I of Greece to witness flying operations

21.04.49 Recommissioned at Sheerness after short refit

00.07.49 Sailed for FEF with 13 CAG embarked; carried out strikes against communist terrorists in Malaya

08.06.50 Anchored off Ominato in Japan

12.06.50 Carried out air group work-up in Japanese waters

24.06.50 Sailed for Hong Kong with destroyer *Cossack* as escort

29.06.50 Ordered to join Task Force 77 under Vice-Admiral C. T. Joy USN to support UN operations in Korea (*Triumph* and *Cossack* joined Rear-Admiral Andrewes, FO2 FEF, flying his flag in cruiser *Belfast,* with *Jamaica* and *Consort* in company, off Okinawa; 827 NAS flew constant AS patrols, 800 NAS stood by for CAP)

02.07.50 Joined USS *Valley Forge* off Korea and both carriers flew familiarization sorties around combined RN/USN task force

03.07.50 Commenced strike operations: 12 Seafires and 9 Fireflies attacked Haeju airfield (100 per cent serviceability in 800 NAS—no mean feat); hangars rocketed and strafed but no enemy aircraft seen

06.07.50 Replenished in Sasebo (black and white 'invasion stripes' painted on to RN aircraft because it was feared that with their in-line engines the USN might mistake them for North Korean Yak-9s); British base rapidly established in Sasebo

15.07.50 Sailed with *Valley Forge* to strike at targets on east coast of Korea (Fireflies maintained AS patrol and Seafires 4-aircraft CAP)

19.07.50 Ship's SAR Sea Otter rescued USN Corsair pilot from sea (last recorded operational rescue of this type)

21.07.50 Stern gland trouble caused ship to leave operational area early

22.07.50 Arrived in Sasebo, where replacement Seafires were taken on from *Unicorn*

24.07.50 Sailed for Korean east coast, where *Valley Forge* flew strikes and, because of limited range of her aircraft, *Triumph* flew CAP and AS patrols

26.07.50 Transferred to the Korean west coast with *Comus* as escort

28.07.50 Seafire shot down in error by USAF B-29

31.07.50 Arrived in Kure for aircraft maintenance period

09.08.50 Sailed for Sasebo, where FO2 FEF was embarked, after which ship joined *Kenya*, *Comus*, *Sioux* and *Athabaskan* for operations off west coast of Korea

13.08.50 Photographic sorties by Seafires over Mokpo and Kunsan

14.08.50 Strikes carried out against shipping in Chinnampo

16.08.50 In Sasebo

18.08.50 Operational off west coast; 150ft gunboat sunk off Inchon

21.08.50 Ship's Seafires spotted for bombardment by *Consort*

23.08.50 Entered Sasebo

26.08.50 Sailed for operations off Korean west coast; 800 NAS reduced to only 9 aircraft, which concentrated on CAP sorties

29.08.50 Propeller blade from Firefly which had hit barrier crashed through Operations Room scuttle and killed CO of 800 NAS (buried at sea that evening); SP took over command

30.08.50 Arrived in Sasebo and embarked last reserve Seafires in FEF from *Unicorn*

	(Fireflies of 827 NAS also proving difficult to support)
03.09.50	Sailed for operations off west coast
04.09.50	Sorties included CAP, reconnaissance and strikes on coastal shipping
05.09.50	Deployed to Korean east coast to replace USN carriers whilst they replenished; road and rail communications successfully rocketed and strafed but with loss of 3 aircraft in operational accidents
10.09.50	Alongside in Sasebo
12.09.50	Sailed flying flag of FO2 FEF in company with *Warramunga*, *Concord*, *Charity* and *Cockade* as Commonwealth Task Force 91, to support UN landing at Inchon; ship's few remaining aircraft covered assault convoy as it passed south of Korea on passage from Japan
13.09.50	Armed reconnaissence and bombardment spotting sorties flown in support of USMC landings
20.09.50	Only 11 aircraft remained serviceable: FO2 FEF decided that ship had reached end of her operational usefulness and she was withdrawn from combat area
21.09.50	Docked in Sasebo for temporary repairs to starboard stern gland
29.09.50	Arrived in Hong Kong
00.11.50	Returned to Portsmouth and recommissioned for service as troopship operating between UK and Middle East
00.02.52	Flying trials carried out to assess practicability of angled deck layout: angled deck painted on flight deck and variety of aircraft flew approaches without landing, although wires remained set for for fore and aft landings and could not, thus, arrest an aircraft landing on the 3-degree painted angle with safety (trials extremely successful and led to joint RN/USN trials in USS *Antietam*, fitted with full 8-degree angled deck with wires modified to match)
00.09.53	Relieved cruiser *Devonshire* as DTS after short refit which equipped her with extra accommodation and classrooms in former hangar (some air facilities retained and Ship's Flight of Sea Balliols operated to give air experience to young officers)
00.10.55	Visited Leningrad
00.00.56	Dartmouth Training task taken on by frigates and ship paid off into reserve; Board approval given to convert her into heavy repair ship
00.12.57	Conversion started in Portsmouth Dockyard
00.00.60	Conversion suspended
Mid. 62	Conversion re-started
09.10.64	Commenced preliminary sea trials
07.01.65	Commissioned as heavy repair ship at Portsmouth; allocated to FEF, ship based in Singapore and used to maintain destroyers and frigates; helicopter landing spot retained forward on former flight deck for use by Wasp Flights in ships undergoing

HMS *Triumph* with an interesting range of aircraft on deck, including a Sea Vampire, a Sea Mosquito, a Firefly, a Seafire and a Barracuda. (FAA Museum)

maintenance (ship spent several periods at sea, including spells on Beira Patrol and disaster relief work in Pakistan)
00.02.72 Returned to Portsmouth after disbandment of FEF
00.03.72 Refitted at Chatham
00.12.75 Refit completed; ship placed in maintained reserve at Chatham
00.00.81 Placed on disposal list and sold to Spanish shipbreakers
09.12.81 Towed from Chatham to be broken up in Spain

Trouncer (D85) Ruler *Class Ferry Carrier*

Laid down: 1 February 1943
Launched: 16 July 1943
Completed: 31 January 1944

Builder: Seattle-Tacoma Shipbuilding Corp., Seattle; completed by Commercial Ironworks
Machinery: 1-shaft Allis-Chalmers geared turbine; 2 Foster Wheeler boilers; 8,500shp = 18 knots
Displacement: 11,400 tons standard; 15,390 tons deep load
Dimensions: 492ft overall x 108ft 6in max beam x 25ft 5in max draught
Gun armament: 2 single 5in US Mk 12 (2); 8 twin 40mm Bofors (16); 27 single 20mm Oerlikon (27)
Fuel: 3,160 tons FFO
Endurance: 27,500 miles @ 11 knots
Complement: 646
Protection: Splinter protection for bomb room
Flight deck: 450ft x 80ft wood-covered steel
Arrester wires: 9 x 19,800lb @ 55 knots; 3 barriers
Hangar: 260ft x 62ft x 18ft
Catapults: 1 x H4C; 16,000lb @ 74 knots (tail-down method only)
Lifts: *Fwd* 42ft long x 34ft wide; *aft* 34ft long x 42ft wide; both 14,000lb
Aircraft: Up to 90 could be ferried; up to 30 could be operated
Aircraft fuel: 36,000 gallons AVGAS
Air weapons: None carried

Notes: One of 23 units of the USN *Prince William* class transferred to the RN under Lend/Lease arrangements to become the *Ruler* class. Built from the outset as a carrier but based on the US C3 mercantile design. Originally named USS *Perdido* (CVE-47) and renamed on transfer.

Summary of service
31.01.44 Transferred to RN and commissioned in Tacoma
29.02.44 Arrived in Vancouver for modification to RN standards
15.05.44 Sailed for Norfolk, Va, via Panama Canal
04.06.44 Arrived in Norfolk, Va
18.06.44 Sailed for Casablanca with cargo of US aircraft
10.07.44 Arrived in Casablanca
13.07.44 Sailed for Norfolk, Va
28.07.44 Sailed for Liverpool via New York
02.08.44 Embarked 1843 NAS (Corsair) for passage to UK
22.08.44 Disembarked 1843 NAS and arrived in Liverpool
26.08.44 Sailed for Norfolk, Va
05.09.44 Sailed for Gibraltar
02.10.44 Sailed for Norfolk, Va
22.10.44 Sailed for Clyde
02.11.44 Employed temporarily in Clyde as DLT carrier
08.12.44 Sailed for New York; returned ferrying aircraft
18.01.45 Defect repairs in Clyde
05.03.45 Arrived in Belfast for refit
14.09.45 Allocated to 21 ACS, EIF; embarked 1702 NAS (Firefly) for passage to Malta
22.09.45 Disembarked 1702 NAS to RNAS Hal Far, Malta
14.10.45 Arrived in Colombo
18.10.45 Sailed for Durban
28.10.45 Arrived in Durban
17.11.45 Sailed for Clyde via Cape Town
14.12.45 Arrived in Clyde to de-store
26.01.46 Sailed for Trinindad
13.02.46 Sailed for Bermuda
19.02.46 Sailed for Norfolk, Va
03.03.46 Returned to USN at Norfolk, Va; sold by USN as mercantile *Greystoke Castle*
00.00.54 Renamed *Gallic*
00.00.59 Renamed *Benrinnes*
03.11.73 Commenced breaking-up in Taiwan

HMS *Trouncer*. (Author)

Trumpeter **(D09)** Ruler *Class Escort Carrier*

Laid down: 25 August 1942
Launched: 15 December 1942
Completed: 4 August 1943

Builder: Seattle-Tacoma Shipbuilding Corp., Seattle; completed by Commercial Ironworks
Machinery: 1-shaft Allis-Chalmers geared turbine; 2 Foster Wheeler boilers; 8,500shp = 18 knots
Displacement: 11,200 tons standard; 15,390 tons deep load
Dimensions: 492ft overall x 108ft 6in max beam x 25ft 6in max draught
Gun armament: 2 single 5in US Mk 12 (2); 8 twin 40mm Bofors (16); 14 twin 20mm Oerlikon (28); 7 single 20mm Oerlikon (7)
Fuel: 3,290 tons FFO
Endurance: 27,500 miles @ 11 knots
Complement: 646
Protection: Splinter protection for bomb room

Flight deck: 450ft x 80ft wood-covered steel
Arrester wires: 9 x 19,800lb @ 55 knots; 3 barriers
Hangar: 260ft x 62ft x 18ft
Catapults: 1 x H4C; 16,000lb @ 74 knots (tail-down method only)
Lifts: *Fwd* 42ft long x 34ft wide; *aft* 34ft long x 42ft wide; both 14,000lb, 50-second cycle
Aircraft: Up to 30 could be operated; up to 90 could be ferried
Aircraft fuel: 48,000 gallons AVGAS
Air weapons: 22.4in torpedoes; 500lb SAP bombs; 250lb MC bombs; 3in RP; aircraft mines; Mk 11 depth charges; .5in gun ammunition; flares and pyrotechnics

Notes: Built from the outset as a carrier but based on the US C3 mercantile design. Laid down as USS*Bastian* (CVE-37) of the *Prince William* class but transferred to RN under Lend/Lease. Renamed on transfer.

Summary of service

04.08.43 Transferred to RN and commissioned in Portland, Oregon
26.08.43 Sailed for Norfolk, Va
29.09.43 Passed through Panama Canal
06.10.43 Arrived in Norfolk, Va; embarked 848 (Avenger) and 1831 and 1833 (Corsair) NAS for passage to UK
23.10.43 Sailed for Belfast via New York
01.11.43 Disembarked 848, 1831 and 1833 NAS to Belfast; allocated to WAC as ferry carrier and ferried aircraft from New York to Clyde in two Atlantic crossings
04.02.44 Arrived in Dundee for refit
21.05.44 Sailed for Rosyth for further modifications
04.06.44 Allocated to HF; started work-up, based on Clyde, with 846 NAS (Avenger/Wildcat)
18.07.44 Post work-up defect rectification in Clyde
01.08.44 Arrived in Scapa Flow
08.08.44 Sailed with HF for air strikes on Gossan with 846 NAS embarked
22.08.44 Operation 'Goodwood' (HF naval air strike on *Tirpitz* in Kaafjord) with *Formidable*, *Furious*, *Indefatigable* and *Nabob*
28.09.44 Sailed from Scapa Flow for operations off Norwegian coast with 846 (Avenger only) and 852 (Avenger) NAS embarked
13.10.44 Minelaying operations off Norway
23.10.44 Minelaying operations off Norway
29.10.44 Repairs in Clyde
24.11.44 Returned to Scapa Flow
12.12.44 Operations off Norway with 881 NAS (Wildcat) embarked
21.12.44 Operations off Norway with 881 NAS
02.01.45 Part of HF sweep based on Scapa Flow with 846 (Avenger/Wildcat) and 881 (Wildcat) NAS embarked
05.02.45 Refit on Clyde
13.03.45 Sailed from Scapa Flow with escort for JW.65 with 846 NAS embarked
21.03.45 Arrived in Kola
23.03.45 Sailed with RA.65
06.04.45 Minelaying operations off Norway
01.05.45 Strike on German shipping in Kilbotn, near Harstad, in company with *Queen* and *Searcher* (last RN air strike of European war): 846 NAS sank depot ship *Black Watch* and *U711* which had been secured alongside
04.05.45 Covered Allied liberation of Denmark
15.05.45 Refit in Clyde
07.07.45 Allocated to EF; sailed for Colombo
30.07.45 Arrived in Colombo; used as DLT carrier in Ceylon area
04.09.45 Allocated for trooping duties in EF
08.09.45 Arrived in Port Swettenham
26.09.45 Arrived in Singapore
07.10.45 Arrived in Trincomalee
06.11.45 Arrived in Bombay
16.11.45 Arrived in Singapore
23.11.45 Arrived in Trincomalee
09.12.45 Arrived in Cochin
03.01.46 Arrived in Colombo
05.01.46 Sailed for UK via Bombay, Suez, Malta and Toulon
10.02.46 Arrived in Clyde; paid off for de-storing
06.04.46 Returned to USN at Norfolk, Va; sold by them as mercantile *Alblasserdijk*
00.00.66 Renamed *Irene Valmas*
01.05.71 Broken up at Castellon

HMS *Trumpeter* serving with the Home Fleet in 1944. (J. D. Brown via Author).

Unicorn (R72) *Aircraft Repair Ship*

Laid down: 29 June 1939
Launched: 20 November 1941
Completed: 12 March 1943

Builder: Harland & Wolff, Belfast
Machinery: 2-shaft Parsons geared turbines; 4 Admiralty 3-drum boilers; 40,000shp = 24 knots
Displacement: 14,750 tons standard; 20,300 tons deep load
Dimensions: 640ft overall x 90ft max beam x 24ft 10in max draught
Gun armament: 4 twin 4in QF Mk 16 HA (8); 4 quadruple 2-pdr pompom (16); 5 twin 20mm Oerlikon (10); 6 single 20mm Oerlikon (6); 4 single 3pdr saluting (4)
Fuel: 3,000 tons FFO
Endurance: 7,500 miles @ 20 knots
Complement: 1,200
Protection: 2in flight deck; 2in magazine crowns; 4in–4.5in magazine sides; 1in NC lift platforms; 1.25in internal anti-torpedo bulkhead
Flight deck: 640ft x 90ft armoured steel
Arrester wires: 6 x 20,000lb @ 60 knots; 1 barrier
Hangar: *Upper* 324ft x 65ft x 16ft 6in; *lower* 360ft x 62ft x 16ft 6in
Catapult: 1 x BH3; 12,500lb @ 66 knots
Lifts: *Fwd* 46ft long x 33ft wide; *aft* 46ft long x 24ft wide; both 20,000lb, 46-second cycle
Aircraft: Typically 20 under repair in workshops; 35 as operational carrier
Aircraft fuel: 36,000 gallons AVGAS
Air weapons: 18in torpedoes; 250lb MC bombs; Mk 11 depth charges; 20mm cannon ammunition; .303in gun ammunition; flares and pyrotechnics (as operational carrier in 1943; no air armament carried when operating as aircraft repair ship)

Notes: Designed to provide aircraft support facilities for air groups embarked in fleet carriers on a scale broadly comparable to the support given to destroyers and submarines by depot ships. The requirement for such a ship was identified during extensive carrier exercises by the MF in the 1930s. She was fitted with an elaborate system of hoists and transfer rails in her two hangars to facilitate component replacement. The after end of the upper hangar was open for aircraft engine runs and there was a long flight deck extension aft under which a self-propelled aircraft lighter was suspended from davits. Aircraft could be moved on to this from the upper hangar and conveyed, once it was lowered into the water, to another carrier. A comprehensive range of engine, radio, electrical and airframe workshops was incorporated together with an extensive stores complex carrying spares for all front-line aircraft. *Unicorn* was a useful and successful ship and she formed the basis of the 1942 light fleet carrier design. Her pennant number was changed to A195 in 1953 when she was redesignated as a ferry carrier.

Summary of service

00.03.43	Allocated temporarily to HF
00.05.43	Ferried Beaufighter aircraft to Gibraltar in MKF.15
00.07.43	Operation 'Governor' off Norway (intended to divert German interest from operations in Mediterranean); air group comprised 887 (Seafire) and 818 and 824 (Swordfish) NAS
00.08.43	Deployed to Mediterranean to act as assault carrier
09.09.43	Operation 'Avalanche' (invasion of Italy at Salerno): air group comprised 809, 887 and 897 (Seafire) NAS and 818 (Swordfish) Flight; ship formed part of Force V under Rear-Admiral Sir Philip Vian in company with *Attacker*, *Battler*, *Hunter* and *Stalker*; during operation, air group reinforced by aircraft from 885 (Seafire) and 888 and 893 (Martlet) NAS transferred from *Formidable* and 894 (Seafire) NAS from *Illustrious*
12.09.43	Deployed 2 Seafires ashore to operate from advanced landing ground at Paestum
20.09.43	Sailed for UK after short visit to Bizerta
00.10.43	Refitted in Belfast to carry out original role as aircraft repair carrier
30.12.43	Sailed from Clyde in company with *Illustrious*, *Renown*, *Queen Elizabeth* and *Valiant* for new EF, deploying via Mediterranean
30.01.44	Arrived in Colombo; acted as aircraft supply and repair ship and as DLT carrier (based in Colombo, then in Trincomalee)
10.12.44	Allocated to BPF and refitted in Durban
01.01.45	Sailed to join BPF via Diego Suarez, Addu Atoll and Colombo
07.02.45	Arrived in Fremantle
12.02.45	Arrived in Sydney
28.02.45	Sailed with replacement aircraft for BPF's forward operating base at Manus; ship

supported 1 ACS throughout operations in support of American landings on Okinawa (Operation 'Iceberg')

00.08.45 Formed part of Task Force 112 under Rear-Admiral Fleet Train based at Manus
00.01.46 Returned to Devonport and paid off into reserve
00.00.49 Refurbished for service in Far East
18.09.49 Sailed for FEF with supply of replacement aircraft to support *Triumph*
21.10.49 Arrived in Singapore
25.06.50 In Singapore de-storing when South Korea was invaded by communist North; ship made ready hastily and sailed for Sasebo with aircraft to sustain operations by *Triumph*
20.07.50 Arrived in Sasebo
24.07.50 Sailed for Iwakuni to collect spare aircraft; subsequently ran 'shuttle service' between Hong Kong and Sasebo collecting aircraft, equipment and victualling stores for *Triumph* and her consorts, including 300 barrels of rum
25.08.50 Embarked Middlesex Regiment and Argyll and Sutherland Highlanders from Hong Kong for Korea (first British troops to be allocated to UN)
29.08.50 Troops landed at Pusan
02.09.50 Sailed from Korean waters for refit in Hong Kong
17.10.50 Sailed for Sasebo with aircraft, stores and ammunition
02.12.50 Ferried troops to Korea from Japan
03.12.50 Rendezvoused with *Theseus* off west coast of Korea and transferred 5 Sea Furies and 1 Firefly
12.12.50 In Sasebo
27.12.50 Sailed for Kure
05.01.51 Sailed for Singapore via Hong Kong
25.01.51 Sailed from Singapore with replacement troops and stores for Korea
14.02.51 Passed through Shimonoseki Strait between Honshu and Kyushu en route to Sasebo (largest RN warship to do so)
16.02.51 Sailed for Singapore
12.03.51 Embarked Meteor fighters for No 77 Squadron RAAF and troops for passage to Iwakuni
27.03.51 Arrived in Sasebo to act as base ship
17.06.51 Sailed for refit in Singapore
03.09.51 Sailed for Korean waters
22.09.51 Recovered 2 aircraft from *Glory* that had force-landed at Paengyong-do
01.10.51 Struck overhead power cables whilst passing through Shimonoseki Strait, causing major 'black-out' in Kyushu
22.11.51 Paid off for major refit in Singapore; old ship's company sailed home in *Warrior*
09.12.51 Docked in Singapore
24.01.52 Embarked Vampires to be delivered to RAF at Kai Tak and Vampires for RAAF at Iwakuni
09.02.52 In Iwakuni
15.02.52 Fired 56-gun salute to mark funeral of HM King George VI
16.02.52 Provided DLP for replacement pilots for *Glory*
29.06.52 Transferred aircraft and stores to *Ocean* at Sasebo
03.07.52 Sailed with *Ocean* to act as 'spare deck' in operational area
10.07.52 Disembarked Sea Fury and Firefly aircraft to AHU at Iwakuni
27.07.52 In Singapore to transfer aircraft to *Vengeance* for passage to UK
09.08.52 Sailed with Meteors for RAAF at Iwakuni
01.09.52 Joined *Ocean* in operational area off west coast of Korea and flew CAP sorties with Sea Furies of 802 NAS loaned from *Ocean*
15.09.52 Maintenance period in Kure
10.10.52 Visited by Admiral Sir Roderick McGrigor (First Sea Lord)
08.12.52 Arrived in Singapore for refit
16.03.53 Sailed for Sasebo
30.05.53 In Singapore with *Glory* for Coronation celebrations
17.07.53 Sailed for Japan with replacement aircraft
30.07.53 With *Ocean* in operational area with 4 Sea Furies of 802 NAS embarked
25.08.53 Carried out last patrol in Korean waters (during four years' service in Far East, *Unicorn* had steamed over 130,000 miles, handled over 600 aircraft and carried more than 6,000 troops into war zone; her support for Commonwealth carriers was essential to conduct of their operations)
21.09.53 In Singapore
15.10.53 Sailed for UK
17.11.53 Returned to Devonport and paid off into reserve
00.03.57 Reduced to extended reserve
00.00.58 Approved for disposal
00.06.59 Towed from Devonport
15.06.59 Arrived at Dalmuir to be stripped by Arnott Young
00.00.60 Hull scrapped in Troon

HMS *Unicorn* post-war with late-production Seafires on deck. Note the pronounced overhang of the flight deck aft, under which the lighter was stowed. (FAA Museum)

Venerable (R04) Colossus *Class Light Fleet Carrier*

Laid down: 3 December 1942
Launched: 30 December 1943
Completed: 17 January 1945

Builder: Cammell Laird & Co., Birkenhead
Machinery: 2-shaft Parsons geared turbines; 4 Admiralty 3-drum boilers; 40,000shp = 25 knots
Displacement: 13,190 tons standard; 18,040 tons deep load
Dimensions: 695ft overall x 112ft 6in max beam x 23ft 5in max draught
Gun armament: 6 quadruple 2pdr pompom (24); 11 twin 20mm Oerlikon (22); 10 single 20mm Oerlikon (10); 4 single 3pdr saluting (4)
Fuel: 3,196 tons FFO
Endurance: 8,300 miles @ 20 knots
Complement: 1,300
Protection: Armoured mantlets over torpedo warheads in magazine

Flight deck: 690ft x 80ft steel
Arrester wires: 10 x 15,000lb @ 60 knots; 2 barriers
Hangar: 275ft (plus 57ft extension aft of aft lift) x 52ft x 17ft 6in
Catapults: 1 x BH3 (twin-track); 16,000lb @ 66 knots
Lifts: *Fwd* 45ft long x 34ft wide; *aft* 45ft long x 34ft wide; both 15,000lb
Aircraft: 42 in 1945
Aircraft fuel: 98,600 gallons AVGAS
Air weapons: 18in torpedoes; 1,000lb MC bombs; 500lb SAP bombs; 250lb GP bombs; B bombs; 3in RP; Mk 11 depth charges; aircraft mines; .5in gun ammunition; .303in gun ammunition; flares and pyrotechnics

Notes: In order to speed production and enable manufacturers not used to warship construction to contribute, this class was built to merchant ship strengths up to the hangar deck level. The original specification called for the 1942 light fleet carriers to last for three years or the duration of the war, whichever was less. It is a tribute to the inherent strength of her design and construction that *Venerable* is still operating, albeit in another navy, fifty years after her first commissioning.

Summary of service

17.01.45 Commissioned in Birkenhead; worked up for operational service in Clyde with 1851 (Corsair) and 814 (Barracuda) NAS embarked (flew flag of Rear-Admiral C. H. J. Harcourt, FO 11 ACS)
12.03.45 Sailed for Far East in company with remainder of 11 ACS comprising *Vengeance*, *Glory* and *Colossus*
20.03.45 Arrived in Malta; air group landed to continue intensive work-up based at RNAS Hal Far
22.05.45 Re-embarked aircraft for passage to Far East
08.06.45 Arrived in Colombo
07.07.45 Sailed for Sydney
22.07.45 Arrived in Sydney (four light fleet carriers intended to join *Indomitable* in expanded 11 ACS for operations in East Indies)
15.08.45 VJ-Day; Admiral Harcourt shifted his flag to *Indomitable* and, with *Venerable* in company, sailed for Hong Kong
31.08.45 Launched last sorties against Japanese forces (Corsairs, Hellcats, Avengers and Barracudas from the two carriers dive-bombed and strafed suicide boats that had sortied for an attack; other craft, hidden to north of Hong Kong Island, were also destroyed); continuous CAP maintained
02.09.45 Japanese forces in Hong Kong surrendered
20.10.45 Sailed for Trincomalee with Indian former POWs on board (for remainder of 1945 ship ferried men and equipment to and from Bombay, Singapore, Batavia and Fremantle)
01.01.46 Arrived in Sydney for refit
00.00.46 Operational service in BPF with 814 and 1851 NAS embarked
21.10.46 Refit in Singapore
00.02.47 Sailed for UK
30.03.47 Returned to Devonport; de-stored and paid off into reserve
01.04.48 Sold to Dutch government
28.05.48 Commissioned as HMNLS *Karel Doorman* (replacing ex British *Nairana* which had also been named *Karel Doorman*); ship operated air group of Sea Furies and Fireflies
00.00.54 Extensive modernisation commenced at Wilton-Fijenoord shipyard with steam catapult, angled deck, mirror landing sight and latest radar mounted on tall, combined mast and funnel (known as 'mack')
00.00.58 Re-commissioned with air group of Sea Hawks and Trackers (Sikorsky S-58 helicopters added later)

HMS *Venerable* off Malta in May 1945. (J. D. Brown)

00.00.68 Damaged by major fire in engine room; sold to Argentina and refitted for Argentine Navy at Wilton-Fijenoord (turbines and boilers from incomplete *Leviathan* made available to replace those damaged in fire)
01.09.69 Commissioned as Argentine *25 de Mayo* and sailed for her new home with air group of Skyhawks and Trackers
00.00.81 Super Étendard aircraft purchased from France for air group
00.00.82 During Falklands War, *25 de Mayo* sortied against RN Task Force but loss of cruiser *General Belgrano* to torpedo attack by nuclear submarine *Conqueror* led to her being withdrawn into safer coastal waters (her aircraft operated from ashore with considerable success)
00.00.95 Extant in Argentine Navy

Vengeance (R71) Colossus *Class Light Fleet Carrier*

Laid down: 16 November 1942
Launched: 23 February 1944
Completed: 15 January 1945

Builder: Swan Hunter & Wigham Richardson, Wallsend-on-Tyne; machinery by Wallsend Slipway & Engineering Co.
Machinery: 2-shaft Parsons geared turbines; 4 Admiralty 3-drum boilers; 40,000shp = 25 knots
Displacement: 13,190 tons standard; 18,040 tons deep load
Dimensions: 693ft 9in overall x 112ft 6in max beam x 23ft 5in max draught
Gun armament: 6 quadruple 2pdr pompom (24); 19 single 40mm Bofors (19); 4 single 3pdr saluting (4)
Fuel: 3,196 tons FFO
Endurance: 8,300 miles @ 20 knots
Complement: 1,300
Protection: Armoured mantlets over torpedo warheads in magazine
Flight deck: 690ft x 80ft steel
Arrester wires: 10 x 15,000lb @ 60 knots; 2 barriers
Hangar: 275ft (plus 57ft extension aft of aft lift) x 52ft x 17ft 6in
Catapults: 1 x BH3 (twin-track); 16,000lb @ 66 knots
Lifts: *Fwd* 45ft long x 34ft wide; *aft* 45ft long x 34ft wide; both 15,000lb
Aircraft: 42
Aircraft fuel: 98,600 gallons AVGAS
Air weapons: 18in torpedoes; 1,000lb MC bombs; 500lb SAP bombs; 250lb MC bombs; 3in RP; Mk 11 depth charges; aircraft mines; .5in gun ammunition; flares and pyrotechnics

Notes: Built to mercantile standards up to the hangar deck in order to speed production and save cost. Like other units of the *Colossus* and *Majestic* classes, *Vengeance* was designed to last for three years or for the duration of the war—whichever was less. She is still in existence in 1995, has given many years of valuable service in three navies and, by any standards, must be adjudged a most successful ship that has given excellent value for money.

Summary of service

15.01.45 Commissioned in Newcastle; allocated to 11 ACS under Rear-Admiral C. H. J. Harcourt (flying his flag in *Venerable*); destined for BPF
12.03.45 Sailed for work-up in Mediterranean with 1850 (Corsair) and 812 (Barracuda) NAS embarked, in company with *Glory*, *Colossus* and *Venerable*
20.03.45 Disembarked air group to Malta and returned to Gibraltar for repairs
18.04.45 Sailed for Suez Canal
28.05.45 Passed Port Said en route to Colombo
23.07.45 Arrived in Sydney
15.08.45 Sailed for BPF forward operating base at Manus
00.09.45 Arrived in Hong Kong (remained there for rest of year)
00.01.46 Sailed for refit in Sydney
16.01.46 Arrived in Sydney
01.03.46 Allocated to EIF but actually used to ferry aircraft from Singapore to Kure in Japan before joining it in Ceylon
20.07.46 Sailed from Colombo for UK
13.08.46 Returned to Devonport; taken in hand for refit
14.12.46 Refit completed; allocated to Rosyth Command as training carrier
05.06.47 Visited Oslo, flying flag of Admiral Sir John Cunningham (First Sea Lord) as part of HF

HMAS *Vengeance* on 22 July 1953. (RAN Official)

	summer cruise; went on to visit number of Norwegian ports
00.07.47	Visited Clyde with HF to express RN's gratitude for work of Clydeside during WW2
05.08.47	In Portsmouth for docking and repairs
16.09.47	Sailed to join BPF
00.02.48	Returned to UK
03.05.48	Taken in hand in Rosyth Dockyard for refit
01.07.48	Sailed to join 3 ACS, HF; 15 CAG, comprising 802 (Sea Fury) and 814 (Firefly) NAS, embarked; took part in HF cruises to West Indies and South Africa
16.12.48	Modified in Portsmouth Dockyard for Operation 'Rusty' (6-week cruise in Arctic to study effects of extreme cold weather on men, ships and aircraft; flying operations by range of aircraft, including Sea Vampires and Dragonflies, proved highly successful)
08.03.49	Returned to Rosyth for refit
19.08.49	Took part in HF autumn cruise
00.01.50	HF spring cruise to Mediterranean
09.01.51	Relieved *Illustrious* as trials and training carrier
00.08.51	Entered Portsmouth Dockyard for conversion for trooping duties to and from Far East
20.01.52	Sailed for Singapore carrying aircraft and men
18.02.52	Arrived in Singapore
28.03.52	Returned to Portsmouth
00.06.52	Sailed to ferry aircraft to Malta
20.06.52	Sailed to Singapore for further trooping duties
28.08.52	Returned to Portsmouth
22.09.52	Entered Devonport Dockyard for DED in preparation for transfer to RAN
13.11.52	Commissioned in Devonport for service in RAN on loan prior to completion of *Melbourne*
22.01.53	Sailed for Australia
11.03.53	Arrived in Sydney and joined 5 ACS, RAN; air group comprised 808 and 850 (Sea Fury) with 817 (Firefly) ANAS
00.09.53	850 ANAS transferred to *Sydney*
00.00.54	Used as training ship during last months with RAN
00.06.55	Sailed from Sydney for UK (ship's company manned new *Melbourne* on arrival)
13.08.55	Returned to Devonport and reduced to Class 3 reserve
13.12.56	Sold to Brazilian government and renamed *Minas Gerais*
00.00.57	Completely rebuilt to modernised standards by Rosenburg Yard of Verolme United Shipyards, Rotterdam, Holland, with a full 6-degree angled deck, steam catapult, mirror landing aid and rebuilt island
06.12.60	Commissioned into Brazilian Navy with AS air group of Trackers and Sea Kings
00.00.95	Extant (after refit that should enable ship to serve until the turn of the century, improvements including new electrical generators, new boilers, improved command facilities and new radar)

HMS *Victorious* refuelling from a US Navy oiler whilst serving with the US Pacific Fleet in 1943. Note that the Avengers and Wildcats on deck have USN-style 'star' markings. (Author)

Victorious (R38) Illustrious *Class Fleet Carrier*

Laid down: 4 May 1937
Launched: 14 September 1939
Completed: 15 May 1941

Builder: Vickers-Armstrong, Newcastle-upon-Tyne; machinery by Wallsend Slipway & Engineering Co.
Machinery: 3-shaft Parsons SR geared turbines; 6 Admiralty 3-drum boilers; 110,000shp = 31 knots
Displacment: 30,300 tons standard; 35,500 tons deep load
Dimensions: 778ft 3in overall x 145ft 9in max beam x 31ft max draught
Gun armament: 6 twin 3in US Mk 33 (12); 1 sextuple 40mm Bofors (6); 4 single 3pdr saluting (4)
Fuel: 4,180 tons FFO
Endurance: 11,000 miles @ 12 knots
Complement: 2,400
Protection: 3.25in flight deck; 4.5in belt and hangar sides; 2.5in hangar deck
Flight deck: 775ft x 145ft armoured steel; 8-degree angled deck
Arrester wires: 5 x 35,000lb @ 103 knots; emergency nylon barriers
Hangar: 360ft (plus 52ft extension fwd of fwd lift) x 62ft 6in x17ft 6in
Catapults: 2 x BS4 (145ft stroke); 50,000lb @ 97 knots
Lifts: *Fwd* 58ft long x 40ft wide; *aft* 54ft long x 34ft wide; both 42,000lb, 22-second cycle
Aircraft: 36
Aircraft fuel: 327,800 gallons AVCAT
Air weapons: Firestreak AAM; Sidewinder AAM; Red Top AAM; Bullpup ASM; Mk 30,44 and 46 homing torpedoes; 1,000lb MC bombs; 500lb MC bombs; 3in RP; 2in RP in pods; Mk 11 depth charges;

aircraft mines; 30mm gun ammunition; 20mm gun ammunition; flares and pyrotechnics

Notes: Built as one of the first three units of the *Illustrious* class. For details of *Victorious* as completed, see *Formidable* which was closely similar; the details given here show the ship after completion of rebuilding in Portsmouth Dockyard between 1950 and 1958, at the end of which, she emerged as one of the world's most advanced carriers. The original hangar was heightened and a new accommodation deck built over it. She was re-boilered and given two steam catapults, a fully angled deck, a mirror landing aid and a new island with the technically advanced Type 984 three-dimensional radar mounted on top of it. It would, arguably, have been cheaper and quicker to have built a new carrier to the fully revised design but the sum total of necessary improvements was not known when work started, such was the rapid progress made in carrier design at the time. When she emerged in 1958 with a new generation of naval aircraft and the huge range of weapons to support them, there can be no doubt that *Victorious* was one of the most capable ships ever deployed by the RN, only the modernised *Eagle* exceeding her potential.

Summary of service

29.03.41 Commissioned in Walker Naval Yard, Tyneside

16.04.41 Sailed for sea trials and passage to Rosyth

04.05.41 Embarked 48 crated Hurricanes for shipment to RAF in Malta

15.05.41 Sailed for Scapa Flow, intention being to join WS.8 for Middle East (there was insufficient time to work up)

22.05.41 Allocated to HF as part of force hastily put together to contain German battleship *Bismarck* and heavy cruiser *Prinz Eugen*; embarked 800Z Flight (Fulmar) and 825 NAS (Swordfish); Fulmars carried out surface searches in bad weather

25.05.41 825 NAS carried out torpedo attack on *Bismarck* in terrible weather: one torpedo struck and further damaged *Bismarck*'s No 2 boiler room, hit during action with *Hood* and *Prince of Wales* the day before

29.05.41 Returned to Clyde

31.05.41 Sailed with WS.8X

04.06.41 Swordfish of 825 NAS sighted German tanker *Gonzenheim*, which was subsequently intercepted by *Neptune*

13.06.41 Operation 'Tracer' (ship flew off assembled RAF Hurricanes to Malta)

29.06.41 Re-joined HF with 809 (Fulmar) and 827 and 828 (Albacore) NAS embarked

30.07.41 Following political decision to support Russia, which had recently been attacked by Germany, *Victorious* and *Furious* attacked Petsamo and Kirkenes; surprise not achieved but one 2,000-ton freighter sunk, another damaged and 5 enemy aircraft shot down (but HF lost 11 Albacores and 2 Fulmars, only 1 of former returning undamaged)

23.08.41 Sailed with HF to provide cover for first Russian convoy with 809 (Fulmar) and 817 and 832 (Albacore) NAS embarked; strikes carried out in Bodø area

22.02.42 Participated in sweep for pocket battleship *Lützow* off Norwegian coast (missed in heavy snowstorm)

07.03.42 Whilst HF covered PQ.12, *Tirpitz* was discovered at sea by air search; torpedo attack by 817 and 832 NAS failed because of lack of recent training and high winds into which enemy was steaming at high speed (disappointment in *Victorious* tempered by Hitler's decree that *Tirpitz* was never to sail again if HF included a carrier)

04.08.42 Sailed for Mediterranean to form part of fighting escort for 'Pedestal' convoy to Malta with 809 and 884 (Fulmar), 885 (Sea Hurricane) and 817 and 832 (Albacore) NAS embarked

10.08.42 Entered Mediterranean in company with *Indomitable*, *Eagle* and *Furious* and escorted convoy (subsequent action legendary, with 5 ships, including tanker *Ohio*, reaching Malta; 30 enemy aircraft shot down for loss of 13 fleet fighters)

16.08.42 Sailed from Gibraltar to re-join HF

08.11.42 Detatched from HF to Force H to provide cover for Operation 'Torch' (invasion of North Africa), with 809 (Fulmar), 882 (Martlet), 884 (Seafire) and 817 and 832 (Albacore) NAS embarked; French airfield at Blida captured by Lt Nations of 882 NAS and his Flight when he landed after seeing white flags raised

11.11.42 Albacore of 817 NAS sank *U517* in mid Atlantic whilst *Victorious* was on passage to UK

20.11.42 Loaned to USN to reinforce its depleted carrier fleet; refitted with USN equipment in Norfolk, Va

02.02.43 Passed through Panama Canal into Pacific

HMS *Victorious* during replenishment operations in San Pedro Bay, Leyte, in late April 1945. (FAA Museum)

11.03.43 Arrived in Pearl Harbor to join CinCPac's Fast Carrier Task Force; air group comprised 882, 896 and 898 (Wildcat) and 832 (Avenger) NAS with aircraft issued by USN and wearing USN-style 'star' markings and flight deck operations carried out using US methods (ship operated in company with USS *Saratoga* and aircraft frequently cross-decked: such was superiority of experienced fighter direction team in *Victorious* that she frequently took on most of the fighters while the strike aircraft concentrated on *Saratoga*)

01.09.43 Returned to Norfolk and returned US equipment

27.09.43 Arrived in Liverpool for refit

04.03.44 Sailed to re-join HF with 47 Naval Fighter Wing (comprising 1834 and 1836 NAS with Corsairs) and 827 and 829 (Barracuda) NAS embarked

03.04.44 Operation 'Tungsten' (carrier air strike on *Tirpitz* in Kaafjord); striking force comprised *Victorious* and *Furious* with *Emperor*, *Pursuer*, *Searcher* and *Fencer* in support (14 direct hits scored by 40 Barracudas, which caused extensive damage and 438 casualties, and 2 Barracudas were lost over target plus a third and a Hellcat on take-off; repairs to make *Tirpitz* seaworthy took 3 months)

12.06.44 Sailed from Scapa Flow to join EF

03.07.44 Arrived in Bombay

25.07.44 Operation 'Crimson' (carrier support for battleship bombardment of Sabang) in company with *Illustrious*; 1834, 1836 and 1838 (Corsair) NAS embarked

29.08.44 Strikes against Emmahaven and Indaroeng in company with *Indomitable*; 47 Naval Fighter Wing and 822 (Barracuda) NAS embarked

18.09.44 Operation 'Light' (strikes against Sigli) with same air group

17.10.44 Operation 'Mullet' (strikes against Nicobar Islands) with 47 Naval Fighter Wing embarked

10.12.44 Became part of 1 ACS, BPF, with air group comprising 1834 and 1836 (Corsair) NAS, 849 (Avenger) NAS and 2 SAR Walrus (this group did not change for rest of war)

04.01.45 Struck at Pangkalan Brandan in company with *Indomitable* and *Indefatigable*

24.01.45 Operation 'Meridian' (strikes on refineries in Palembang complex by whole BPF): Pladjoe hit first by 43 Avengers supported by 12 Fireflies and about 50 fighters (172 x 500lb bombs dropped accurately, halving output for next 3 months and burning all oil in storage tanks; 34 enemy aircraft

HMS *Victorious* after her reconstruction, with Buccaneers, Sea Vixens, Gannets and Wessexes on deck. She is seen about to enter the Johore Straits and is flying a paying-off pennant. Aircraft are ranged ready but hands are not yet fallen in for a ceremonial entry into Singapore Naval Base. (Author)

	destroyed on ground); 1 ACS comprised *Indomitable* (flag), *Illustrious*, *Victorious* and *Indefatigable*
29.01.45	Soengi Gerong, second refinery struck by BPF: all production stopped for two months and did not recover fully until after war (one of the most strategically significant attacks carried out by British aircraft in WW2; 38 enemy aircraft were destroyed on ground and 30 in air for the loss of 9 naval aircraft over target)
04.02.45	Arrived in Fremantle
11.02.45	Arrived in Sydney
08.03.45	Sailed with BPF, comprising Task Force 57 of Allied fleets covering Okinawa landings
26.03.45	Operation 'Iceberg' (cover for Okinawa camapaign): 1 ACS struck at airfields in Sakashima Gunto to prevent Japanese reinforcement aircraft staging through
09.05.45	Hit by Kamikaze aircraft near forward lift which caused fire and damage; second Kamikaze crashed into deck park aft, destroying 4 Corsairs, but armoured deck prevented any damage to ship (temporary repairs allowed ship to continue flying in short term but she had to return to Sydney for more permanent repairs)
07.06.45	Arrived in Sydney
12.07.45	In Manus (forward operating base) with *Formidable* (flag). *Implacable* and *Indefatigable* (BPF now comprised Task Force 37, which formed part of US Third Fleet for strikes on Japanese home islands)
11.08.45	Lack of available fuel in fleet train compelled bulk of BPF to return to Sydney, leaving token force, including *Indefatigable* off Tokyo
15.08.45	At sea on passage on VJ-Day
25.09.45	Sailed from Sydney for UK
31.10.45	Arrived in Portsmouth
00.12.45	Trooping voyages to and from UK, Australia and Far East with no aircraft on board
00.01.47	Paid off into reserve
00.10.47	Commissioned with limited ship's company and no aircraft for service in HFTS at Portland
00.03.50	Taken in hand for major modernisation work in Portsmouth Dockyard
14.01.58	Re-commissioned at Portsmouth
03.02.58	Sailed for extensive sea trials
23.06.58	First deck landing on modernised deck by Cdr S. J. A. Richardson RN in Gannet; air group comprised 803 (Scimitar), 893 (Sea Venom), 849B (Skyraider) and 824 (Whirlwind) NAS
03.09.58	In Portsmouth after work-up
28.09.58	Sailed for Mediterranean
13.10.58	In Malta; faults with both catapults and Whirlwind engine defects limited flying, but visits made to Toulon and Messina
14.01.59	Returned to Portsmouth
20.02.59	Exercise 'Dawn Breeze IV' with *Eagle*, *Centaur* and Allied ships
Spr. 59	Visited Oslo, Aarhus and Torquay
04.05.59	Embarked 700Y NAS (Sea Vixen) for sea trials
00.06.59	Sailed for USA to demonstrate new equipment and Scimitar fighter
10.07.59	In Norfolk, Va
00.07.59	Exercise 'Riptide' with USN, followed by visits to Boston and New York
Aut. 59	Exercise 'Blue Frost' off northern Norway (during which ditched Skyraider crew were rescued by Soviet trawler)
00.12.59	Radio Luxemburg 'Take Your Pick' programme broadcast from on board whilst ship alongside in Portsmouth
16.01.60	Sailed to carry out initial deck landing trials with NA.39 Buccaneer (31 successful launches and recoveries achieved)
02.04.60	Minor refit in Portsmouth, after which 892 NAS (Sea Vixen) replaced 893 NAS (Sea Venom) in air group
00.00.61	Provided aid for victims of flooding in Kenya in company with *Centaur*
29.06.61	Ordered to Persian Gulf 'with all dispatch', having been on passage to Hong Kong; provided air defence for British forces defending newly independent state of Kuwait against threat of Iraqi aggression
31.07.61	Relieved in Gulf by *Centaur*; proceeded to Mombasa for restful visit
00.12.61	Re-joined HF
02.04.62	Paid off for major refit in Portsmouth
12.06.63	Recommissioned for service with FEF with 801 (Buccaneer), 893 (Sea Vixen), 849A (Gannet AEW) and 814 (Wessex ASW) NAS
00.00.63	Operations in support of Malaysia during confrontation with Indonesia
00.05.64	Visited Yokosuka Naval Base, Japan
Late 64	After short refit in Singapore, new ship's company flown out from UK to man her (first time this was done for a carrier)
00.07.65	Returned to UK; 801 NAS re-equipped with Buccaneer S.2

00.04.66 Buccaneer of 801 NAS carried out simulated strike on Gibraltar from launch position in Irish Sea (round trip of 2,300 miles) as part of demonstration of RN capability to Press
07.04.66 Recommissioned in Portsmouth
08.07.66 Sailed to re-join FEF
00.06.67 Passed through Suez Canal just before Arab-Israeli 'Six-Day War'; held in Malta area in case needed to support British intervention (when this did not happen, ship returned to Portsmouth)
21.06.67 Portsmouth for refit
00.11.67 Slightly damaged by fire and withdrawn from service two years before planned retirement (given the minimal nature of the damage, and the proven capability of this successful ship, it is difficult not to judge this as a mistaken decision)
00.07.69 Broken up at Faslane

Vikrant (R11) Majestic *Class Light Fleet Carrier*

Laid down: 12 October 1943
Launched: 22 September 1945
Completed: 4 March 1961
Builder: Vickers-Armstrong, Newcastle-upon-Tyne (completed by Harland & Wolff, Belfast)
Machinery: 2-shaft Parsons geared turbines; 4 Admiralty 3-drum boilers; 40,000shp = 25 knots
Displacement: 16,000 tons standard; 19,500 tons deep load
Dimensions: 700ft overall x 128ft max beam x 25ft max draught
Gun armament: 4 twin 20mm Bofors (8); 7 single Bofors (7)
Fuel: 3,200 tons FFO
Endurance: 8,300 miles @ 20 knots
Complement: 1,343 as built
Protection: Armoured mantlets for 32 torpedo warheads
Flight deck: 700ft x 80ft steel
Arrester wires: 4 x 20,000lb @ 104 knots; emergency nylon barriers
Hangar: 273ft (plus 63ft extension aft of aft lift) x 52ft x 17ft 6in
Catapults: 1 x BS4 (103ft stroke); 40,000lb @ 78 knots
Lifts: *Fwd* 54ft long x 34ft wide; *aft* 54ft long x 34ft wide; both 24,000lb, 23-second cycle
Aircraft: 22
Aircraft fuel: 212,000 gallons AVCAT
Air weapons: Magic AAM; Sea Eagle ASM; homing torpedoes; 1,000lb MC bombs; Mk 11 depth charges; 30mm gun ammunition; 20mm gun ammunition; flares and pyrotechnics

Notes: Laid down and built as HMS *Hercules*. Like other units of the *Colossus* and *Majestic* classes, she was built to mercantile standards up to the hangar deck. This hastened production and enabled yards that did not normally build warships to participate. These ships were designed with austerity in mind and wereintended to last three years or for the duration of the war. *Vikrant* represents a remarkable return on her original investment as she is still in service in 1995. She has an up-to-the-minute air group of Sea Harriers and Sea Kings and is likely to last until the turn of the century.

Summary of service
00.05.46 Construction suspended
00.05.47 Laid up at Faslane
00.01.57 Sold to India
00.04.57 Arrived at Harland & Wolff, Belfast, for reconstruction and completion
04.03.61 Commissioned in Belfast
18.05.61 First deck landing by IN Sea Hawk
09.07.61 INAS 300 (Sea Hawk) embarked off Portsmouth
04.08.61 Commenced work-up off Malta
06.10.61 Sailed for India
03.11.61 Arrived in Bombay; remainder of air group comprised INAS 310 (Alizé) and SAR Flight with Alouette III helicopters
00.12.61 Operation 'Vijay' (acquisition of former Portuguese colonies of Goa, Daman and Diu): ship formed part of covering fleet 100 miles offshore
00.09.65 In refit during Indo-Pakistan war (despite extraordinary efforts, she joined Fleet two days before cease-fire that ended war)
26.07.71 INAS 330 (Sea King) embarked for first time but disembarked during subsequent action in Bay of Bengal
03.12.71 Took part in operations in Bay of Bengal

INS *Vikrant* working up in UK waters during 1961. (World Ship Society Photographic Library)

during fighting that led to formation of Bangladesh; Sea Hawks of INAS 300 flew 160 strike and CAP sorties without loss

00.07.72 BAe Harrier G-VTOL carried out demonstrations on board

00.00.79 Re-boilered

21.12.82 First deck landing by IN Sea Harrier

00.02.84 INAS 300 (Sea Harrier) embarked for first time since re-equipment

00.04.86 Exercise 'Trishakti' off west coast of India, involving both strike and defensive operations

00.00.86 Phase I modernisation carried out with new radar and command and control systems (to 00.00.87)

09.05.87 Last Alizé of INAS 310 catapult-launched; INAS to be shore-based at INAS Dabolim

00.00.87 Phase II modernisation carried out, including removal of steam catapult, fitting of 12 degree ski-jump and fitting of white f light deck floodlighting and Sea Harrier visual landing aids (to 1988)

00.00.95 Extant (expected to operate throughout decade with air group of up to 22 Sea Harriers and Sea Kings; IN hopes to replace ship with new carrier at turn of century and a number of designs are being studied)

Vindex (1943) (R15) *Escort Carrier*

Laid down: 1 July 1942
Launched: 4 May 1943
Completed: 3 December 1943

Builder: Swan Hunter & Wigham Richardson, Wallsend-on-Tyne
Machinery: 2-shaft Doxford diesels; 10,700bhp = 17 knots
Displacement: 14,500 tons standard; 17,200 tons deep load
Dimensions: 525ft 6in overall x 68ft max beam x 25ft 8in max draught
Gun armament: 1 twin 4in QF Mk XVI HA (2); 4 quadruple 2 pdr pompom (16); 8 twin 20mm Oerlikon (16)
Fuel: 1,655 tons FFO
Endurance: 13,000 miles @ 16 knots
Complement: 639
Protection: 1in plating on magazine crowns; splinter protection for bomb room; empty oil drums used to fill void spaces
Flight deck: 502ft x 66ft steel
Arrester wires: 6 x 15,500lb @ 60 knots; 1 barrier
Hangar: 231ft x 61ft x 17ft 6in
Catapults: None
Lifts: *Aft* 45ft long x 34ft wide; 15,000lb

Aircraft: 20
Aircraft fuel: 52,000 gallons AVGAS
Air weapons: Mk XXIV mines (homing torpedoes); 18in torpedoes; 500lb SAP bombs; 3in RP; Mk 11 depth charges; 20mm gun ammunition; .5in gun ammunition; .303in gun ammunition; flares and pyrotechnics

Notes: Laid down as fast cargo ship for Ministry of War Transport and taken over by Admiralty on 29 June 1942. Original merchant ship structural design generally followed. Internal decks made watertight and extra transverse bulkheads added. Hangar and flight deck worked in as part of the hull rather than as superstructure. Extra structure all-welded by Smith's Dock Co. of Tyneside. The ship was used for arctic operations since it was felt that the original mercantile lower part of the hull, being riveted, was less prone to cracking than the all-welded hulls of the US-built escort carriers.

HMS *Vindex* with Swordfish ranged aft. (G. M. Hughes via FAA Museum)

Summary of service

15.11.43 Commissioned in Wallsend
30.11.43 Sailed to Rosyth for modifications and installation of RN equipment; allocated to WAC
11.12.43 Arrived in Clyde area for trials with 825 NAS (Swordfish/Sea Hurricane) embarked
21.01.44 Post work-up defect recticifation in Clyde (some damage had to be repaired after collision)
02.03.44 Arrived in Londonderry
11.03.44 AS sweep with 2nd Support Group
15.03.44 Swordfish aircraft shared sinking of *U653* with surface escorts
24.03.44 Swordfish crashed on deck, detonating depth charge which caused fire and damage
28.03.44 Clyde for repairs
26.04.44 AS sweep with 6th Escort Group
06.05.44 Swordfish shared sinking of *U765* with surface escorts
15.05.44 Arrived in Clyde for defect rectification
06.06.44 AS sweep in Western Approaches
11.08.44 Arrived in Scapa Flow; loaned to HF
16.08.44 Covered JW.59
20.08.44 Swordfish sank *U354*
25.08.44 Arrived in Kola
28.08.44 Escorted RA.59A
02.09.44 Swordfish shared sinking of *U394* with surface escorts
07.09.44 Clyde for defect rectification
26.09.44 Collided with *Queen Mary* in Clyde; further repairs carried out
15.10.44 Returned to Scapa Flow
21.10.44 Escorted JW.61 with 811 NAS (Swordfish/Wildcat) embarked
28.10.44 Arrived in Kola Inlet
31.10.44 Escorted RA.61 (no kills in this operation but no ships lost)
10.11.44 Clyde for defect rectification
27.12.44 In Scapa Flow
31.12.44 Escorted JW.63 with 825 NAS (Swordfish/Wildcat) embarked
08.01.45 Arrived in Kola
11.01.45 Escorted RA.63
21.01.45 Arrived in Scapa Flow
23.01.45 Clyde for defect rectification
17.04.45 Escorted JW.66 with 813 NAS (Swordfish/Wildcat) embarked
25.04.45 Arrived in Kola Inlet
29.04.45 Escorted RA.66
17.05.45 Arrived in Clyde shipyard for conversion to replenishment carrier
01.07.45 Allocated to 30 ACS, BPF, as replenishment carrier with 1790 NAS (Firefly NF) embarked; sailed for Far East via Suez and Colombo
11.08.45 Anchored off Brisbane to unload some aircraft and stores; on completion, sailed for Sydney
12.08.45 Arrived in Sydney; took on draft of 300

	extra men and humanitarian stores for relief of Hong Kong (remaining aircraft were landed)
20.08.45	Sailed for Brisbane to take on extra stores
23.08.45	Sailed for Hong Kong via Leyte and Manus
08.09.45	Arrived off Hong Kong; port propeller damaged by wreck when moving alongside berth in Kowloon
14.09.45	300 Australian former POWs and civilians from Stanley Internment Camp taken on board for passage to Australia
18.09.45	Sailed for Australia
03.10.45	Arrived in Sydney; spent rest of year on trooping duties, carrying stores, deck cargoes of aircraft and passengers to and from Australia, Hong Kong and Iwakuni
30.11.45	Collided with junk in Hong Kong
09.02.46	Refit in Sydney; on completion, transported shore HQ of BPF from Sydney to Colombo; once there, took loads of Lend/Lease aircraft to sea to jettison them over side (to avoid having to pay USN for them)
23.09.47	Stripped of naval equipment in Rosyth
02.10.47	Bought by Port Line (original owners) and renamed *Port Victor*
04.10.47	Towed to Wallsend for conversion to fast cargo ship
23.08.71	Broken up in Taiwan

Vindictive (–) *Modified* Cavendish *Class Cruiser*

Laid down: 26 June 1916
Launched: 17 January 1918
Completed: 21 September 1918

Builder: Harland & Wolff, Belfast
Machinery: 4-shaft Parsons geared turbines; 12 Yarrow boilers; 60,000shp = 30 knots
Displacement: 9,750 tons standard; 12,400 tons deep load
Dimensions: 605ft overall x 65ft 2in max beam x 20ft 6in max draught
Gun armament: 4 single 7.5in LA Mk VI (4); 4 single 3in LA (4); 4 single 3in AA (4); 4 x .303in MG (4); 6 x 21in torpedo tubes
Fuel: 1,600 tons FFO; 800 tons coal
Endurance: 5,400 miles @ 14 knots
Complement: 648
Protection:1.5in–3in belt; 1.5in upper deck; 1.5in main deck; 1in magazine crowns
Flight deck: *Fwd* 78ft x 49ft aft tapering to 44ft fwd; *aft* 193ft x 57ft; both steel
Arrester wires: None
Hangar: 78ft x 49ft tapering to 44ft fwd
Catapults: 1 x HIII hydraulic; 12,000lb @ 55 knots (fitted in 1925)
Lifts: Hatch giving access to after part of the hangar (aircraft hoisted out by derrick)
Aircraft: 12 in 1919
Aircraft fuel: Varying amounts carried in 2-gallon tins
Air weapons: .303 gun ammunition; flares and pyrotechnics

HMS *Vindictive* in 1918. (J. D. Brown via Author)

Notes: Laid down as the name-ship of a class of heavy cruisers; renamed in honour of the ship that played a key role in the WW1 Zeebrugge raid. Converted into second fast carrier for GF along the lines of*Furious*. The gun armament was reduced and a hangar was fitted forward, the roof of which formed the flying-off deck. A landing-on deck was fitted aft. However, the failure of the landing trials in *Furious* and the success of those in *Argus* showed that the design had no future. Although she carried aircraft, *Vindictive* never operated them in the intended manner.

Summary of service

01.10.18 Commissioned
18.10.18 Joined Flying Squadron, GF, at Scapa Flow; used mainly for aircraft trials
01.11.18 Only landing on after deck carried out by W. W. Wakefield in Sopwith Pup
02.07.19 Sailed for operations against Bolshevik forces in Baltic with air group of Camels, Short 184s, 1½-Strutters and Grain Griffins
06.07.19 Grounded near Reval and only refloated after 8 days with great difficulty
30.07.19 Ship's aircraft, operating from airstrips ashore, bombed Kronstadt (as well as supporting aircraft operations ashore, *Vindictive* acted as depot ship for 8 motor torpedo boats)
24.12.19 Paid off into reserve at Portsmouth
00.02.20 Alternated between reserve and duty as troopship
01.03.23 Taken in hand at Chatham Dockyard for conversion back to cruiser (all air facilities, except hangar, removed and two 7.5in guns added; catapult added over hangar—first major British warship to have one—and crane added starboard forward to lift aircraft out of hangar on to catapult; older derricks removed)
03.10.25 First catapult launch of Fairey IIID (trials also carried out with float-fitted Flycatchers)
01.01.26 Sailed for China Station with air group of 6 Fairey IIIDs; employed on anti-piracy patrols as well as working with Fleet
14.03.28 Sailed for UK
00.05.28 Returned to Chatham Dockyard for refit, during which catapult and all aircraft support facilities removed (ship never again able to operate aircraft)
00.00.29 Maintained in reserve
00.05.37 Demilitarised under terms of London Naval Treaty; converted into cadet training ship
07.09.37 Commissioned for DTS
00.00.39 Converted into heavy repair ship (hangar structure removed)
00.00.40 Served as repair ship off Norway (for remainder of WW2 ship served in South Atlantic, Mediterranean and home waters)
08.09.45 Paid off into unmaintained reserve
24.01.46 Sold for scrap and later broken up in Blyth

Warrior (R31) Colossus *Class Light Fleet Carrier*

Laid down: 12 December 1942
Launched: 20 May 1944
Completed: 14 March 1946

Builder: Harland & Wolff, Belfast
Machinery: 2-shaft Parsons geared turbines; 4 Admiralty 3-drum boilers; 40,000shp = 24.5 knots
Displacement: 14,000 tons standard; 19,600 tons deep load
Dimensions: 695ft overall x 112ft 6in max beam x 23ft 7in max draught
Gun armament: 4 twin 40mm Bofors (8); 18 single 40mm Bofors (18)
Fuel: 3,200 tons FFO
Endurance: 8,300 miles @ 20 knots
Complement: 1,300
Protection: Armoured mantlets over 32 torpedo warheads in magazine
Flight deck: 690ft x 93ft steel; 4-degree angled deck
Arrester wires: 8 x 15,000lb @ 60 knots; emergency nylon barrier
Hangar: 275ft (plus 57ft extension aft of aft lift) x 52ft x 17ft 6in
Catapults: 1 x modified BH3 hydraulic; 20,000lb @ 60 knots
Lifts: *Fwd* 45ft long x 34ft wide; *aft* 45ft long x 34ft wide; both 20,000lb
Aircraft: 42
Aircraft fuel: 155,000 gallons AVCAT; 24,000 gallons AVGAS
Air weapons: 18in torpedoes; 1,000lb MC bombs; 500lb SAP bombs; Mk 11 depth charges; aircraft mines; 20mm cannon ammunition; flares and pyrotechnics

Notes: Last of the *Colossus* class carriers to be completed and subsequently modernised to a greater extent than any of her sister ships, being fitted with an angled deck, a mirror landing aid and strengthened arrester gear. She was capable of operating any of the generation of aircraft in service in the late 1950s. The flexible deck trials in 1949 represented a remarkable attempt to

HMCS *Warrior* in November 1946. (Canadian Department of National Defence)

improve the performance of carrier-borne fighters by removing the need for an undercarriage, thus making them lighter and/or allowing more fuel to be carried. The Achilles' heel of the whole concept was of course the inability of the aircraft to move once it had landed until it had been lifted on to a trolley by a crane. Recovery times could hardly have been better than one aircraft every five minutes in good weather and considerably worse in bad weather. Furthermore, a worldwide system of airfields equipped with flexible decks would have been necessary for aircraft to disembark or divert to. The idea seems so impractical that is difficult to understand, years after the event, how so much serious effort was devoted to it. Details are for the ship as she was in 1957.

Summary of service

00.05.45	Admiralty approved transfer of ship on loan to RCN on completion
24.01.46	Commissioned in Belfast as HMCS *Warrior*
23.03.46	Sailed from Portsmouth for Halifax
31.03.46	Arrived in Halifax and commenced work-up with 803 (Seafire) and 825 (Firefly) CNAS embarked
00.05.47	Allocated to Canadian Atlantic Fleet based on Halifax; 803 and 825 incorporated into 19 CAG
00.01.48	Sailed for Belfast to deliver stores and personnel for HMCS *Magnificent* which was nearing completion
01.03.48	Arrived in Portsmouth
23.03.48	Formally returned to RN and recommissioned as HMS *Warrior*; refitted in Portsmouth with experimental flexible rubber deck designed to allow jet aircraft to land without undercarriages following trials at RAE Farnborough
00.03.49	Trials with Vampire F.21 aircraft carried out on flexible deck (Lt-Cdr E. M. Brown RN awarded Boyd Trophy for this experimental work)
00.06.49	Trials completed (athough technically successful, concept proved completely unworkable in practice and was not adopted; flexible deck removed)
00.09.49	Paid off into Category B reserve in Portsmouth
00.06.50	Brought forward for service as aircraft and

troop transport between UK and Far East
00.08.50 Sailed on first of four trooping runs to Far East
00.06.51 Transported 16 Parachute Brigade Group to Cyprus as result of security crisis in island
00.12.51 Ceased trooping duties and returned to Devonport
00.04.52 Started limited modernisation in Devonport Dockyard, during which bridge was extended and tripod mast was replaced by improved lattice structure
08.09.53 Recommissioned in Devonport
00.10.53 Post-refit trials
15.02.54 Sailed for work-up in Mediterranean with 811 (Sea Fury) and 825 (Firefly) NAS embarked
12.05.54 Joined FEF and relieved *Sydney* in UN Force monitoring cease-fire after armistice in Korea
25.08.54 Ordered to assist in evacuation of refugees from North to South Vietnam following request to British government from Vietnamese Prime Minister
31.08.54 Sailed from Singapore to Haiphong following hasty modifications (including installation of extra 'heads')
04.09.54 Transported over 3,000 refugees who wanted to escape communist regime in north of country, from Haiphong to Saigon
13.09.54 Evacuation completed
23.09.54 Sailed from Singapore for UK via Durban, Port Elizabeth, Cape Town and Dakar
00.10.54 Ship received Unit Citation from President of Vietnam for her work
14.12.54 Returned to Devonport and paid off for extended refit and modernisation (including fitting of angled deck and improved arrester gear)
21.08.56 Recommissioned in Devonport: intention was for ship to relieve *Bulwark* as trials and training carrier but ship was instead allocated to squadron supporting Operation 'Grapple' (British nuclear tests in Pacific planned for 1957)
02.02.57 Sailed from Portsmouth with Ship's Flight of Avengers and Whirlwind helicopters embarked
04.03.57 Arrived off Christmas Island (during tests ship provided aircraft to collect samples and provide SAR, weather reporting and radar tracking facilities)
00.08.57 Sailed for UK

HMS *Warrior* in late 1956 after her modernisation. (Author)

11.10.57 Arrived in Portsmouth
00.02.58 Paid off into extended reserve at Portsmouth
00.03.58 Placed on Disposal List (Sales)
04.07.58 Purchased by Argentina
24.07.58 Renamed *Independencia*
04.11.58 Argentine ensign hoisted for first time during ceremony in Portsmouth
10.12.58 Sailed for Buenos Aires (in Argentine Navy ship operated air group of F4U Corsairs and AT-6 Harvards
00.00.71 Withdrawn from service and broken up

A Sea Vampire landing on HMS *Warrior*'s flexible deck during 1948. (FAA Museum)

Part 2: Seaplane Carriers

Albatross (I22) *Seaplane Carrier*

Laid down: 5 May 1926
Launched: 23 February 1928
Completed: January 1929

Builder: Cockatoo Island Dockyard, Sydney
Machinery: 2-shaft Parsons geared turbines; 4 Yarrow small-tube boilers; 12,000shp = 20 knots
Displacement: 4,800 tons standard; 6,350 tons deep load
Dimensions: 443ft 9in overall x 68ft max beam x 16ft 6in max draught
Gun armament: 4 single 4.7in HA/LA (4); 4 quadruple 2pdr (16); 6 single 20mm Oerlikon (6)
Fuel: 942 tons FFO
Endurance: 9,500 miles @ 10 knots
Complement: 450
Protection: None
Flight deck: None
Arrester wires: None
Hangar: 130ft x 60ft x 21ft
Catapults: 1 x EIII hydraulic; 12,000lb @ 55 knots
Lifts: Hatch 40ft x 24ft through which aircraft were lifted by crane
Aircraft: 9 (6 normally carried)
Aircraft fuel: 8,300 gallons AVGAS
Air weapons: 250lb SAP bombs; 100lb AS bombs; Mk VII depth charges; Mk VIII depth charges; .303in gun ammunition; flares and pyrotechnics

Notes: *Albatross* was designed to provide modest air support for the Australian Squadron more cheaply than would have been possible with a conventional carrier. Transferred to the RN in 1938 in partial payment for the new cruiser HMS *Apollo*, which became HMAS *Hobart*. Details apply to the ship as she was in 1942.

Summary of service

00.01.29 Patrolled and surveyed dependent territories north of Australia with 101 Flight RAAF (6 Seagull III seaplanes) embarked
00.12.31 Paid off for refit
00.00.32 Recommissioned as gunnery training ship, retaining 4 aircraft of 101 Flight
19.03.32 Anchored off Garden Island, Sydney, for ceremonial opening of Harbour Bridge
26.04.33 Paid off into Class E Reserve at Garden Island (aircraft transferred to cruisers *Australia* and *Canberra* but ship still used to support seaplanes visiting harbour, with manpower from RAAF Richmond)
00.00.36 Designed hydraulic catapult fitted for first time
00.08.36 Carried out trials with Seagull V (Walrus), which proved to be too high for hangar and had to be stowed on special trolley with undercarriage retracted
00.09.36 Proposed reactivation postponed owing to economic difficulties
00.00.38 Transferred to RN
19.04.38 Recommissioned
11.07.38 Sailed for UK manned by crew intended to commission HMAS *Hobart*
00.08.38 Ship's company provided part of funeral cortège in Gibraltar for Spanish sailors killed in Republican destroyer action with Nationalist cruiser during Spanish Civil War
09.09.38 Arrived in Devonport
29.09.38 Commissioned into RN at Devonport as trials ship
15.12.38 Paid off into reserve (catapult removed and *Albatross* then used as accommodation ship in Devonport)
25.08.39 Recommissioned at Devonport
31.08.39 Embarked 710 NAS (Walrus)
14.09.39 Sailed for Sierra Leone (based in Freetown, ship and her aircraft proved only way of

HMS *Albatross*. (FAA Museum)

providing AS protection for convoys on these distant trade routes); moored near Hastings while RNAS Hastings was being constructed ashore

26.01.40 Cruised convoy routes based mainly on Freetown

24.06.40 Embarked CinC South Atlantic, Vice-Admiral d'Oyly Lion

25.06.40 Led force which attempted to neutralise French Fleet in Dakar

26.06.40 Walrus aircraft detected breakout by French battleship *Richelieu*

03.07.40 Returned to Freetown

14.05.41 710 NAS disembarked to RNAS Hastings and ship proceeded to refit in Simonstown, during which replacement EIII catapult, removed from HMS *Orion*, was fitted

13.09.41 Resumed AS operations with 710 NAS embarked

22.12.41 Sailed via Trinidad for refit in Mobile, Alabama

02.04.42 Sailed from Mobile

20.04.42 Re-embarked 710 NAS from RNAS Hastings

31.05.42 Allocated to EIF for convoy protection duties in western Indian Ocean

21.07.42 Carried out AS patrols in Mozambique Channel based at Mayotte, Madagascar

09.09.42 Moved to Majunga, from where ship's aircraft carried out reconnaissence patrols in support of military operations ashore

09.10.42 In Majunga, used as command ship for forces occupying southern Madagascar

20.10.42 Arrived in Diego Suarez

00.10.42 Ferried 795 NAS (fighter pool) from Madagascar to RNAS Tanga, East Africa

27.11.42 Refit in Durban

04.03.43 Sailed for Bombay with 710 NAS embarked

27.03.43 Disembarked 710 NAS to RAF Santa Cruz, then used for some months as Combined Operations training ship

20.07.43 Re-embarked 710 NAS and sailed for Kilindini, where aircraft and stores landed

17.08.43 Sailed for UK with personnel from 710 NAS embarked

06.10.43 Arrived in Devonport

00.10.43 Carried out sea trials with new Sea Otter amphibian

05.11.43 Paid off into care and maintenance at Devonport

17.04.44 Refitted for duty as landing craft repair ship

23.05.44 Grounded on Goodwin Sands and attacked by German aircraft (no damage)

02.06.44 In Southend; allocated to forces for D-Day landing on 'Sword' beach

06.06.44 Flagship of follow-up Force L, Eastern Naval Task Force; used to repair landing craft to get them back into service quickly (whilst so doing, ship engaged shore batteries and shot down Ju 88); during Operation 'Neptune' ship saved 79 landing

	craft from total loss and repaired 132 others
24.06.44	Hit by German 5.9in shell (minor damage)
01.07.44	Moved to 'Gold' Force
11.08.44	Hit by long-range torpedo which killed 50 and caused extensive damage; towed to UK
12.08.44	Temporary repairs to keep ship afloat carried out but not returned to active service
30.08.44	Paid off into reserve.
00.11.44	Recommissioned for use as minesweeper depot ship at Portsmouth
00.07.45	Paid off into reserve
00.08.45	Towed to Falmouth for Category C Reserve
08.08.45	Paid off completely at Falmouth; subsequently laid up off Isle of Wight
19.08.46	Sold for conversion to luxury liner (plan fell through)
21.11.47	Sold to Greek Yannaulatos Group who converted her to passenger ship renamed *Hellenic Prince*
00.00.49	Carried 1,000 refugees from Europe to Australia
12.08.54	Broken up in Hong Kong

Anne (–) *Seaplane Carrier*

Laid down: ?
Launched: ?
Completed: 1911

Builder: Rickmers AG, Bremerhaven
Machinery: 1-shaft triple-expansion steam engine; ? boilers; ?ihp = 11 knots
Displacement: 4,083 tons deep load
Dimensions: 367ft 1in overall x 47ft 7in max beam x 27ft 3in draught
Gun armament: 1 single 12pdr LA (1); 1 single .303in MG (1)
Fuel: ?
Endurance: ?
Complement: ?

Protection: None
Flight deck: None
Arrester wires: None
Hangar: Canvas windscreens for up to 3 seaplanes
Catapults: None
Lifts: None
Aircraft: Up to 3 seaplanes
Aircraft fuel: Variable amounts AVGAS carried in 2-gallon tins
Air weapons: Grenades; .303in gun ammunition

Notes: Built as the merchant ship *Änne Rickmers* for Rickmers Reismuhlen Reederai & Schiffbau AG and captured in Port Said in August 1914. Temporary modifications were carried out to enable her to fulfil a role as

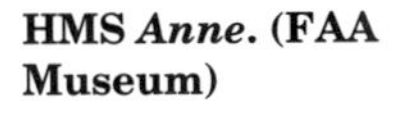
HMS *Anne*. (FAA Museum)

a seaplane carrier, after which she operated in the Eastern Mediterranean. She retained her original name at first and flew the red ensign with a mixed RN and civilian crew whilst operating French seaplanes.

Summary of service

00.01.15 Operated off Sinai, Syrian and Turkish coasts with French Nieuport seaplanes manned by French pilots and British observers (operations contributed to successful British naval and military actions that halted Turkish thrust towards Suez Canal)
11.03.15 Torpedoed by Turkish torpedo boat *Demir Hisar*; deliberately beached at Mudros and seaplanes transferred to *Raven*
12.05.15 Refloated and towed to Alexandria for repairs and improvements to aviation facilities
00.07.15 Sailed for further operations off Turkish coast with French seaplanes embarked
05.08.15 Commissioned into RN and renamed *Anne*
00.01.16 Joined East Indies & Egypt Seaplane Squadron
09.05.16 Replaced French seaplanes with British Short 184s and Schneiders at Malta; then returned to Eastern Mediterranean
08.08.17 Paid off and no longer used by RN
29.01.18 Entered service with F. C. Strick & Co as collier
00.00.22 Sold to Greek interests and renamed *Ithaki*
00.00.39 Sold to Romanian interests and renamed *Moldova*
00.00.42 Registered in Panama
00.00.49 Sold to Wallen & Co, Panama
00.00.54 Renamed *Jagrahat*
00.00.55 Renamed *Moldova*
00.00.58 Broken up in Hong Kong

Ark Royal (1914) (I35) *Seaplane Carrier*

Laid down: 7 November 1913
Launched: 5 September 1914
Completed: 10 December 1914

Builder: Blyth Shipbuilding and Dry Dock Co., Blyth
Machinery: 1-shaft triple-expansion reciprocating steam engine; 3 single-ended tank boilers; 3,000ihp = 11 knots
Displacement: 7,080 tons standard; 7,450 tons deep load
Dimensions: 366ft overall x 50ft 6in max beam x 18ft 6in max draught
Gun armament: 4 single 12pdr QF (4); 2 single .303in Maxim MG (2)
Fuel: 500 tons FFO
Endurance: 3,030 miles @ 10 knots
Complement: 180
Protection: None
Flight deck: 130ft x 44ft steel
Arrester wires: None
Hangar: 150ft x 45ft x 20ft
Catapults: 1 x 12,000lb @ 55 knots (fitted in 1930)
Lifts: None (aircraft lifted through hatch 40ft x 30ft by 2 x 6,000lb steam cranes)
Aircraft: Designed to take 10 seaplanes
Aircraft fuel: 4,000 gallons AVGAS in 2-gallon tins plus 1,000 gallons lube oil in tins
Air weapons: Built to carry torpedoes, light bombs and machine-gun ammunition

Notes: The first aviation vessel procured (at a cost of £81,000) for the RN. The keel and frames of a merchant ship were used to save time but the redesign was so extensive that she can be said to have been designed and built as a seaplane carrier. Anchors and cables were on No 2 deck, leaving a clear flat space forward on the the upper deck which could have been used to launch wheeled aircraft. However, there is no evidence of its being used for this purpose. Renamed *Pegasus* on 21 December 1934 to free the name *Ark Royal* for the carrier being built by Cammell Laird.

Summary of service

00.01.15 Completed working up
01.02.15 Sailed to join Allied fleet assembling to attempt to force passage of Dardanelles; air group comprised 8 aircraft (1 Short Type 135, 2 Wright floatplanes, 3 Sopwith Type 807s and 2 Tabloid landplanes) but none of these could fly high enough to spot fall of shot from battleship gunfire effectively
15.02.15 First combat flight over Dardanelles carried out (20lb bomb dropped)
05.03.15 Ship's seaplane spotted for battleship

HMS *Ark Royal* in Mudros Harbour during operations off the Dardanelles in April 1915. (Arnold Hague)

	Queen Elizabeth, sending corrections by W/T for first time
07.04.15	Schneider floatplanes replaced Tabloids (spotting role taken over by more suitable landplanes based on Tenedos Island)
00.06.15	Relieved on station by faster *Ben-My-Chree*, which was less vulnerable to submarine attack
00.11.15	Based on Salonika as seaplane depot ship
00.03.16	Used as depot ship for 2 Wing RNAS at Mudros Island
00.04.18	Used as depot ship for 62 and 63 Wings RAF at Syra
00.10.18	Ferried aircraft across Black Sea in support of anti-Bolshevik operations
00.12.18	Ferried No 2 Squadron RAF to British Somaliland, where they helped put down revolt by native insurgents
00.00.22	Used as aircraft transport and depot ship in Dardanelles during Chanak crisis (to 00.00.23)
00.00.23	Used as fleet auxiliary, aircraft ferry and minesweeper depot ship (to 00.00.30)
00.00.30	Fitted with catapult and used as trials and training ship
00.00.33	Carried out trials with 'Hein Mat' method of recovering seaplanes (method not successful)
00.09.39	Allocated to HF as aircraft transport; used to ferry aircraft to Orkneys

HMS ***Pegasus*** **(ex *Ark Royal*) operating as a fighter catapult ship in 1941. (Author)**

00.11.40 Allocated to WAC as fighter catapult ship; allocated 3 Fulmars to protect Gibraltar-bound convoys from increased air threat from German-occupied France

08.12.40 Joined escort of convoy OG.76 (decision to launch rested with CO, but he was hampered by lack of radar and suitable RT for communication with aircraft)

11.01.41 Launched Fulmar against FW 200 whilst with convoys SL.60 and HG.49 (enemy evaded into cloud and not intercepted)

07.06.41 Launched Fulmar against FW 200 whilst with convoy HG.63 (enemy driven off but not shot down)

07.07.41 Launched Fulmar against FW 200 whilst supporting convoys SL.78 and OG.67 (fighter failed to intercept; pilot flew back to Ireland rather than ditch but crashed into hillside in bad weather and was killed)

26.07.41 Returned to catapult training duties in Clyde area

00.02.44 Reduced to reserve and used as accommodation vessel

00.05.46 De-stored ready for disposal

00.06.46 Placed on disposal list

18.10.46 Purchased for conversion to merchant ship and renamed *Anita 1* (conversion never completed and ship sold on to succession of breakers)

00.00.50 Scrapped at Grays, Essex

Athene (D25) *Seaplane Carrier/Aircraft Transport*

Laid down: December 1939
Launched: 1 October 1940
Completed: October 1941

Builder: Greenock Dockyard Co; completed by John Brown, Clydebank; machinery by Kincaid
Machinery: 2-shaft vertical triple-expansion driving double reduction gears; 5 cylindrical boilers; 8,300ihp = 17 knots

Displacement: 9,435 tons standard; 10,890 tons deep load
Dimensions: 487ft 8in overall x 63ft max beam x 23ft max draught
Gun armament: 1 single 4.7in BL Mk 1 (1); 1 single 4in QF Mk V HA (1); 4 single 2pdr pompom (4); 10 single 20mm Oerlikon (10)
Fuel: 980 tons FFO; 146 tons diesel
Endurance: 8,550 miles @ 9 knots

Complement: ?
Protection: 1.5in magazine sides; 2in magazine crowns; buoyancy drums over magazines
Flight deck: None
Arrester wires: None
Hangar: 5 holds plus deck hangar designed to hold 3 Walrus amphibians
Catapult: None as built; designed to take a single E IIIH
Lifts: None; original numbers 1 and 4 cargo hatches retained and aircraft worked through them by cranes
Aircraft: Up to 10 seaplanes; up to 40 densely stowed or crated as aircraft transport
Aircraft fuel: 28,500 gallons AVGAS
Air weapons: None carried as transport

Notes: Laid down for the Clan Line in 1939 as a fast cargo liner. Taken up by the Admiralty for conversion to a seaplane carrier together with a sister-ship which became HMS *Engadine* (a third vessel was converted into the X-Craft depot ship *Bonaventure*). They were hastened into service as transports and never used in their designed role.

Summary of service

01.11.41	Sailed from Greenock with 40 crated RAF Hurricanes intended for Middle East
08.11.41	In Gibraltar for defect repairs
23.12.41	Sailed from Gibraltar
08.01.42	Arrived in Takoradi; disembarked Hurricanes, which were assembled to fly on to Middle East, and embarked aircraft intended for Bombay
07.02.42	Diverted to Batavia, where ship unloaded aircraft cargo; from then on, employed ferrying aircraft throughout East Indies Command and Australia
24.11.42	Allocated to USPF, which used her to ferry aircraft in South-West Pacific area
00.06.43	Sailed from Cristobal for New York, where ship reverted to RN control
10.09.43	Arrived in Clyde; allocated to WAC and used to ferry aircraft to UK from USA (ship usually routed independently)
03.03.44	Sailed from Clyde to East Indies Station; allocated to EIF for further aircraft ferrying
00.07.44	Returned to Clyde
29.07.44	Refit on Tyne
00.10.44	Returned to ferrying operations; used to carry aircraft from USA to Cochin via Mediterranean
00.12.44	Returned to Clyde
00.01.45	Laid up in reserve at Loch Alsh
00.00.46	Returned to merchant service and reconstructed as *Clan Brodie*
00.06.63	Broken up in Hong Kong

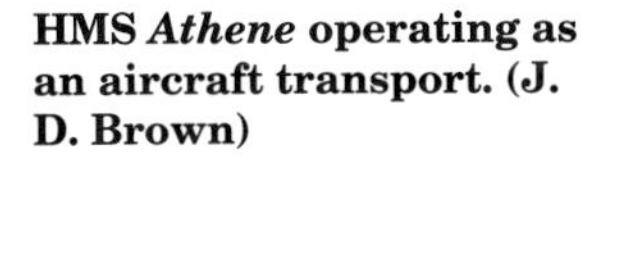
HMS *Athene* operating as an aircraft transport. (J. D. Brown)

Ben-My-Chree (–) *Seaplane Carrier*

Laid down: 1908
Launched: 23 April 1908
Completed: 8 August 1908

Builder: Vickers, Barrow-in-Furness; converted by Cammell Laird, Birkenhead
Machinery: 3-shaft steam turbines; 4 boilers; 14,500shp = 22 knots
Displacement: 3,888 tons
Dimensions: 375ft overall x 46ft max beam x 16ft max draught
Gun armament: 4 single 12pdr LA (4) ; 1 single 12pdr AA (1); 2 single 3pdr (2)
Fuel: 552 tons coal
Endurance: ?
Complement: 250
Protection: None
Flight deck: Trackway 63ft long x 12ft wide for launching seaplanes on wheeled trolleys
Arrester wires: None
Hangar: 80ft x 42ft x 21ft
Catapults: None
Lifts: None
Aircraft: Up to 6
Aircraft fuel: Variable amounts AVGAS carried in 2-gallon tins
Air weapons: 18in torpedoes; 20lb bombs; .303in gun ammunition; flares and pyrotechnics

Notes: Formerly owned by the Isle of Man Steam Packet Co.; the name is Manx for 'Woman of My Heart'. The fire that caused *Ben-My Chree*'s loss was made worse by the explosion of petrol vapour in supposedly empty AVGAS tins. Analysis of this danger led to the steps subsequently taken by the RN to protect AVGAS stowage, and no subsequent British-built carrier has been lost to fire.

Summary of service

01.01.15	Taken up from Isle of Man Steam Packet Co. for conversion to seaplane carrier (work included fitting large hangar and operating deck aft and small flying-off deck forward)
23.03.15	Commissioned in Birkenhead
00.04.15	Replaced *Empress* in Harwich Force with Schneider fighter floatplanes embarked
00.05.15	Operations off German coast
11.05.15	Attempts to fly Schneider off launching platform unsuccessful so latter removed
12.06.15	Replaced *Ark Royal* in fleet off Dardanelles (air group comprised first Short Type 184s to see operational service)
12/17.08.15	Aircraft carried out first aerial torpedo attacks in history, targets being Turkish merchant ships
00.01.16	Became flagship of East Indies & Egypt Seaplane Squadron on its formation at Port Said (from then on, ship operated

HMS *Ben-My-Chree* on fire and sinking off Castelorizzo Island in 1917. (FAA Museum)

throughout Eastern Mediterranean, Red Sea and Aegean Sea areas)
13.03.16 Drydocked in Suez for repairs
09.01.17 Set on fire and sunk by Turkish shore batteries whilst anchored off Castelorizo Island (only aircraft carrier sunk in WW1)
00.00.21 Wreck raised and subsequently broken up in Italy

Campania (1915) (–) *Seaplane Carrier*

Laid down: 1892
Launched: 8 September 1892
Completed: 13 April 1894

Builder: Fairfield Shipbuilding & Engineering Co., Glasgow; converted by Cammell Laird & Co., Birkenhead
Machinery: 2-shaft triple-expansion steam engines; 13 boilers; 30,000shp = 23 knots
Displacement: 18,000 tons standard; 20,611 tons deep load
Dimensions: 622ft overall x 65ft max beam x 29ft 3in max draught
Gun armament: 6 single 4.7in LA (6); 1 single 3in AA (1)
Fuel: 3,270 tons coal
Endurance: 2,600 miles @ 21 knots
Complement: 600
Protection: None
Flight deck: 245ft x 50ft max/30ft min; wood planking
Arrester wires: None
Hangars: *Fwd* 210ft x 60ft x 20ft for seaplanes; *aft* 100ft x 50ft fwd/40ft aft x 20ft canvas structure for kite balloons
Catapults: None
Lifts: *Fwd* hatch 45ft x 20ft; *aft* hatch 45ft x 30ft through which aircraft were hoisted by derricks
Aircraft: 10 seaplanes; 1 kite balloon after 1915
Aircraft fuel: Variable amounts AVGAS carried in 2-gallon tins
Air weapons: 18in torpedoes; 20lb bombs; .303in gun ammunition; flares and pyrotechnics

Notes: Built for the Cunard Steamship Company. *Campania* won the Atlantic Blue Riband in 1893 and 1894 but by the outbreak of war she was worn out and had actually been sold to T. W. Ward for scrapping. However, she was still intact and was purchased by the Admiralty as an auxiliary cruiser. On the advice of the Director of the Air Department, she was converted to a seaplane carrier as she had the speed to operate with the

HMS *Campania* launching a Short seaplane. Note the split forward funnels and lengthened flight deck fitted in 1915. (FAA Museum)

Fleet. She was, however, always vulnerable to underwater damage because of the limited number of watertight bulkheads fitted and her loss after a collision in 1918 bears testimony to this. However, she was a successful seaplane carrier and was able to launch her aircraft on wheeled trolleys from her flight deck. The Fairey Campania, the first aeroplane in the world designed to fly from a carrier deck, was intended to fly reconnaissance sorties from her.

Summary of service

27.11.14 Purchased from T. W. Ward and converted to seaplane carrier by Cammell Laird; fitted with forward hangar and with launching platform for trolley-mounted seaplanes built over it
17.04.15 Commissioned in Birkenhead and subsequently joined GF at Scapa Flow
11.06.15 First operational cruise with GF
00.08.15 Schneiders successfully took off from launching platform but latter too short for heavier aircraft
00.11.15 Returned to Cammell Laird for launching platform to be lengthened (achieved by fitting 2 side-by-side funnels forward, between which deck now passed) and new, larger hangar and equipment to operate balloon fitted aft (all proved most successful)
02.04.16 Re-joined GF with air group of Schneiders and Short 184s
31.05.16 Missed Battle of Jutland because of signalling error (ship sailed late)
00.00.18 Machinery defects proved increasing problem and ship relegated to training duties although still attached to GF
05.11.18 Dragged anchors during gale in Firth of Forth and collided with *Royal Oak* and *Glorious*; foundered and sank (fortunately no loss of life)

HMS *Empress* hoisting out a Short seaplane. (FAA Museum)

Empress (1914) (–) *Seaplane Carrier*

Laid down: ?
Launched: 13 April 1907
Completed: 25 August 1914 (as carrier)

Builder: William Denny & Bros, Dumbarton
Machinery: 3-shaft direct drive turbines; 6 boilers; 8,800shp = 18 knots
Displacement: 2,540 tons standard
Dimensions: 316ft overall x 41ft max beam x 13ft 8in max beam
Gun armament: 4 single 12pdr LA (4); 2 single 3pdr HA (2)
Fuel: 425 tons coal
Endurance: 1,355 miles @ 15 knots
Complement: 197
Protection: None
Flight deck: None
Arrester wires: None
Hangar: 82ft x 37ft x 20ft
Catapults: None
Lifts: None
Aircraft: 4 seaplanes
Aircraft fuel: Variable amounts AVGAS carried in 2-gallon tins
Air weapons: 18in torpedoes; light bombs; Ranken darts; .303in gun ammunition; flares and pyrotechnics

Notes: Originally owned by the South Eastern & Chatham Railway Co. and operated as a cross-Channel packet. Details are for September 1914.

Summary of service

11.08.14 Hired by Admiralty and employed as RNAS transport and dispatch vessel taking equipment for Eastchurch Squadron to Ostend
30.08.14 Taken in hand by Chatham Dockyard for temporary conversion to seaplane carrier with canvas screens for one seaplane forward and two aft, together with handling derricks
30.09.14 Joined Harwich Force and employed on raids against German coastal targets
25.12.14 Took part in Cuxhaven Raid
09.05.15 Taken in hand by Cunard Steamship Co. at Liverpool for more extensive conversion to seaplane carrier, including fitting of steel hangar and operating deck aft
18.07.15 Conversion completed; stationed at Queenstown, Ireland
00.01.16 Assigned to East Indies & Egypt Seaplane Squadron, stationed in Port Said

00.04.16	Detached for operations off Bulgarian coast based in various Aegean ports
00.11.16	Used in operations off Sinai/Syrian coast
00.01.18	Reallocated to anti-submarine work in Port Said and finally Gibraltar
00.11.19	Returned to former owners
00.00.23	Sold to Southern Railway Co.; later that year sold to French Société Anonyme de Gérance et d'Armament
00.00.33	Scrapped in France

Engadine (1914) (–) *Seaplane Carrier*

Laid down: ?
Launched: 1 April 1911
Completed: 11 August 1914

Builder: William Denny & Bros, Dumbarton
Machinery: 3-shaft direct-drive turbines; 6 boilers; 13,800shp = 22 knots
Displacement: 2,400 tons standard; 2,550 tons deep load
Dimensions: 316ft overall x 41ft max beam x 13ft 8in max draught
Gun armament: 4 single 12pdr (4); 2 single 3pdr (2)
Fuel: 960 tons coal
Endurance: 1,250 miles @ 15 knots
Complement: 197
Protection: None
Flight deck: None
Arrester wires: None
Hangar: 80ft x 36ft x 20ft
Catapults: None
Lifts: None
Aircraft: 4 seaplanes
Aircraft fuel: Variable amounts AVGAS carried in 2-gallon tins
Air weapons: 18in torpedoes; 100lb bombs; grenades; .303in gun ammunition; flares and pyrotechnics

Notes: Built for and operated by the South Eastern & Chatham Railway Co. before being requisitioned by the Admiralty. Many different types of seaplane were operated during the ship's career. Details are for March 1915.

Summary of service

11.08.14	Hired and later purchased outright by Admiralty; converted at Chatham Dockyard to operate seaplanes with canvas shelters

HMS *Engadine* in 1915. (Author)

for 2 aft and 1 forward; light gun armamentadded

01.09.14 Commissioned and allocated to Harwich Force

00.10.14 Took part in series of raids against German Zeppelin bases

25.12.14 Took part in the Cuxhaven raid

10.02.15 Taken in hand by Cunard Steamship Co. in Liverpool for incorporation of improvements, including steel 'box' hangar for 4 seaplanes aft with operating platform and derricks

23.03.15 Modifications completed

00.07.15 Based in Granton

00.10.15 Joined BCF based in Rosyth; carried out tests involving high-speed towing of kite balloons (successful)

31.05.16 Launched Short 184 seaplane which carried out successful reconnaissance during Battle of Jutland; later took damaged cruiser *Warrior* in tow and rescued her ship's company when she foundered

00.00.18 Transferred to MF; based in Malta

00.12.19 Returned to former owners.

00.00.23 Sold to Southern Railway Co.

00.00.32 Sold to Instone Hire

00.00.33 Sold to Hermanos Inc. in Philippines and renamed *Corregidor*

00.12.41 Sunk by mine in Manila Bay during Japanese invasion (heavy loss of life)

Engadine (1941) (D71) *Seaplane Carrier / Aircraft Transport*

Laid down: 16 March 1940
Launched: 26 May 1941
Completed: 17 November 1941

Builder: William Denny & Bros, Dumbarton; machinery by Kincaid
Machinery: 2-shaft, 6-cylinder triple-expansion reciprocating steam engines driving through double reduction gears; 5 single-ended cylindrical boilers; 8,300ihp = 16.5 knots
Displacement: 9,190 tons standard; 10,650 tons deep load
Dimensions: 487ft 8in overall x 63ft max beam x 21ft 11in max draught
Gun armament: 1 single 4.7in (1); 1 single 4in HA (1); 4 single 2pdr (4); 7 single 20mm Oerlikon (7; fitted in 1943)
Fuel: 980 tons FFO
Endurance: 8,550 miles @ 9 knots
Complement: ?
Protection: 2in NC magazine crowns; 1.5in NC magazine sides; buoyancy drums over magazines
Flight deck: None
Arrester wires: None
Hangar: 5 holds and deck hangar (latter designed to contain 3 Walrus amphibians)
Catapults: None as built (designed to take 1 x EIIIH)
Lifts: None
Aircraft: Up to 10 seaplanes (up to 40 densely stored or crated as aircraft transport)
Aircraft fuel: 28,500 gallons AVGAS
Air weapons: None carried as transport

Notes: Laid down for the Clan Line in 1939 as a fast cargo liner. One sister-ship, also purchased by Admiralty, became *Athene*, a second, *Clan Davison*, was taken up to become the X-Craft depot ship *Bonaventure* and a third, *Clan Buchanan*, was lost in 1941. *Engadine* and *Athene* were intended for use as seaplane carriers for AS work on the trade routes (a similar role to that carried out by *Albatross*). Both completed with warship-style bridges, hangars, workshops and fuel and air weapons stowage and were designed to take a catapult. In the event they were hastened into service as aircraft transports without the catapult being fitted. They were never used as seaplane carriers but they retained that capability.

Summary of service

08.12.41 Sailed from Clyde with convoy WS.11 for Middle East via Cape

06.02.42 Arrived in Suez; allocated to EIF and used to ferry aircraft between bases

00.08.42 Port Elizabeth for repairs

00.11.42 Durban for repairs

24.11.42 Proceeded to Noumea via Australia in company with *Athene*; on arrival in South Pacific came under operational control of CinC USPF

19.12.42 Arrived in Fremantle

30.12.42 Arrived in Sydney

26.01.43 Arrived in Suva, Fiji

HMS *Engadine* operating as an aircraft transport. (Author)

00.07.43 Reverted to RN control
23.08.43 Left New York for UK
19.09.43 Arrived in Clyde; allocated to WAC as aircraft ferry
11.10.43 Sailed for New York with convoy ON.206; returned with aircraft
00.11.43 Refitted on Clyde
03.03.44 Sailed with *Athene* for EIF
04.04.44 Arrived in Colombo
00.06.44 Returned to UK
00.07.44 Refitted in Clyde
19.09.44 Sailed for New York to pick up cargo of aircraft
06.11.44 Arrived in Cochin to discharge aircraft
23.11.44 Sailed for UK
17.12.44 Arrived in Clyde
09.01.45 Paid off into RF at Kyle of Lochalsh
00.08.45 Placed on disposal list
00.00.46 Sold to Clan Line and renamed *Clan Buchanan*
14.11.62 Sold to G. M. Alacren and arrived in Cartagena for scrapping

Hermes (1899) (–) *Seaplane Carrier (Modified Cruiser)*

Laid down: 30 April 1897
Launched: 7 April 1898
Completed: 5 October 1899

Builder: Fairfield Shipbuilding and Engineering Co., Glasgow
Machinery: 2-shaft triple-expansion steam engines; 18 Babcock boilers; 10,000ihp = 20 knots
Displacement: 5,650 tons deep load
Dimensions: 372ft overall x 54ft max beam x 20ft 6in max draught
Gun/torpedo armament: 8 single 6in QF (8); 9 single 12pdr QF (9); 6 single 3pdr QF (6); 2 single 18in torpedo tubes (2)
Fuel: 1,100 tons coal
Endurance: ?
Complement: 450
Protection: 1.5in–3in deck; 3in gun shields; 6in conning tower; 5in engine hatches
Flight deck: Troughs 70ft long to launch seaplanes equipped with wheels
Arrester wires: None
Hangar: Canvas screens, 1 forward and 1 aft, to provide some protection for one aircraft each
Catapults: None
Lifts: None
Aircraft: Up to 3 seaplanes (usually only 2)
Aircraft fuel: 2,000 gallons AVGAS in 2-gallon tins
Air weapons: Grenades; .303in gun ammunition; flares and pyrotechnics

Notes: *Highflyer* class cruiser modified to test the ability of aircraft to operate under realistic conditions at sea. The forward 6in gun was landed to make space for wooden flying-off rails similar to those fitted temporarily to the battleship *Hibernia*. The after two 6in were removed to make space for a canvas hangar on the quarterdeck capable of accommodating a single seaplane. A second canvas hangar was constructed forward to protect a seaplane on the launch rails. Improved derricks were fitted to move aircraft on to and off the water. She embarked Borel Seaplane No 48 and the prototype Short S.64 Folder for the 1913 Manoeuvres. The latter type was fitted with a wireless transmitter and was the first aircraft in the world to have folding wings to facilitate stowage in a carrier. The success of the manoeuvres convinced the Admiralty that aircraft operations at sea were viable and led to the order for *Ark Royal*.

Summary of service

00.05.13 Converted to seaplane carrier in Chatham Dockyard
07.05.13 Commissioned for flying trials
05.07.13 Embarked 2 seaplanes for trials
14.07.13 Sea trials completed after 9 flights
18.07.13 Sailed to join 'Red Fleet' for summer manoeuvres; ship based on Yarmouth with force commanded by Vice-Admiral Jellicoe (Borel No 48 damaged during gale and replaced by Caudron No 55)
28.07.13 Caudron No 55 took off from launch rails forward
31.07.13 Folder made forced landing on water after engine failure and broke several struts
03.09.13 Second launch from rails by Caudron No 55
00.10.13 Manoeuvres completed (ship's aircraft had carried out 30 successful flights)
30.12.13 Paid off into reserve in Chatham
31.08.14 Recommissioned at Chatham for service as RNAS transport and supply ship; used to ferry aircraft, men and material to France
31.10.14 Torpedoed and sunk by *U27* off Ruylingen Bank

HMS *Hermes* sinking off the Ruylingen Bank in 1914. Note the wreckage of the canvas hangar aft and of the aircraft that it contained. (Author)

Manxman (–) *Seaplane Carrier*

Laid down: 1903
Launched: 15 June 1904
Completed: 1904

Builder: Vickers, Sons & Maxim, Barrow-in-Furness
Machinery: 3-shaft direct-drive turbines; 3 boilers; 6,500shp = 21 knots
Displacement: 2,048 tons standard; 3,090 tons deep load
Dimensions: 343ft overall x 43ft 1in max beam x 15ft 9in max draught
Gun armament: 2 single 12pdr LA (2); 1 single 6 pdr AA (1)
Fuel: 430 tons coal
Endurance: ?
Complement: 250
Protection: None
Flight deck: 86ft x 28ft fwd launching platform
Arrester wires: None
Hangar: 80ft x 36ft x 20ft
Catapults: None
Lifts: Hatch 18ft x 14ft served by derricks
Aircraft: 8 (normally 4 seaplanes and 4 landplanes)
Aircraft fuel: Variable amounts AVGAS carried in 2-gallon tins
Air weapons: 18in torpedoes; light bombs; .303in gun ammunition; flares and pyrotechnics

Notes: Former Isle of Man packet operated by the Midland Railway Company. She was converted to a seaplane carrier by Chatham Dockyard to a design more advanced than that used in *Riviera*, *Engadine* and *Empress*. A launching deck forward was the first at sea capable of flying off Pup fighters. The jib cranes aft were theoretically capable of hoisting in seaplanes while the ship was making way but were not successful in practice; they represented an attempt to overcome the requirement for the carrier to have to stop to hoist in or lower seaplanes. With a flight deck forward but no means of recovering wheeled fighters, *Manxman* represented an intermediate step between the early conversions and *Argus*, the first true carrier.

Summary of service

17.04.16 Purchased by Admiralty; taken in hand for conversion in Chatham Dockyard
00.12.16 Conversion completed; attached to BCF in Rosyth

HMS *Manxman*. (FAA Museum)

00.04.17 Supported minelaying operations in North Sea (speed was found to be insufficient to work with battlecruisers)
00.10.17 Transferred to MF (operated more as depot ship for air operations than as carrier); based in turn at Syracuse, Taranto and Brindisi
00.01.18 Moved to Mudros for air strike on battlecruiser *Goeben* which was aground in Dardanelles (strike cancelled)
12.02.20 Sold to Isle of Man Packet Co.
00.10.41 Requisitioned by Admiralty again and converted to radar training ship, renamed *Caduceus*
00.00.45 Paid off and placed on disposal list
00.00.49 Broken up

Nairana (1917) (–) *Seaplane Carrier*

Laid down: ?
Launched: 21 June 1915
Completed: 25 August 1917

Builder: William Denny & Bros, Dumbarton
Machinery: 2-shaft geared turbines; 6 boilers; 6,700shp = 19 knots
Displacement: 3,070 tons deep load
Dimensions: 352ft overall x 45ft 6in max beam x 14ft 5in max draught
Gun armament: 2 single 12pdr LA (2); 2 single 12 pdr AA (2)
Fuel: 448 tons coal
Endurance: ?
Complement: 278
Protection: None
Flight deck: 94ft x 23ft fwd launching platform
Arrester wires: None
Hangar: 80ft x 36ft x 20ft
Catapults: None
Lifts: Hatch 22ft x 14ft served by derricks
Aircraft: 8
Aircraft fuel: Variable amounts AVGAS carried in 2-gallon tins
Air weapons: 18in torpedoes; light bombs; .303in gun ammunition; flares and pyrotechnics

Notes: Under construction for the Australian firm Huddart & Parker when she was taken over by the Admiralty. The ship was completed as an enhanced seaplane carrier able to launch Pups from the flight deck forward and to operate Short 184s using the gantry aft. Like *Manxman*, she represented an intermediate step between the early conversions and *Argus*. It was hoped that *Manxman*, *Nairana* and *Pegasus* would form a squadron of ships with the speed to remain with the Fleet whilst operating seaplanes. This proved not to be the case.

HMS *Nairana* in 1918. (Author)

Summary of service

00.00.17 Taken up from trade by Admiralty

00.08.17 Allocated to BCF in Rosyth; used to train pilots in deck launch techniques and to ferry replacement aircraft to warships fitted with take-off platforms

00.00.18 Allocated to MF with air group of Short 184s and Beardmore WB.IIIs

00.00.19 Deployed to Archangel to support British and White Russian forces; air group comprised 5 Campanias and 2 Camels

00.00.20 Sold to Tasmanian Steamers Pty and refitted for mercantile service

18.02.51 Ran aground in Port Melbourne and damaged beyond economic repair; subsequently broken up

Pegasus (–) *Seaplane Carrier/Aircraft Tender*

Laid down: ?
Launched: 9 June 1917
Completed: 14 August 1917

Builder: John Brown & Co, Clydebank
Machinery: 2 shaft Brown-Curtis geared turbines; 6 boilers; 9,500shp = 20 knots
Displacement: 2,070 tons standard; 3,315 tons deep load
Dimensions: 332ft 4in overall x 43ft 0¾in max beam x 18ft 9in max draught
Gun armament: 2 single 3in AA (2); 2 single 12 pdr AA (2)
Fuel: 350 tons FFO
Endurance: ?
Complement: 258
Protection: None
Flight deck: 82ft x 28ft fwd launching platform
Arrester wires: None
Hangar: *Fwd* 40ft x 40ft x 20ft; *aft* 80ft x 40ft x 20ft
Catapults: None
Lifts: Hatch 18ft x 14ft served by derricks
Aircraft: 9 seaplanes and wheeled fighters
Aircraft fuel: 1,300 gallons AVGAS
Air weapons: 18in torpedoes; light bombs; .303in gun ammunition; flares and pyrotechnics

HMS *Pegasus*. (FAA Museum)

Notes: The last to complete and the most sophisticated of the enhanced seaplane carriers to enter service in WW1, *Pegasus* was laid down as the mercantile *Stockholm* for the Great Eastern Railway Company. Five Beardmore WB.III fighters were stowed in the forward hangar and launched from the flying-off deck. Four seaplanes were carried aft and the ship was fitted with a much improved fuel system incorporating all the wartime lessons.

Summary of service

27.02.17 Purchased for Admiralty whilst building
28.08.17 Commissioned on Clyde
00.00.17 Served with GF based at Rosyth (ship took part in several sweeps with BCF but was used mainly to train pilots in shipborne operations and to ferry aircraft to ships with take-off platforms)
00.00.18 Camels replaced WB.IIIs
00.05.19 Deployed to Archangel in support of British intervention forces during Russian Civil War; air group at this time comprised Fairey IIICs
00.09.19 Returned to UK
00.00.20 Deployed 'L' Flight of No 267 Squadron RAF to MF during Chanak crisis.; allocated to MF on completion
00.00.23 Forward flying-off deck removed
00.00.24 Reclassified as aircraft tender; employed as aircraft ferry based on Singapore (to 00.00.25)
05.07.25 Paid off into reserve in Devonport
00.00.29 Recommissioned as ferry carrier
22.08.31 Sold and broken up at Morecambe

Raven II (–) *Seaplane Carrier*

Laid down: ?
Launched: ?
Completed: December 1903

Builder: Swan Hunter & Wigham Richardson, Wallsend-on-Tyne
Machinery: 1-shaft quadruple-expansion steam reciprocating engine; ? boilers; ?ihp = 10 knots
Displacement: 4,706 tons deep load
Dimensions: 394ft 5in overall x 51ft 6in max beam x 27ft 6in max draught
Gun armament: 1 single 12pdr LA (1)
Fuel: ?
Endurance: ?
Complement: ?
Protection: None
Flight deck: None
Arrester wires: None
Hangar: Canvas screens to protect aircraft
Catapults: None
Lifts: None
Aircraft: Up to 6 seaplanes
Aircraft fuel: Variable amounts AVGAS carried in 2-gallon tins
Air weapons: Grenades; .303in gun ammunition; flares and pyrotechnics

Notes: Built as the merchant ship *Rabenfels* for Deutsche DampfschiffahrtsGesellschaft, this ship was seized together with *Anne* at Port Said on the outbreak of the First World War. Like *Anne*, she operated initially under the red ensign with a mixed Anglo-French air group.

Summary of service

00.12.14 Operated French seaplanes with French pilots and British observers in Eastern Mediterranean
00.03.15 Embarked *Anne*'s seaplanes at Mudros
12.06.15 Commissioned into RN and renamed *Raven II*
00.01.16 Allocated to East Indies & Egypt Seaplane Squadron operating RN Short Type 184 and 827s and Schneiders
01.09.16 Damaged in Port Said by bomb dropped by German aircraft
16.03.17 Passed through Suez Canal with French cruiser *Pothuau* to search Indian Ocean for German commerce raider *Wolf*
10.06.17 Returned to Eastern Mediterranean and paid off
00.01.18 Bought by Graham & Co. and renamed *Ravenrock*
00.00.23 Sold to British Dominion Steamship Co.; then sold to Karafuto KKK and renamed *Heiyei Maru 7*
00.00.35 Sold to Innui KKK (ship finally lost in Pacific in WW2)

HMS *Raven II* moored in Castelorizzo Harbour in 1915 or 1916. (FAA Museum)

Riviera (–) *Seaplane Carrier*

Laid down: ?
Launched: 1 April 1911
Completed: 1911

Builder: William Denny & Bros, Dumbarton
Machinery: 3-shaft diesel direct-drive turbines; 6 boilers; 11,000shp = 20.5 knots
Displacement: 2,400 tons standard; 2,550 tons deep load
Dimensions: 323ft overall x 41ft max beam; x 16ft 6in max draught
Gun armament: 4 single 12pdr LA (4); 2 single 3pdr AA (2)
Fuel: 400 tons coal
Endurance: ?
Complement: 197
Protection: None
Flight deck: None
Arrester wires: None
Hangar: 82ft x 37ft x 20ft 3in (pigeon loft fitted over hangar)
Catapults: None
Lifts: None
Aircraft: 4 seaplanes
Aircraft fuel: 1,200 gallons in 2-gallon tins in forward hold
Air weapons: Light bombs; .303in gun ammunition; flares and pyrotechnics

Notes: Some idea of how extensive the seaplane carrier conversions were may be gained from these notes. The hangar was heated by 14 steam radiators and there were bomb racks and racks for air bottles. Rails were fitted on the deck for trolleys on which seaplanes could be moved. Two cranes were provided for lifting aircraft and engines. Roller blinds were fitted to close the hangar. There was an armament workshop, a W/T workshop, an engine workshop which contained lathes, a milling ma-

HMS *Riviera* in 1914 with the canvas hangars fitted by Chatham Dockyard. (FAA Museum)

chine, a vertical drilling machine, hand shearing machines, an emery wheel, a coppersmith brazing hearth, four benches with vices, an engine washing tank and engine trolleys. There was even a portable forge and anvil which were kept in the hangar. A carpenter's workshop contained a circular saw, a spindle moulding machine, an emery wheel and five benches with vices. Stores could be lowered and raised between workshops and the hangar through a trunking. There was also a dark room for photography and a W/T office for communicating with aircraft that were airborne. *Riviera* was requisitioned from the South East & Chatham Railway Company together with *Engadine*.

Summary of service

11.08.14	Requisitioned and converted in Chatham Dockyard with canvas hangar aft
06.09.14	Conversion and trials completed; allocated to Harwich Force
00.10.14	Took part in attacks on German coastal airship bases
25.12.14	Took part in Cuxhaven raid
14.02.15	Taken in hand by Cunard Steamship Co. in Liverpool for more elaborate conversion, including construction of steel hangar aft
07.04.15	Reconstruction completed; allocated to Dover Patrol
00.06.15	Used for gunfire spotting and other duties off Belgian coast
00.00.18	Transferred to MF and based in Malta
00.00.19	Sold back to original owners
00.00.23	Sold to Southern Railway Co.
00.00.32	Sold to Burns & Laird Lines and renamed *Laird's Isle*
00.09.39	Requisitioned by Admiralty again; used variously as torpedo training ship, armed boarding vessel and infantry landing ship
00.00.45	Returned to Burns & Laird
00.00.57	Sold for scrap

Vindex (1915) (–) *Seaplane Carrier*

Laid down: 1904
Launched: 7 March 1905
Completed: 26 June 1905

Builder: Sir W. G. Armstrong Whitworth & Co., Newcastle-upon-Tyne
Machinery: 3-shaft direct drive turbines; 4 boilers; 11,000shp = 23 knots
Displacement: 1,951 tons standard; 2,950 tons deep load
Dimensions: 361ft overall x 42ft max beam x 13ft 3ft max draught
Gun armament: 2 single 12pdr LA (2)
Fuel: 475 tons coal
Endurance: 995 miles @ 10 knots
Complement: 218

HMS *Vindex*. Note the lightweight flying-off deck over the forecastle with derricks forward of the bridge to lift aircraft on to it. (FAA Museum)

Protection: None
Flight deck: 64ft x 25ft fwd launching platform
Arrester wires: None
Hangar: 80ft x 36ft x 20ft
Catapults: None
Lifts: None
Aircraft: 7 (normally 5 seaplanes and 2 landplanes)
Aircraft fuel: Variable amounts AVGAS carried in 2-gallon tins
Air weapons: 18in torpedoes; light bombs; .303in gun ammunition; flares and pyrotechnics

Notes: Formerly the Isle of Man Steam Packet Co. passenger vessel *Viking*. This ship was the first of the second-generation seaplane carrier conversions and was designed to operate fighters forward (to defend the Fleet against Zeppelins) and seaplanes aft. She was converted by the Cunard Steamship Co. at Liverpool.

Summary of service

26.03.15	Hired by Admiralty and began conversion
03.11.15	Flew off Bristol Scout landplane during trials
11.11.15	Purchased outright and renamed *Vindex*; commissioned at Liverpool; allocated to Harwich Force and used in North Sea and on anti-airship patrols off The Nore
02.08.16	Bristol Scout carried out first interception of airship by carrier-based fighter (though Zeppelin *L17* escaped)
00.00.18	Allocated to MF
12.02.20	Sold back to original owner and reverted to former name
00.00.39	Requisitioned by Admiralty for use as troopship
00.00.45	Returned to her owners
00.00.54	Sold to British Shipbreakers for scrap

Part 3: Helicopter Support and Training Ships

Kanimbla (51) *Training and Helicopter Support Ship*

Laid down: 24 May 1969
Launched: 27 February 1970
Completed: 23 January 1971

Builder: National Steel and Shipbuilding Co., USA
Machinery: 2 shafts and bow thruster; 6 ARCO diesels; 16,500bhp = 20 knots
Displacement: 8,342 tons deep load
Dimensions: 522ft 4in overall x 69ft 6in max beam x 17ft 6in max draught
Gun armament: 1 single 20mm Vulcan Phalanx CIWS (1)
Fuel: 200 tons diesel
Endurance: 2,500 miles @ 14 knots
Complement: 170 plus squadron personnel, plus embarked force of up to 450
Protection: None
Flight deck: *Aft* large enough for 2 running Seahawk helicopters; *fwd* single helicopter spot
Arrester wires: None
Hangar: Amidships; capable of accommodating 4 SH-60 Seahawk or 3 Sea King helicopters
Catapults: None
Lifts: None

HMAS *Kanimbla* entering Sydney Harbour for the first time in 1994. (RAN Official)

Aircraft: 4 to 6 helicopters (depending on type)
Aircraft fuel: 575,000 gallons AVCAT
Air weapons: Homing torpedoes; depth charges; .5in gun ammunition; 7.62mm gun ammunition; flares and pyrotechnics

Notes: Formerly the USS *Saginaw*, this vessel is one of two tank landing ships purchased by the RAN for conversion to helicopter support ships with secondary amphibious and training roles. Both ships were selected from the USN Atlantic Reserve Fleet, having been found to be in a good state of preservation and capable of running for another 20 years. They were due to arrive in Sydney for conversion in August 1994, one with an RAN and one with a USN crew. After conversion, both ships will have a flight deck aft capable of operating two helicopters, a hangar amidships and a single-spot flight deck forward. Seahawk, Sea King and Army Blackhawk helicopters will all be operated, with enough aviation fuel to allow three Seahawks to fly six hours each per day for a month. The ships will retain the capability to carry landing craft, vehicles and an embarked force of up to 450 men or alternatively a 100-bed hospital facility. The projected cost, including the purchase of the ships and the conversion, is $85 million. This represents excellent value for money, and thc RAN is putting into service a type of warship that many other navies would do well to copy.

Lofoten (K07) *Helicopter Training Ship*

Laid down: 30 May 1944
Launched: 25 January 1945
Completed: 24 October 1945

Builder: Blyth Shipbuilding & Dry Dock Co., Blyth
Machinery: 2 shaft reciprocating steam engines; 2 Admiralty 3-drum boilers; 5,500shp = 12.5 knots
Displacement: 2,140 tons standard; 4,820 tons deep load
Dimensions: 345ft 9in overall x 55ft max beam x 8ft 3in max draught
Gun armament: 2 single 40mm Bofors (2)
Fuel: 1,400 tons FFO
Complement: 110
Protection: None
Flight deck: 120ft x 55ft steel
Arrester wires: None
Hangar: None
Catapults: None
Lifts: None
Aircraft: 2 helicopters up to Wessex size with rotors running on deck; deck park up to 6 folded Wessex type
Aircraft fuel: 20,000 gallons AVCAT

HMS *Lofoten* with a Wessex helicopter on deck. (IWM FXL.17208)

Air weapons: Practice torpedoes; flares and pyrotechnics

Notes: Formerly *LST(3) 3027*. Converted into a helicopter training ship at Devonport during 1964. The upper deck forward was strengthened to form a flight deck with a flying control position in the former forward gun platform. The bow doors were welded closed and two 10,000-gallon aircraft fuel tanks were built into the forward part of the former tank deck. No provision was made for live aircraft armament. Workshops and accommodation in after part of former tank deck. The ship provided deck-landing facilities for helicopter-training squadrons based at RNAS Culdrose and Portland.

Summary of service

00.00.64 Based at Portland for helicopter training
00.00.67 Replaced in service by RFA *Engadine*
00.00.69 Laid up in Rosyth; used for many years as accommodation ship for dockyard staff
26.10.93 Towed from Rosyth by tug *Towing Chieftain*
29.10.93 Arrived at Bruges scrapyard of Jacques Bakker & Son for breaking up

Manoora (52) *Training and Helicopter Support Ship*

Laid down: 29 March 1970
Launched: 19 December 1970
Completed: 16 October 1971

Builder: National Steel and Shipbuilding Co., USA
Machinery: 2 shafts and bow thruster; 6 ARCO diesels; 16,500bhp = 20 knots
Displacement: 8,342 tons deep load
Dimensions: 522ft 4in overall x 69ft 6in max beam x 17ft 6in max draught
Gun armament: 1 single 20mm Vulcan Phalanx CIWS (1)
Fuel: 200 tons diesel
Endurance: 2,500 miles @ 14 knots
Complement: 170 plus squadron personnel, plus embarked force of up to 450
Protection: None
Flight deck: *Aft* large enough for 2 running Seahawk helicopters; *fwd* single helicopter spot
Arrester wires: None
Hangar: Amidships; capable of accommodating 4 SH-60 Seahawk or 3 Sea King helicopters
Catapults: None
Lifts: None
Aircraft: 4 to 6 helicopters (depending on type)
Aircraft fuel: 575,000 gallons AVCAT
Air weapons: Homing torpedoes; depth charges; .5in gun ammunition; 7.62mm gun ammunition; flares and pyrotechnics

Notes: Formerly the USS *Fairfax County*, one of two USN tank landing ships purchased by the RAN for conversion to helicopter support ships with secondary amphibious and training roles. See HMAS *Kanimbla*.

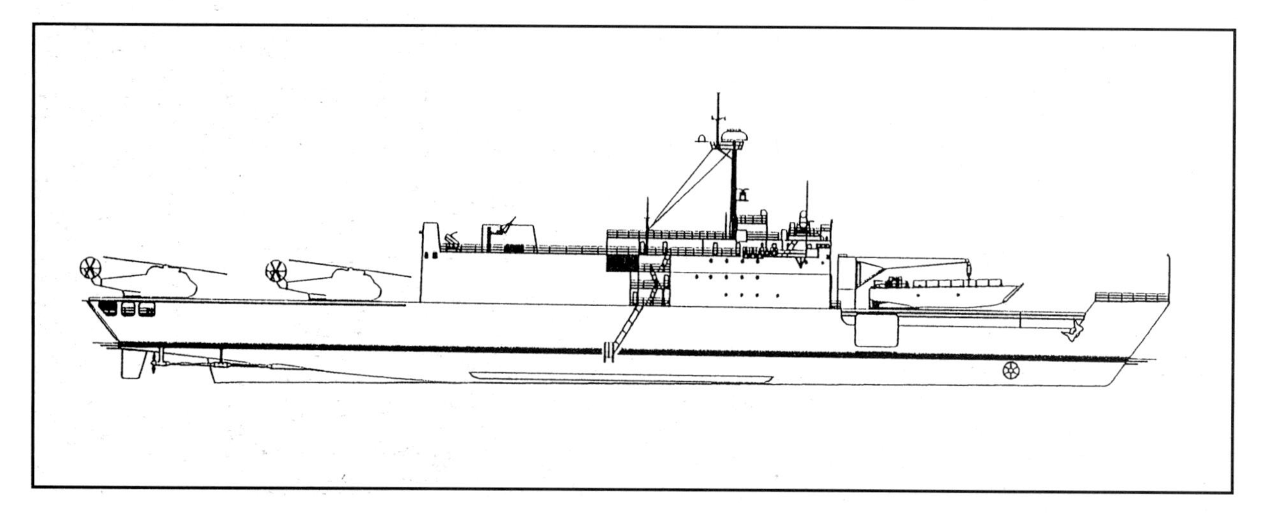

How HMAS *Manoora* will appear when fully modified for RAN service. (RAN Official)

Part 4: Merchant Aircraft Carriers

Acavus (–) *Merchant Aircraft Carrier*

Laid down: ?
Launched: 24 November 1934
Completed: October 1943 (as carrier)

Builder: Workman Clark, Belfast; converted by Silley Cox & Co., Falmouth
Machinery: 1-shaft Sulzer direct-drive diesel; 3,500bhp = 11.5 knots
Displacement: 8,000 tons standard; 16,000 tons deep load
Dimensions: 481ft overall x 62ft max beam x 27ft 6in max draught
Gun armament: 1 single 4in QF Mk IV (1); 2 single 40mm Bofors (2); 6 single 20mm Oerlikon (6)
Fuel: 3,100 tons diesel
Endurance: ?
Complement: 118
Protection: None
Flight deck: 461ft x 62ft steel
Arrester wires: 4 x 15,000lb @ 55 knots; 1 barrier
Hangar: None
Catapults: None
Lifts: None
Aircraft: 3 Swordfish
Aircraft fuel: 5,000 gallons AVGAS
Air weapons: Mk XXIV mines (homing torpedoes); Mk XI depth charges; 100lb AS bombs; 3in RP; .303in gun ammunition; flares and pyrotechnics

Notes: Originally owned by the Anglo-Saxon Petroleum Company, whose employee John Lambe proposed the idea of modifying bulk tankers to operate aircraft. The Admiralty was put off by the theoretical risk of fire at first, but, desperate to increase the number of escorting aircraft that could sail with a convoy, in September 1943 they agreed to proceed with the idea. The fuel piping arrangements in a tanker made it impossible to build a hangar under the flight deck and so, unlike their bulk grain carrying counterparts, tanker 'MAC-ships' were limited to three Swordfish which had to be kept on deck. Tanker MAC-ships were able to carry about 80 per cent of their original cargo, the remaining space being taken for AVGAS stowage to Admiralty safety standards. Collapsible wind breaks were fitted on the flight deck aft to provide some protection for parked aircraft.

Summary of service

00.10.43	Conversion completed in Falmouth; after work-up 836F Flight (Swordfish) embarked and ship worked with ON/ HX convoys in North Atlantic
00.03.44	836V Flight replaced 836F
00.00.52	Restored to mercantile standard and sold; renamed *Iacra*
18.04.63	Arrived at La Seine for scrapping

A tanker MAC-ship of the *Acavus* type ferrying Thunderbolt aircraft across the Atlantic in March 1944. With no hangar, the three Swordfish of her own Flight are lashed aft, protected to some extent by wind breaks at the deck-edge. Stores in crates are secured amidships. (FAA Museum)

Adula (–) *Merchant Aircraft Carrier*

Laid down: ?
Launched: 28 January 1937
Completed: February 1944 (as carrier)

Builder: Blythwood, Scotstoun; converted by Silley Cox & Co., Falmouth
Machinery: 1-shaft Sulzer direct-drive diesel; 3,000bhp = 12 knots
Displacement: 8,000 tons standard; 16,000 tons deep load
Dimensions: 481ft overall x 62ft max beam x 27ft 6in max draught
Gun armament: 1 single 4in QF Mk IV (1); 2 single 40mm Bofors (2); 6 single 20mm Oerlikon (6)
Fuel: 3,100 tons diesel
Endurance: ?
Complement: 118
Protection: None
Flight deck: 461ft x 62ft steel
Arrester wires: 4 x 15,000lb @ 55 knots; 1 barrier
Hangar: None
Catapults: None
Lifts: None
Aircraft: 3 Swordfish
Aircraft fuel: 5,000 gallons AVGAS
Air weapons: Mk XXIV mines (homing torpedoes); Mk XI depth charges; 100lb AS bombs; 3in RP; .303in gun ammunition; flares and pyrotechnics

Notes: See sister-ship *Acavus*.

A tanker MAC-ship of the same type, believed to be MV *Adula*. (FAA Museum).

Summary of service

00.02.44	Completed conversion in Falmouth
00.03.44	Embarked 836P Flight (Swordfish) for work-up, after which ship operated on North Atlantic convoy routes
00.07.44	836G Flight replaced 836P
00.09.44	836P Flight replaced 836G
00.12.44	836M Flight replaced 836P
00.05.45	Disembarked aircraft to RNAS Maydown for last time
Post-war	Reconverted back to original tanker configuration and operated commercially
15.05.53	Sold to T. W. Ward and arrived at Briton Ferry for scrapping

Alexia (–) *Merchant Aircraft Carrier*

Laid down: ?
Launched: 20 December 1934
Completed: December 1943 (as carrier)

Builder: Vulkan, Vegesack; converted by T. W. Greenwell & Co., Sunderland
Machinery: 1-shaft Sulzer direct-drive diesel; 4,000bhp = 12 knots
Displacement: 8,000 tons standard; 16,000 tons deep load
Dimensions: 481ft 6in overall x 62ft max beam x 27ft 6in max draught
Gun armament: 1 single 4in QF Mk IV (1); 2 single 40mm Bofors (2); 6 single 20mm Oerlikon (6)
Fuel: 3,100 tons diesel
Endurance: ?
Complement: 118
Protection: None
Flight deck: 461ft x 62ft steel
Arrester wires: 4 x 15,000lb @ 55 knots; 1 barrier
Hangar: None
Catapults: None
Lifts: None
Aircraft: 3 Swordfish

MV *Alexia* seen from the TAG's cockpit of a Swordfish seconds after launch. The steam jet at the forward end of the deck shows that the ship was not quite into wind for the launch. (FAA Museum)

Aircraft fuel: 5,000 gallons AVGAS
Air weapons: Mk XXIV mines (homing torpedoes); Mk XI depth charges; 100lb AS bombs; 3in RP; .303in gun ammunition; flares and pyrotechnics

Notes: See *Acavus*.

Summary of service

00.12.43	Completed conversion in Sunderland and started work-up
00.01.44	Embarked 836F Flight (Swordfish) and commenced operations on North Atlantic convoy routes
00.05.44	836J Flight replaced 836F
00.07.44	836Q Flight replaced 836J
00.12.44	Disembarked 836Q Flight to RNAS Maydown
00.05.45	Embarked 836L Flight for one last convoy
Post-war	Converted back to mercantile tanker
00.00.51	Sold and renamed *Ianthina*
17.08.54	Sold to Hughes Bölkow and arrived at Blyth for scrapping

Amastra (–) *Merchant Aircraft Carrier*

Laid down: ?
Launched: 18 December 1934
Completed: September 1943 (as carrier)

Builder: Lithgow, Port Glasgow; converted by Smith Dock Co., North Shields
Machinery: 1-shaft Sulzer direct-drive diesel; 3,500bhp = 12 knots
Displacement: 8,000 tons standard; 16,000 tons deep load
Dimensions: 482ft 9in overall x 62ft max beam x 27ft 6in max draught
Gun armament: 1 single 4in QF Mk IV (1); 2 single 40mm Bofors (2); 6 single 20mm Oerlikon (6)
Fuel: 3,100 tons diesel
Endurance: ?
Complement: 118
Protection: None
Flight deck: 461ft x 62ft steel
Arrester wires: 4 x 15,000lb @ 55 knots; 1 barrier
Hangar: None
Catapults: None
Lifts: None
Aircraft: 3 Swordfish
Aircraft fuel: 5,000 gallons AVGAS
Air weapons: Mk XXIV mines (homing torpedoes); Mk XI depth charges; 100lb AS bombs; 3in RP; .303in gun ammunition; flares and pyrotechnics

Notes: See *Acavus*.

Summary of service

00.09.43	Completed conversion in North Shields
00.10.43	Embarked 836E Flight (Swordfish) from RNAS Maydown and employed on North Atlantic convoy routes after work-up
00.07.44	836C replaced 836E Flight
00.09.44	836C Flight disembarked to RNAS Maydown for last time (ship ran for remainder of war as tanker with no operational aircraft embarked; empty deck often used to ferry aircraft from USA to UK)
00.00.46	Converted back to mercantile tanker configuration
00.00.51	Sold and renamed *Idas*
27.06.55	Sold to Italian shipbreakers and arrived in La Spezia for scrapping

MV *Amastra* with two Swordfish of 'E' Flight, 836 NAS, on deck photographed by the third. The forward aircraft is about to launch while that behind it is still folded and covered, ready to be pushed forward of the barrier for the imminent recovery. (FAA Museum)

Ancylus (–) *Merchant Aircraft Carrier*

Laid down: ?
Launched: 9 October 1934
Completed: October 1943 (as carrier)

Builder: Swan Hunter & Wigham Richardson, Wallsend-on-Tyne; converted by Palmers, Hebburn-on-Tyne
Machinery: 1-shaft Sulzer direct-drive diesel; 3,500bhp = 12 knots

Displacement: 8,000 tons standard; 16,000 tons deep load
Dimensions: 482ft 9in overall x 62ft max beam x 27ft 6in max draught
Gun armament: 1 single 4in QF Mk IV (1); 2 single 40mm Bofors (2); 6 single 20mm Oerlikon (6)
Fuel: 3,100 tons diesel
Endurance: ?
Complement: 118

MV *Ancylus* in convoy with a deck cargo of B-25 Mitchell bombers. (FAA Museum)

Protection: None
Flight deck: 461ft x 62ft steel
Arrester wires: 4 x 15,000lb @ 55 knots; 1 barrier
Hangar: None
Catapults: None
Lifts: None

Aircraft: 3 Swordfish
Aircraft fuel: 5,000 gallons AVGAS
Air weapons: Mk XXIV mines (homing torpedoes); Mk XI depth charges; 100lb AS bombs; 3in RP; .303in gun ammunition; flares and pyrotechnics

Notes: See *Acavus*.

Summary of service

00.10.43 Completed conversion on Tyne and commenced work-up
02.11.43 Embarked 836G Flight (Swordfish); employed on North Atlantic convoy routes
31.05.44 Disembarked 836G Flight to RNAS Maydown
18.08.44 Embarked 836D Flight from RNAS Maydown
02.10.44 Disembarked 836D Flight to RNAS Maydown (ship used on tanking duties without operational aircraft embarked for remainder of war; often used to transport aircraft on deck from USA to UK)
00.00.45 Converted back to mercantile tanker
00.00.52 Sold and renamed *Imbricaria*
04.12.54 Sold to Italian shipbreakers and arrived in La Spezia for scrapping

Argus (1987) (A135) *Training/Ferry Carrier*

Laid down: ?
Launched: 1981
Completed: 1 June 1988

Builder: Cantieri Navali, Breda, Italy; converted by Harland & Wolff, Belfast
Machinery: 2-shaft Lindholmen-Pielstick diesels driving electric propulsion motors; 23,400shp = 22 knots
Displacement: 22,256 tons standard; 28,480 tons deep load
Dimensions: 574ft 6in overall x 99ft 7in max beam x 27ft max draught
Gun armament: 1 twin 30mm BMARC DS-30B (2); 1 twin 20mm Oerlikon GAM-BO1 (2)
Fuel: 5,617 tons diesel
Endurance: 20,000 miles @ 19 knots
Complement: 250 RFA and RN
Protection: 6in concrete under flight deck
Flight deck: 369ft x 92ft steel over concrete
Arrester wires: None
Hangar: 370ft x 90ft x 20ft
Catapults: None
Lifts: *Fwd* 54ft 8in long x 31ft 8in wide; *aft* 54ft 8in long x 31ft 8in wide; both 40,000lb
Aircraft: 14
Aircraft fuel: 812,750 gallons AVCAT
Air weapons: Sidewinder AAM; Sea Eagle ASM; Sea Skua ASM; Stingray homing torpedoes; laser-guided bombs; 1,000lb MC bombs; practice bombs and grenades; 30mm ADEN cannon ammunition; 7.62mm gun ammunition; flares and pyrotechnics (only practice weapons normally carried in training role; no weapons carried in PCRS role)

Notes: Originally a 'ro-ro' container ship named *Contender Bezant*. She was taken up from trade (STUFT) during the Falklands conflict in 1982, subsequently purchased outright and converted into an RFA training/ferry carrier. The original vehicle and cargo deck was converted into a hangar capable of taking 8 Sea Harriers and 3 Sea Kings. Two *Invincible*-type lifts were fitted although they were poorly positioned and take up a great deal of space in the hangar 'box' that could have been used to park more aircraft. The flight deck was built up by inverting the former hatch covers and filling them with six inches of concrete. This put weight high in the ship, compensating for the lack of cargo and improving stability. The resultant surface was covered with steel. Extra accommodation was provided in an unimaginative box structure added to the original bridgework. A small starboard-side island with funnel simulates the after structure of a destroyer for helicopter deck landing training purposes. The ship can actually carry a tactically useful air group but with such meagre support facilities and accommodation that it would not be operable; similarly, she can carry a Commando-size force and its vehicles a considerable distance but lacks the ability to support it adequately. The shortage of heads and galleys would also be a limiting factor. She was fitted as a Primary Casualty Receiving Ship with medical facilities and the necessary staff during the Gulf War of 1990–91 and retains some capability for this role. The lack of a ski-jump drastically reduces the effectiveness of any Sea Harrier operations but she can carry a range of weapons and has full electronic and visual landing aids. This huge ship, which could have been a valuable fleet unit in addition to its training duties, has been rendered less useful by the unimaginative and pedestrian conversion.

Summary of service

00.00.81 Entered service as commercial ro-ro ship
00.05.82 Taken up from trade for conversion to aircraft ferry; converted in Devonport Dockyard and used successfully in

RFA *Argus*. (FAA Museum)

	Falklands conflict
02.03.84	Purchased by Ministry of Defence for conversion to helicopter training ship to replace RFA *Engadine*
28.10.87	Initial sea trials
03.03.88	Accepted into RFA though still incomplete
01.06.88	Dedicated and entered service as training ship based in Portland
17.07.89	Refitted to improve aviation standards
03.10.89	Replaced *Engadine* as helicopter training ship
16.10.90	Fitted with 100-bed emergency hospital and sailed the Persian Gulf as a Primary Casualty Receiving Ship (PCRS) with helicopters of 846 NAS (Sea King Commando) embarked for casevac duties
00.03.91	Operated in Gulf with 846 NAS and visiting Lynx Flights; on completion, returned to training role at Portland
00.00.93	Deployed to Adriatic in company with *Ark Royal* and other warships to support UN operations in former Republic of Yugoslavia (ship carried Army units which were held poised offshore ready to land, if necessary, in support of British forces ashore in Bosnia)
Late 93	Returned to training role
00.00.95	Extant

Empire MacAlpine (–) *Merchant Aircraft Carrier*

Laid down: 11 August 1942
Launched: 23 December 1942
Completed: 21 April 1943

Builder: Burntisland Shipbuilding Co., Burntisland; converted by William Denny & Bros, Dumbarton
Machinery: 1-shaft Doxford diesel; 3,500bhp = 12.5 knots
Displacement: 7,950 tons standard; 12,000 tons deep load
Dimensions: 459ft overall x 62ft max beam x 24ft 6in max draught
Gun armament: 1 single 4in QF Mk IV (1); 2 single 40mm Bofors (2); 4 single 20mm Oerlikon (4)
Fuel: 3,000 tons diesel
Endurance: ?
Complement: 107
Protection: None
Flight deck: 414ft x 62ft steel
Arrester wires: 4 x 15,000lb @ 55 knots
Hangar: 142ft x 38ft x 24ft
Catapults: None
Lifts: *Aft* 42ft long x 20ft wide; 10,000lb, 50-second cycle
Aircraft: 4 Swordfish
Aircraft fuel: 5,000 gallons AVGAS
Air weapons: Mk XXIV mines (homing torpedoes); Mk XI depth charges; 100lb AS bombs; 3in RP; .303in gun ammunition; flares and pyrotechnics

Notes: The first MAC-ship to enter service. Grain tankers under construction were chosen for completion as limited carriers since they could be brought into service more rapidly than full escort carriers. Unlike the oil tanker conversions, it was possible to work in a small hangar aft with a lift to move aircraft to and from the flight deck. This allowed 4 rather than 3 Swordfish to be carried. The extra topweight of flight deck, hangar, island and armament meant that a reduction of about 3,000 tons (or 30 per cent) of the original cargo of grain had to be accepted. The ship was manned by an MN crew, the RN provided the air department, aircraft, air crews and maintainers and the guns were manned by DEMS soldiers—a truly joint effort. The barrier used on the tanker MAC-ships was not fitted as the aircraft were struck down into the hangar instead of remaining in a permament deck park.

Summary of service

00.04.43	First MAC-ship to complete and work up
00.05.43	Lt-Cdr Slater RN, CO of 836 NAS (Swordfish), landed on board (first time aircraft had ever landed on merchant ship)
29.05.43	Sailed as part of ONS.9 with 836B Flight (Swordfish) embarked
22.09.43	Whilst ship with ONS.18, Swordfish sighted and attacked surfaced U-boat but failed to sink it
00.02.44	836D Flight replaced 836B
00.12.44	836D Flight disembarked to RNAS Maydown
00.04.45	Embarked 836Y (ship's last Flight from RNAS Maydown)
12.04.45	Whilst with ON.296, Swordfish sighted and

MV *Empire MacAlpine* with all four of her Swordfish on deck. (FAA Museum)

attacked U-boat schnorkel and evidently damaged it as three hours later *U1024* surfaced and surrendered to escort vessels

00.00.47 Sold and converted to conventional mercantile grain ship; renamed *Derrynane*

00.00.51 Renamed *Huntsbrook*

00.00.60 Renamed *Suna Breeze*; later resold and renamed *Djatinegeleh* and then *San Ernesto*

00.00.68 Renamed *Pacific Endeavour*

00.04.70 Sold to Wise Investment Co. and scrapped in Hong Kong

Empire MacAndrew (–) *Merchant Aircraft Carrier*

Laid down: ?
Launched: 3 May 1943
Completed: July 1943

Builder: William Denny & Bros, Dumbarton

Machinery: 1-shaft Burmeister & Wain diesel; 3,300bhp = 12.5 knots
Displacement: 7,950 tons standard; 12,000 tons deep load
Dimensions: 448ft 6in overall x 62ft max beam x 24ft

MV *Empire MacAndrew*, showing the more slab-sided appearance of the bulk grain-carrying MAC-ships. (FAA Museum)

9in max draught
Gun armament: 1 single 4in QF Mk IV (1); 2 single 40mm Bofors (2); 4 single 20mm Oerlikon (4)
Fuel: 3,000 tons diesel
Endurance: ?
Complement: 107
Protection: None
Flight deck: 414ft x 62ft steel
Arrester wires: 4 x 15,000lb @ 55 knots
Hangar: 142ft x 38ft x 24ft
Catapults: None
Lifts: *Aft* 42ft long x 20ft wide; 10,000lb, 50-second cycle
Aircraft: 4 Swordfish
Aircraft fuel: 5,000 gallons AVGAS
Air weapons: Mk XXIV mines (homing torpedoes); Mk XI depth charges; 100lb AS bombs; 3in RP; .303in gun ammunition; flares and pyrotechnics

Notes: See *Empire MacAlpine.*

Summary of service

00.07.43	Completed as MAC-ship and worked up
00.08.43	Embarked 836M Flight (Swordfish) and began convoy duty in North Atlantic
00.11.43	836H Flight replaced replaced 836M
00.06.44	836R Flight replaced 836H.; number of aircrew in Flight reduced to provide extra crews for NAS involved in Operation 'Neptune'
26.09.44	Whilst with ON.255, Swordfish on dusk patrol saw U-boat dive but was unable to carry out successful attack on it
00.11.44	836B Flight replaced 836R
00.03.45	836Z Flight replaced 836B
26.04.45	Whilst with ON.298, Swordfish observed periscope and carried out depth-charge attack on U-boat but failed to sink it
00.05.45	Disembarked 836Z Flight to RNAS Maydown for last time
00.00.47	Sold and reconverted to mercantile standards; renamed *Derryheen*
00.00.51	Renamed *Cape Grafton*
00.00.64	Renamed *Patricia*
00.00.70	Sold to Chinese shipbreakers and scrapped

Empire MacCabe (–) *Merchant Aircraft Carrier*

Laid down: ?
Launched: 18 May 1943
Completed: December 1943

Builder: Swan Hunter & Wigham Richardson, Wallsend-on-Tyne
Machinery: 1-shaft Doxford diesel; 3,300bhp = 11 knots
Displacement: 9,249 tons deep load
Dimensions: 485ft 9in overall x 62ft max beam x 27ft 6in max draught
Gun armament: 1 single 4in QF Mk IV (1); 8 single 20mm Oerlikon (8)
Fuel: ?
Endurance: ?
Complement: 122
Protection: None
Flight deck: 461ft x 62ft steel
Arrester wires: 4 x 15,000lb @ 55 knots; 1 trickle wire; 1 barrier
Hangar: None
Catapults: None
Lifts: None
Aircraft: 3 Swordfish
Aircraft fuel: 5,000 gallons AVGAS
Air weapons: Mk XXIV mines (homing torpedoes); Mk XI depth charges; 100lb AS bombs; 3in RP; .303in gun ammunition; flares and pyrotechnics

Notes: Originally owned by BP. See *Acavus* for notes.

Summary of service

00.12.43 Completed as MAC-ship and worked up
00.01.44 Commenced Atlantic convoy duty and embarked 836N Flight (Swordfish)
00.09.44 836A Flight replaced 836N
18.01.45 Whilst with ONS.40, Swordfish sighted U-boat but unable to make successful attack
00.05.45 836H Flight replaced 836A
00.06.45 836H Flight disembarked for last time
00.00.46 Converted to conventional oil tanker and sold by BP; renamed *British Escort*
00.00.59 Renamed *Easthill Escort*
00.00.62 Sold to British shipbreakers and scrapped in Hong Kong

Empire MacCallum (–) *Merchant Aircraft Carrier*

Laid down: ?
Launched: 12 October 1943
Completed: December 1943

Builder: Lithgow, Port Glasgow
Machinery: 1-shaft Burmeister & Wain diesel; 3,300bhp = 12.5 knots
Displacement: 8,250 tons deep load
Dimensions: 446ft 6in overall x 62ft max beam x 24ft 6in max draught
Gun armament: 1 single 4in QF Mk IV (1); 2 single 40mm Bofors (2); 6 single 20mm Oerlikon (6)
Fuel: ?
Endurance: ?
Complement: 107
Protection: None
Flight deck: 461ft x 62ft steel
Arrester wires: 4 x 15,000lb @ 55 knots
Hangar: 142ft x 38ft x 24ft
Catapults: None
Lifts: *Aft* 42ft long x 20ft wide; 10,000lb, 50-second cycle
Aircraft: 4 Swordfish
Aircraft fuel: 5,000 gallons AVGAS
Air weapons: Mk XXIV mines (homing torpedoes); Mk XI depth charges; 100lb AS bombs; 3in RP; .303in gun ammunition; flares and pyrotechnics

Notes: See *Empire MacAlpine*.

Summary of service

00.12.43 Completed as a MAC-ship and worked up
00.01.44 Embarked 836K Flight (Swordfish) and operated on North Atlantic convoy routes
00.02.44 836R Flight replaced 836K
00.06.44 836T Flight replaced 836R
08.07.44 Whilst with ONM 243 three Swordfish from *Empire MacCallum* and *Empire MacColl* attacked and probably damaged unidentified U-boat
00.09.44 836Y Flight replaced 836T
00.02.45 836K Flight replaced 836Y
00.05.45 836K Flight disembarked to RNAS Maydown for last time
00.00.45 Converted to mercantile standard
00.00.47 Sold and renamed *Doris Clunies*
00.00.51 Renamed *Sunrover*
00.00.59 Renamed *Eudoxia*; later renamed *Phorkyss*
00.00.60 Sold to Japanese shipbreakers and scrapped in Osaka

The former *Empire MacCallum*, converted to mercantile standard post-war and re-named *Doris Clunies*. (World Ship Society Merchant Photographic Library)

MV *Empire MacCabe* shows the more open-sided appearance of the tanker conversions. (FAA Museum)

Empire MacColl (–) *Merchant Aircraft Carrier*

Laid down: ?
Launched: 24 July 1943
Completed: November 1943

Builder: Cammell Laird & Co., Birkenhead
Machinery: 1-shaft Burmeister & Wain diesel; 3,300bhp = 11 knots
Displacement: 9,133 tons deep load
Dimensions: 481ft 6in overall x 62ft max beam x 27ft 9in max draught
Gun armament: 1 single 4in QF Mk IV (1); 8 single 20mm Oerlikon (8)
Fuel: ?
Endurance: ?
Complement: 122
Protection: None
Flight deck: 461ft x 62ft steel

MV *Empire MacColl* in convoy. (FAA Museum)

Arrester wires: 4 x 15,000lb @ 55 knots; 1 barrier
Hangar: None
Catapults: None
Lifts: None
Aircraft: 3 Swordfish
Aircraft fuel: 5,000 gallons AVGAS
Air weapons: Mk XXIV mines (homing torpedoes); Mk XI depth charges; 100lb AS bombs; 3in RP; .303in gun ammunition; flares and pyrotechnics

Notes: Converted whilst under construction. Formerly owned by British Petroleum. See notes on *Acavus*.

Summary of service

00.11.43	Completed as MAC-ship and worked up; embarked 836A Flight (Swordfish) and operated on North Atlantic convoy routes
08.07.44	3 Swordfish from *Empire MacColl* and *Empire MacCallum* attacked U-boat that was threatening ONM.243 (U-boat believed damaged, but this not confirmed)
00.07.44	836J Flight replaced 836A
00.08.44	836E Flight replaced 836J
00.11.44	836V Flight replaced 836E
00.01.45	836V Flight disembarked to RNAS Maydown
00.03.45	Embarked 836Q Flight
00.05.45	Disembarked 836Q Flight to RNAS Maydown to disband
00.00.45	Converted to mercantile standard
00.00.46	Renamed *British Pilot* and operated by BP
00.08.62	Sold to Metal Industries and arrived at Faslane for scrapping

Empire MacDermott (–) *Merchant Aircraft Carrier*

Laid down: ?
Launched: 24 January 1944
Completed: March 1944

Builder: William Denny & Bros, Dumbarton
Machinery: 1-shaft Burmeister & Wain diesel; 3,300bhp = 12.5 knots
Displacement: 7,950 tons deep load
Dimensions: 448ft 6in overall x 62ft max beam x 24ft 9in max draught
Gun armament: 1 single 4in QF Mk IV (1); 2 single 40mm Bofors (2); 4 single 20mm Oerlikon (4)
Fuel: ?
Endurance: ?
Complement: 107
Protection: None
Flight deck: 423ft x 62ft steel
Arrester wires: 4 x 15,000lb @ 55 knots

Hangar: 142ft x 38ft x 24ft
Catapults: None
Lifts: *Aft* 42ft long x 20ft wide
Aircraft: 4 Swordfish
Aircraft fuel: 5,000 gallons AVGAS
Air weapons: Mk XXIV mines (homing torpedoes); Mk XI depth charges; 100lb AS bombs; 3in RP; .303in gun ammunition; flares and pyrotechnics

Notes: See *Empire MacAlpine.*

Summary of service

00.03.44 Completed as MAC-ship and worked up for service on North Atlantic convoy routes
00.04.44 836K Flight (Swordfish) embarked
26.09.44 Swordfish on dusk search from *Empire MacDermott* and *Empire MacAndrew* saw U-boat dive but were unable to attack it
00.11.44 836N Flight replaced 836K
00.04.45 836B Flight replaced 836N
00.05.45 836B Flight disembarked to RNAS Maydown to disband
00.00.46 Converted back to mercantile standard

00.00.48 Renamed *La Cumbre*
00.00.59 Renamed *Parnon*
00.00.69 Renamed *Starlight*; eventual fate unknown

Empire Mackay (–) *Merchant Aircraft Carrier*

Laid down: ?
Launched: 17 June 1943
Completed: October 1943

Builder: Harland & Wolff, Govan
Machinery: 1-shaft Burmeister & Wain diesel; 3,300bhp = 11.5 knots
Displacement: 8,908 tons deep load
Dimensions: 479ft 6in overall x 62ft max beam x 27ft 3in max draught
Gun armament: 1 single 4in QF Mk IV (1); 8 single 20mm Oerlikon (8)
Fuel: ?
Endurance: ?
Complement: 122
Protection: None
Flight deck: 460ft x 62ft steel
Arrester wires: 4 x 15,000lb @ 55 knots; 1 barrier
Hangar: None
Catapults: None
Lifts: None
Aircraft: 3 Swordfish
Aircraft fuel: 5,000 gallons AVGAS

Two Swordfish parked forward after a recovery aboard MV *Empire Mackay*. (FAA Museum)

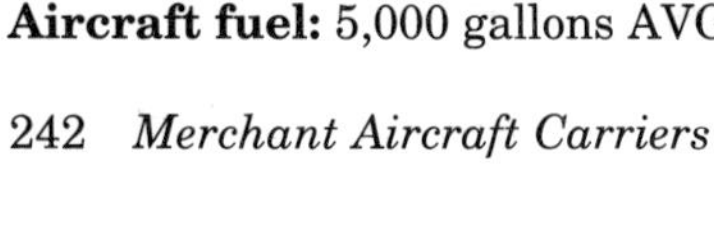

MV *Empire MacDermott* in convoy, seen from a Swordfish that has just launched. A 'Flower' class corvette is acting as planeguard. (Author)

Air weapons: Mk XXIV mines (homing torpedoes); Mk XI depth charges; 100lb AS bombs; 3in RP; .303in gun ammunition; flares and pyrotechnics

Notes: Owned by BP. See *Acavus* for further details.

Summary of service

00.10.43 Completed as MAC-ship and worked up for service with North Atlantic convoy routes; embarked 836D Flight (Swordfish)
00.07.44 836W Flight replaced 836D
00.12.44 836R Flight replaced 836W
00.06.45 836R Flight disembarked to RNAS Maydown to disband
00.00.46 Retained by BP but converted to mercantile tanker standard; renamed *British Swordfish* as tribute to those who operated from her during war
21.05.59 Arrived at Rotterdam for scrapping, having been sold to Dutch shipbreakers

Empire MacKendrick (–) *Merchant Aircraft Carrier*

Laid down: ?
Launched: 29 September 1944
Completed: December 1943

Builder: Burntisland Shipbuilding Co., Burntisland
Machinery: 1-shaft Burmeister & Wain diesel; 3,500bhp = 12.5 knots
Displacement: 7,950 tons deep load
Dimensions: 459ft overall x 62ft max beam x 28ft 9in max draught
Gun armament: 1 single 4in QF Mk IV (1); 2 single 40mm Bofors (2); 4 single 20mm Oerlikon (4)
Fuel: ?
Endurance: ?
Complement: 107
Protection: None

Flight deck: 413ft 9in x 62ft steel
Arrester wires: 4 x 15,000lb @ 55 knots
Hangar: 142ft x 38ft x 24ft
Catapults: None
Lifts: *Aft* 42ft long x 20ft wide; 10,000lb, 50-second cycle
Aircraft: 4 Swordfish
Aircraft fuel: 5,000 gallons AVGAS
Air weapons: Mk XXIV mines (homing torpedoes); Mk XI depth charges; 100lb AS bombs; 3in RP; .303in gun ammunition; flares and pyrotechnics

Notes: See *Empire MacAlpine.*

MV *Empire MacKendrick* on 9 December 1944. (FAA Museum)

Summary of service

00.12.43 Completed as MAC-ship and worked up for service on North Atlantic convoy routes
00.01.44 836M Flight (Swordfish) embarked
29.05.44 Whilst escorting ON.237, 3 Swordfish from *Ancylus* and *Empire MacKendrick* sighted U-boat on surface and attacked it with 3in RP (U-boat not sunk and all three aircraft slightly damaged by flak)
00.09.44 836Z Flight replaced 836M
00.01.45 836L Flight replaced 836Z
00.03.45 836V Flight replaced 836L
00.06.45 836V Flight disembarked to RNAS Maydown to disband
00.00.45 Converted to mercantile standard
00.00.51 Renamed *Granpond*
00.00.54 Renamed *Condor*
00.00.59 Renamed *Saltersgate*; later renamed *Vassil Levsky*
00.00.67 One of merchant ships trapped in Bitter Lakes during Arab-Israeli 'Six-Day War'; eventual fate unknown

Empire MacMahon (–) *Merchant Aircraft Carrier*

Laid down: ?
Launched: 2 July 1943
Completed: December 1943

Builder: Swan Hunter & Wigham Richardson, Wallsend-on-Tyne
Machinery: 1-shaft Werkspoor diesel; 3,300bhp = 11 knots
Displacement: 8,856 tons deep load
Dimensions: 483ft overall x 62ft max beam x 27ft 6in max draught
Gun armament: 1 single 4in QF Mk IV (1); 8 single 20mm Oerlikon (8)
Fuel: ?
Endurance: ?
Complement: 122
Protection: None
Flight deck: 461ft 6in x 62ft steel
Arrester wires: 4 x 15,000lb @ 55 knots; 1 barrier
Hangar: None
Catapults: None
Lifts: None
Aircraft: 3 Swordfish
Aircraft fuel: 5,000 gallons AVGAS
Air weapons: Mk XXIV mines (homing torpedoes); Mk XI depth charges; 100lb AS bombs; 3in RP; .303in gun ammunition; flares and pyrotechnics

Notes: See *Acavus.*

Summary of service

00.12.43	Completed as MAC-ship and worked up for service on North Atlantic convoy routes; embarked 836J Flight (Swordfish)
00.04.44	836B Flight replaced 836J
00.10.44	836G Flight replaced 836B
00.03.45	836W Flight replaced 836G
00.06.45	836W Flight disembarked to RNAS Maydown to disband
00.00.45	Converted to mercantile standard
00.00.46	Renamed *Navinia*
17.03.60	Arrived in Hong Kong for scrapping, having been sold to British shipbreakers

A MAC-ship similar to MV *Empire MacMahon* on 30 April 1944. (FAA Museum)

Empire MacRae (–) *Merchant Aircraft Carrier*

Laid down: ?
Launched: 21 June 1944
Completed: September 1943

Builder: Lithgow, Port Glasgow
Machinery: 1-shaft Burmeister & Wain diesel; 3,300bhp = 12.5 knots
Displacement: 8,250 tons deep load
Dimensions: 446ft 6in overall x 62ft max beam x 24ft 6in max draught
Gun armament: 1 single 4in QF Mk IV (1); 2 single 40mm Bofors (2); 4 single 20mm Oerlikon (4)
Fuel: ?
Endurance: ?
Complement: 107
Protection: None

Flight deck: 424ft 4in x 62ft steel
Arrester wires: 4 x 15,000lb @ 55 knots
Hangar: 142ft x 38ft x 24ft
Catapults: None
Lifts: *Aft* 42ft long x 20ft wide; 10,000lb, 50-second cycle
Aircraft: 4 Swordfish
Aircraft fuel: 5,000 gallons AVGAS
Air weapons: Mk XXIV mines (homing torpedoes); Mk XI depth charges; 100lb AS bombs; 3in RP; .303in gun ammunition; flares and pyrotechnics

Notes: See *Empire MacAlpine*. Converted to MAC-ship while under construction.

Summary of service

00.09.43	Completed as MAC-ship and worked up
00.10.43	Embarked 836C Flight (Swordfish) and operated on North Atlantic convoy routes
00.05.44	836L Flight replaced 836C
00.11.44	836U Flight replaced 836L
00.03.45	836D Flight replaced 836U
00.06.45	836D Flight disembarked to RNAS Maydown to disband
00.00.45	Converted to mercantile standard
00.00.47	Renamed *Alpha Zambesi*
00.00.54	Renamed *Tobon*
00.00.67	Renamed *Despina P*; eventual fate unknown

Engadine (1967) (K08) *Helicopter Training Ship*

Laid down: 9 August 1965
Launched: 16 September 1966
Completed: 14 December 1967

Builder: Henry Robb, Leith
Machinery: 1-shaft Sulzer turbocharged diesel; 5,500bhp = 15 knots
Displacement: 8,000 tons deep load
Dimensions: 424ft overall x 58ft 4in max beam x 22ft max draught
Gun armament: None
Fuel: ?
Endurance: 6,000 miles @ 14 knots
Complement: 77 RFA personnel plus up to 113 RN
Protection: None
Flight deck: 160ft x 58ft steel
Arrester wires: None
Hangar: 90ft x 50ft 17ft 6in
Catapults: None
Lifts: None
Aircraft: 4 helicopters plus PTA
Aircraft fuel: ?
Air weapons: Stingray homing torpedoes; Mk 46 homing torpedoes; Mk 44 homing torpedoes; Mk XI depth charges; 7.62mm gun ammunition; flares and pyrotechnics

Notes: Built specifically to replace *Lofoten* in the helicopter training role. She was designed to mercantile standards based on the store carriers *Hebe* and *Bacchus* and intended to be an RFA to save costs. She was, however, capable of deploying operationally with up to 4 Wessex ASW. A small hangar, designed to accommodate pilotless target aircraft, was constructed on the roof of the main hangar. Target aircraft could be launched from the main hangar roof or from the flight deck. *Engadine* was often used to support the Fleet Target Group during exercises.

Summary of service

00.00.68	Based at Portland; provided embarked training facilities for 737 (Wessex ASW), 702 (Lynx) and 703 (Wasp) NAS
00.00.82	Deployed to South Atlantic with part of 847 NAS (Wessex Commando) embarked
04.06.82	Overflown by Argentine Air Force Boeing 747

(Left) MV *Empire MacRae* with a Swordfish being struck down into the hangar on the single lift. (FAA Museum)

(Far right) RFA *Engadine* in South Atlantic waters during 1982 with two Wessex helicopters on deck. (FAA Museum)

09.06.82	Provided support for minesweeper group off Port Stanley
00.00.83	Provided training facilities for 810 NAS (Sea King ASW)
00.00.88	Replaced in training role at Portland by *Argus*
00.02.89	De-stored at Portland; laid up in Devonport on completion
00.06.89	Placed on sales list
00.02.90	Towed to Falmouth for modification to mercantile standards; registered in St Vincent by new owners for use as car ferry in Greek waters
00.00.95	Believed extant

Miralda (–) *Merchant Aircraft Carrier*

Laid down: ?
Launched: July 1936
Completed: January 1944 (as carrier)

Builder: Netherlands Dock & Shipbuilding Co.; converted by Palmers, Hebburn-on-Tyne
Machinery: 1-shaft Sulzer diesel; 4,000bhp = 12.5 knots
Displacement: 8,000 tons standard; 16,000 tons deep load
Dimensions: 482ft 9in overall x 62ft max beam x 27ft 6in max draught
Gun armament: 1 single 4in QF Mk IV (1); 2 single 40mm Bofors (2); 6 single 20mm Oerlikon (6)
Fuel: 3,100 tons diesel
Endurance: ?
Complement: 118 (64 RN plus 54 MN)
Protection: None
Flight deck: 461ft 9in x 62ft steel
Arrester wires: 4 x 15,000lb @ 55 knots; 1 barrier
Hangar: None
Catapults: None
Lifts: None
Aircraft: 3 Swordfish
Aircraft fuel: 5,000 gallons AVGAS
Air weapons: Mk XXIV mines (homing torpedoes); Mk XI depth charges; 100lb AS bombs; 3in RP; .303in gun ammunition; flares and pyrotechnics

Notes: See *Acavus.*

Summary of service

00.01.44	Conversion to MAC-ship completed on Tyne; worked up for duty on North Atlantic convoy routes
00.02.44	Embarked 836Q Flight (Swordfish)
21.06.44	Whilst with ON.240, probable sighting of U-boat by 2 Swordfish (both damaged on landing but repairable on board)

00.08.44 836H Flight replaced 836Q
27.12.44 Whilst with ON.274, U-boat attacked by Swordfish with two 100lb AS bombs (no confirmed result)
26.01.45 Whilst with SC.165, U-boat schnorkel sighted in approximately 53° N 24° W but no attack carried out
00.02.45 836P Flight replaced 836H
00.05.45 836P Flight disembarked to RNAS Maydown to disband
Post-war Converted back to mercantile tanker standard
00.00.50 Renamed *Marisa*
21.07.60 Arrived in Hong Kong for scrapping

Rapana (–) *Merchant Aircraft Carrier*

MV *Miralda* in convoy. (FAA Museum)

Laid down: ?
Launched: April 1935
Completed: July 1943 (as carrier)

Builder: Wilton-Fijenoord, Schiedam; converted by Smiths Dock Co., North Shields
Machinery: 1-shaft Sulzer diesel; 4,000bhp = 12.5 knots
Displacement: 8,000 tons standard; 16,000 tons deep load
Dimensions: 482ft 9in overall x 62ft max beam x 27ft 6in max draught
Gun armament: 1 single 4in QF Mk IV (1); 2 single 40mm Bofors (2); 6 single 20mm Oerlikon (6)
Fuel: 3,100 tons diesel
Endurance: ?
Complement: 118 (64 RN plus 54 MN)
Protection: None
Flight deck: 462ft x 62ft steel
Arrester wires: 4 x 15,000lb @ 55 knots; 1 barrier
Hangar: None
Catapults: None
Lifts: None
Aircraft: 3 Swordfish
Aircraft fuel: 5,000 gallons AVGAS
Air weapons: Mk XXIV mines (homing torpedoes); Mk XI depth charges; 100lb AS bombs; 3in RP; .303in gun ammunition; flares and pyrotechnics

Notes: The first tanker MAC-ship to complete. See *Acavus* for further notes.

Summary of service
00.07.43 Completed conversion to MAC-ship on Tyne; worked up for service on North Atlantic convoy routes
00.08.43 Embarked 836L Flight (Swordfish)
08.10.43 Whilst with SC.143, Swordfish carried out attacks on U-boat (thought to have been damaged but unconfirmed)
00.02.44 836L Flight disembarked to RNAS Maydown
00.04.44 836X Flight embarked
00.10.44 836X Flight disembarked to RNAS Maydown
00.00.45 Converted back to mercantile tanker
00.00.50 Renamed *Rotula*
00.01.58 Arrived in Hong Kong for scrapping

MV *Rapana* shortly after conversion to a MAC-ship. (Author)

Reliant (A131) *Helicopter Support Ship*

Laid down: ?
Launched: ?
Completed: 1977

Builder: Gdansk Shipyard, Poland; converted by Cammell Laird & Co., Birkenhead
Machinery: 1-shaft Ceglieski-built Sulzer direct-drive diesel; 29,000bhp = 22 knots
Displacement: 27,867 tons deep load
Dimensions: 670ft overall x 101ft max beam x 26ft 3in max draught
Gun armament: 4 single 20mm GAM-BO1 (4)
Fuel: ?
Endurance: 12,000 miles @ 18 knots
Complement: 201 (60 RFA plus 141 RN)
Protection: None

RFA *Reliant*. (FAA Museum)

Flight deck: 196ft x 85ft galvanised steel mesh
Arrester wires: None
Hangar: 108ft x 42ft x 20ft
Catapults: None
Lifts: None
Aircraft: 5 Sea Kings
Aircraft fuel: ?
Air weapons: Stingray homing torpedoes; Mk 46 homing torpedoes; Mk XI depth charges; 7.62mm gun ammunition; flares and pyrotechnics

Notes: Built as the container ship *Astronomer* for the Harrison Line and chartered by the Ministry of Defence in late 1982 after having been temporarily taken up from trade during the Falklands conflict. She was fitted out with the US-designed Arapaho containerised system, designed to allow merchant ships to be rapidly converted to helicopter support ships. In fact, given the cost of the containerised hangar, workshops and deck, *Reliant* offered little improvement over the merchant conversions carried out so effectively by the Royal Dockyards during the Falklands War. The use of a 27,000-ton ship to operate five helicopters was also questionable when *Reliant* is compared with the 1967 *Engadine*. Despite interest in similar conversions, which may be regarded as a modern development of the MAC-ship concept, *Reliant* was not retained in service. There seems little point in spending money to procure containerised support equipment to sit in a dockyard waiting for a potential emergency: for little extra cost it could have been built into a more effective ship in the first place and put to general use. British Aerospace developed Arapaho into SCADS (Shipborne Containerised Air Defence System) but no production orders followed.

Summary of service

00.05.82 Taken up from trade and proceeded to Devonport Dockyard for conversion to aircraft transport in order to support Task Force in South Atlantic: in a matter of days she was fitted with flight deck amidships, hangar forward, fuel system and workshops (best of the STUFT conversions)
00.06.82 Sailed for South Atlantic with Chinook, Wessex and Scout helicopters but arrived off Falklands too late for war service
00.07.82 Relieved *Engadine* as helicopter support ship in Falklands waters
00.12.82 Chartered by MoD for more permanent conversion to helicopter support ship (US prototype Arapaho facilities fitted by Cammell Laird with project management by British Aerospace)
00.07.83 Renamed *Reliant* and entered service with RFA
02.01.84 Sailed for Mediterranean with 846 NAS (Sea King Commando) embarked to support British forces acting with International Peacekeeping Force in Lebanon
11.01.84 Withdrew 115 British troops from Lebanon to Cyprus
00.10.84 OST at Portland with Flight of 826 NAS (Sea King) embarked
00.11.84 Deployed to South Atlantic to provide ASW protection for Falkland Islands (aircrew and maintainers changed by rotation every three months)
25.05.86 Returned to Devonport and disembarked 826 NAS (apart from visit to Fort Lauderdale on way home, ship had spent 566 days at sea and steamed 100,000 miles during deployment)
00.07.86 Arrived in Seaforth Container Terminal on Merseyside for Arapaho equipment to be removed for return to USN (terms of charter from Harrison Line were that she would have to be restored to her original condition before return and MoD therefore took cheaper option of purchasing her outright and selling her as she lay)
00.10.86 Sailed from Liverpool under Panamanian flag en route for new mercantile owners

Appendices

APPENDIX 1: AIRCRAFT CARRIERS ORDERED BUT NOT COMPLETED

MALTA (D93) Malta *Class Fleet Carrier*

Builder: John Brown, Clydebank
Machinery: 4-shaft Parsons geared turbines; 8 Admiralty 3-drum boilers; 200,000shp = 33 knots
Displacement: 46,900 tons standard; 56,800 tons deep load
Dimensions: 916ft 6in overall x 136ft max beam x 34ft 6in max draught
Gun armament: 8 twin 4.5in QF Mk V HA (16); 8 sextuple 40mm Bofors (48); 7 single 40mm Bofors (7); 4 single 3pdr saluting (4)
Fuel: 7,000 tons FFO and diesel
Endurance: 7,100 miles @ 20 knots
Complement: 3,520
Protection: 1in flight deck; 4in waterline belt; 4in hangar deck; 4in magazines; 2in crowns; 2in bulkheads; 4in steering gear
Flight deck: 888ft x 121ft 9in armoured steel
Arrester wires: 16 x 20,000lb @ 75 knots; 3 barriers
Hangar: 440ft x 90ft x 17ft 6in
Catapults: 2 new design hydraulic; 30,000lb @ 130 knots
Lifts: *Centreline fwd* 54ft long x 46ft wide; *centreline aft* 54ft long x 46ft wide; *side fwd* 60ft long x 35ft wide; *side aft* 60ft long x 35ft wide; all 30,000lb
Aircraft: 90 as designed
Aircraft fuel: 190,000 gallons AVGAS
Air weapons: Extensive magazine space designed to support contemporary aircraft (exact loading never finalised but staff requirement called for torepdoes, bombs, bomb clusters, RP, depth charges, mines, 20mm cannon ammunition, flares and pyrotechnics)

Notes: Name-ship of a class of three fleet carriers upon which design work started in 1943. A considerable number of changes were made to the design during 1944 and the eventual ship, which was intended to launch the maximum number of aircraft in a single strike, owed much to American concepts. The single hangar spanned the width of the ship and was open at the sides to allow aircraft engines to be run. The large lifts, two of them on the ship's side outside the main hull, were designed to bring manned, running aircraft up to the flight deck for launch once the deck range were airborne. All machines were to be launched by newly designed hydraulic catapults. The flight deck was stressed to take 30,000lb aircraft. The engine and boiler rooms were divided into two groups, that for the outer shafts being forward and that for the inner aft. Underwater protection was to be similar to that built in *Eagle*, able to withstand a 2,000lb charge. The 4.5in guns were to be in Mk VII mountings, similar to the Mk VI widely used post-war in many destroyers and frigates but with a larger, 14ft diameter roller path.

There is some doubt as to whether *Malta* was actually laid down. If metal was actually cut, it was scrapped on the slip early in 1946 to make room for mercantile construction. Ordered early in 1945, *Malta* was cancelled on 21 December that year. Her sister-ships *Gibraltar* and *New Zealand* were not laid down and their orders were cancelled in November and December 1945 respectively.

The *Malta* design is enigmatic. The RN could not afford to build such huge ships in 1945, but it is arguable that two of them would have been a better investment than *Eagle* and *Ark Royal*, which proved to be difficult and expensive to modify for the large jet aircraft of the 1960s. The flight deck formed a superstructure and it would therefore have been more amenable to modification to take the angled deck and improved flight-deck machinery.

CVA-01 *Fleet Carrier*

Builder: Never laid down
Machinery: 3-shaft steam turbines; 135,000shp = 30 knots
Displacement: 54,650 tons deep load
Dimensions: 963ft overall x 231ft 4in max beam x 33ft 4in max draught
Missile armament: Sea Dart and Ikara missile systems aft; no guns

Fuel: 6,200 tons diesel
Endurance: 6,000 miles @ 20 knots
Complement: 3,000
Protection: 3in hangar side and roof; 1.5in bulkheads around magazines; 1.5in splinterproof steel bulkheads
Flight deck: 928ft x 230ft steel; 2.5-degree parallel deck
Arrester wires: 4 x 35,000lb @ 103 knots; emergency nylon barriers
Hangar: 660ft x 80ft x 18ft (with two higher bays to allow aircraft to fold/spread)
Catapults: 2 x BS5 steam (250ft stroke); 50,000lb @ 103 knots
Lifts: *Fwd* 54ft long x 44ft wide; *aft (side)* 54ft long x 45ft wide; both 40,000lb
Aircraft: 47 planned
Aircraft fuel: 600,000 gallons AVCAT
Air weapons: 4 magazines capable of carrying full range of naval air weapons

Notes: The result of many years research and development, CVA-01 was authorised on 30 July 1963. In June 1964 it was stated that bids would be requested for construction in April 1966 with completion due in 1973. In the event, the ship was cancelled following a major defence review in February 1966 when the Government announced the withdrawal of forces based east of Suez. The design included many innovative features, most notably the reduced-angle 'parallel' deck which eliminated Fly 4 and made 15 per cent more flight deck area usable to starboard. It would also have simplified landing in bad weather. The wide 'Alaskan highway', outboard of the island to starboard, was intended to be used by taxying aircraft. The forward lift was to use a 'scissors' arrangement (upon which the design of the lift in the *Invincible* class was based). It is believed that CVA-01 would have been named *Queen Elizabeth II*, perpetuating the tradition that the first major warship built during a particular reign is named after the Sovereign.

AFRICA (D06) *Fleet Carrier*

Ordered from Fairfield, Govan, in 1943. Never laid down and cancelled in October 1945. For details see *Eagle* (1951) as completed.

ARROGANT (14) Centaur *Class Light Fleet Carrier*

Ordered from Swan Hunter & Wigham Richardson, Wallsend-on-Tyne, in 1943. Never laid down and cancelled in 1945. For details see *Centaur*.

EAGLE (94) *Fleet Carrier*

Ordered from Vickers-Armstrongs, Walker Yard, Newcastle-upon-Tyne, in 1943. Cancelled in 1945 and such structure as had been built was broken up on the slipway. The sister-ship laid down as *Audacious* was renamed and completed as *Eagle* in order to perpetuate the name. For details see *Eagle* (1951) as completed.

GIBRALTAR (D68) Malta *Class Fleet Carrier*

Ordered from Vickers-Armstrongs, Walker Yard, Newcastle-upon-Tyne, in 1944. Never laid down and cancelled on 5 November 1945. For details see her planned sister-ship *Malta*.

HERMES (95) Centaur *Class Light Fleet Carrier*

Ordered from Cammell Laird, Birkenhead, in 1943. Cancelled in 1945 and such structure as had been built was broken up on the slipway. The sister-ship laid down as *Elephant* was more advanced and was renamed and completed as *Hermes* (1959) in order to perpetuate the name. For details see *Centaur*.

MONMOUTH (96) Centaur *Class Light Fleet Carrier*

Ordered from Fairfield, Govan, in 1943. Cancelled and steelwork scrapped on slipway in October 1945. For details see *Centaur*.

NEW ZEALAND (D43) Malta *Class Fleet Carrier*

Ordered from Cammell Laird, Birkenhead, in 1944. Never laid down and cancelled on 21 December 1945 when such steelwork as had been assembled was broken up on the slipway. For details see *Malta*.

POLYPHEMUS (57) Centaur *Class Light Fleet Carrier*

Ordered from HM Dockyard, Devonport. Never laid down and cancelled in October 1945. For details see *Centaur*.

APPENDIX 2: OTHER VESSELS REQUISITIONED FOR USE AS SEAPLANE CARRIERS

BROCKLESBY

One of only two paddle steamers to operate seaplanes in WW1. Requisitioned from the Great Central Railway on 21 February 1916. Based at Yarmouth and used without modification to carry two Sopwith Baby floatplanes on coastal anti-Zeppelin patrols. When concept of operation proved unsound, she paid off on 9 June 1917 and was returned to her owners.

KILLINGHOLME

The second paddle steamer requisitioned on 21 February 1916. Based at Killingholme and used for similar duties to *Brocklesby*. Damaged by a mine later in 1916. Returned to the Great Central Railway on 21 April 1917.

ORLIONOCH

Former Russian merchant ship taken over by the RN in late 1918. Modified locally to operate two Short floatplanes in support of anti-Bolshevik operations in Caspian Sea. Her aircraft are known to have been used on reconnaissance and bombing missions. She was transferred to the White Russian Forces during the British withdrawal in August 1919.

ALADER YOUSANOFF

Second and larger of the two former Russian merchant ships to operate two Short floatplanes in support of anti-Bolshevik operations in the Caspian Sea. She developed boiler problems and ceased operations in July 1919. Handed over to the White Russian authorities as she lay in August 1919.

CITY OF OXFORD

See Appendix 3.

APPENDIX 3: VESSELS REQUISITIONED FOR USE AS BALLOON CARRIERS

MANICA

Purchased from Ellerman & Bucknall Steamship Co. in March 1915 and modified to operate a single balloon. Successfully spotted for the Fleet's gunfire in the Dardanelles from 9 April 1915. Extensively refitted to improve balloon-operating facilities in early 1916 and deployed to East African coastal waters from April 1916 to May 1917. Renamed *Huntball* in August 1917 and used by Admiralty as a collier.

HECTOR

Taken over from the Ocean Steamship Co. on 12 May 1915 and converted on similar lines to *Manica*. Spotted for ship's guns at the Dardanelles and at Smyrna. Converted for use as an ammunition ship in 1917.

MENELAUS

Taken over by the Admiralty on 5 May 1915 from the Ocean Steamship Co. Used in the Dover Patrol spotting for coastal bombardments of enemy positions in Belgium from July 1915. Transferred to the GF in March 1916 and converted to an ammunition carrier in 1917.

CITY OF OXFORD

Taken over from Ellerman & Bucknall Steamship Co. in October 1914 and modified to act as a dummy battleship on decoy duties. Rebuilt as a balloon ship between July 1915 and March 1916, emerging as the best of the conversions. She saw service with the Dover Patrol and the GF in 1916. Converted to a seaplane carrier in 1917 and employed in the Egypt & East Indies Squadron. She ended the war as a seaplane depot ship alongside in Alexandria.

CANNING

Hired by the Admiralty from the Liverpool, Brazil & River Plate Steam Navigation Co. in May 1915. She saw service as a balloon ship at the Dardanelles and Salonika and was used to carry the wreckage of the Zeppelin *LZ85* back to the UK in May 1916. Refitted for service as a balloon depot ship with the GF, she was responsible for maintaining all balloons used in warships for the remainder of the war.

APPENDIX 4: AIRCRAFT CARRIER FLIGHT DECK RECOGNITION LETTERS

Note: If a ship is not listed below, the deck recognition letter is unknown. Because of the large number of carriers in commission in 1944–45, some duplication occurred.

Ship	Letter
HMS *Albion*	Z (1954), A (1958)
HMS *Ark Royal*	O (1955), R (1958)
HMS *Ark Royal*	R (1985)
HMS *Battler*	B (1945)
HMCS *Bonaventure*	22 (1957)
HMS *Bulwark*	B (1954)
HMS *Campania*	Z (1945)
HMS *Centaur*	L (1953), C (1954)
HMS *Colossus*	D (1945)
HMS *Eagle*	EG (1926)
HMS *Eagle*	J (1951), E (1958)
HMS *Emperor*	E (1944)
HMS *Formidable*	X (1945), R (1945)
HMS *Glory*	L (1945), R (1946)
HMS *Hermes*	HR (1924)
HMS *Hermes*	H (1959)
HMS *Illustrious*	L (1940), Q (1945), D (1946), Y (1953)
HMS *Illustrious*	L (1982)
HMS *Implacable*	N (1945), A (1946), C (1948)
HMS *Indefatigable*	S (1945)
HMS *Indomitable*	W (1945), C (1946), A (1947)
HMS *Invincible*	N (1980)
HMCS *Magnificent*	21 (1948)
HMAS *Melbourne*	Y (1956), M (1957)
HMS *Nairana*	Y (1945)
HMS *Ocean*	O (1945)
HMS *Patroller*	F (1944)
HMS *Premier*	P (1945)
HMS *Puncher*	N (1945)
HMS *Pursuer*	U (1945)
HMS *Queen*	Q (1945)
HMS *Ranee*	F (1945)
HMS *Ravager*	V (1945)
HMS *Reaper*	R (1945)
HMS *Searcher*	S (1945)
HMS *Smiter*	G (1945)
HMAS *Sydney*	K (1949), S (1956)
HMS *Theseus*	T (1946)
HMS *Tracker*	TR (1945)
HMS *Triumph*	P (1946)
HMS *Trouncer*	I (1945)
HMS *Trumpeter*	J (1945)
HMS *Unicorn*	U (1945), Y (1946)
HMS *Venerable*	V (1946)
HMS *Vengeance*	M (1945), Q (1946)
HMS *Victorious*	P (1945), S (1945), G (1946), V (1958)
HMS *Vindex*	V (1945)
HMS *Warrior*	W (1946), J (1953)

MAC-ships

Ship	Letter
Acavus	MA (1944)
Adula	MQ (1944)
Alexia	MP (1944)
Amastra	MC (1944)
Ancylus	MF (1944)
Empire MacAlpine	MH (1944)
Empire MacAndrew	MK (1944)
Empire MacCabe	ML (1944)
Empire MacCallum	MN (1944)
Empire MacColl	MB (1944)
Empire MacRae	MU (1944)
Empire MacDermott	MS (1944)
Empire Mackay	MM (1944)
Empire MacKendrick	MO (1944)
Empire MacMahon	MJ (1944)
Miralda	MW (1944)
Rapana	MV (1944)

APPENDIX 5: ENDURANCE FIGURES FOR SELECTED AIRCRAFT CARRIERS

Ship	*Distance (miles)*	*Speed (knots)*	*Remarks*
Indomitable	3,250	29.25	Full authorised speed
	3,560	28.75	All despatch
	5,300	25.5	Despatch
	6,730	22.5	Convenient despatch
	9,000	18	Moderate despatch
	10,250	12	Economical
Furious	2,090	27.25	Full authorised speed
	2,260	26.75	All despatch
	3,100	23	Despatch
	3,710	20	Convenient despatch
	4,470	16.25	Moderate despatch
	5,080	12	Economical
Smiter	18,050	18.5	Full authorised speed
	18,750	18	All despatch
	22,200	16	Despatch
	25,700	13.5	Convenient despatch
	26,800	12	Moderate despatch
	27,500	11	Economical
Argus	3,360	17	Full authorised speed
	3,770	16.25	All despatch
	4,660	14.5	Despatch
	5,180	12.5	Convenient despatch
	–	–	Moderate dispatch
	5,200	12	Economical
Unicorn	4,600	23	Full authorised speed
	6,000	22	All despatch
	7,620	19.5	Despatch
	8,450	17.25	Convenient despatch
	9,200	14	Moderate despatch
	9,700	10	Economical
Albatross	2,720	19	Full authorised speed
	2,970	18.25	All despatch
	3,410	17	Despatch
	4,720	14	Convenient despatch
	5,700	11.5	Moderate despatch
	5,900	10	Economical
Athene	5,700	16	Full authorised speed
	5,850	15.5	All despatch
	6,500	14	Despatch
	7,220	12.5	Convenient despatch
	8,200	10	Moderate despatch
	8,550	9	Economical

APPENDIX 6: DETAILS FOR SELECTED CARRIER-BORNE AIRCRAFT

Aircraft	*In service*	*Length*	*Span (spread)*	*Span (folded)*	*Height*	*Internal fuel*	*Empty weight*	*Max. weight*
Camel 2F.1	1917	18ft 8in	26ft 11in	–	9ft 1in	37 gallons	1,036lb	1,530lb
Short 184	1917	40ft 7$^1/_2$in	63ft 6$^3/_4$in	16ft 4$^1/_4$in	13ft 6in	80 gallons	3,638lb	5,287lb
Flycatcher	1925	23ft 1in	29ft 0in	–	12ft 0in	53 gallons	2,106lb	2,937lb
Dart	1925	35ft 4$^1/_2$in	45ft 6in	17ft 6in	12ft 11in	78 gallonS	3,599lb	6,383lb
Swordfish	1936	35ft 8in*	45ft 6in	17ft 3in	12ft 4in*	110 gallons	4,700lb	7,510lb
Skua	1938	35ft 7in	46ft 2in	15ft 6in	14ft 2in	166 gallons	3,405lb	4,950lb
Barracuda	1943	37ft 0in	50ft 0in	18ft 0in	14ft 9in	226 gallons	10,818lb	14,250lb
Avenger	1943	40ft 0in	54ft 2in	20ft 8in	13ft 9in	278 gallons	10,687lb	16,325lb
Sea Fury	1950	34ft 8in	38ft 4$^3/_4$in	116ft 1in	15ft 0in	200 gallons	9,240lb	12,500lb
Sea Hawk	1956	39ft 8in	39ft 0in	13ft 3in	16ft 8in*	397 gallons	9,560lb	15,990lb
Gannet	1957	44ft 6in	54ft 4in	19ft 11in	13ft 9in	968 gallons	15,069lb	19,600lb
Sea Vixen	1960	55ft 7in	51ft 0in	22ft 3in	10ft 9in	1,300 gallons	31,715lb	41,575lb
Wessex	1963	65ft 10in	56ft 0in	12ft 0in	15ft 10in	308 gallons	7,600lb	12,600lb
Sea King	1971	55ft 9$^3/_4$in	62ft 0in	15ft 6in	–	800 gallons	12,170lb	20,500lb
Sea Harrier	1980	47ft 7$^1/_2$in	25ft 3$^1/_2$in	–	11ft 10$^1/_2$in	600 gallons	12,950lb	26,000lb

Powerplant	*Crew*	*Weapons*	*Guns*	*RPG*	*Sensors*	*Remarks*
150hp piston	1	2 x 50lb bombs	2 x .303in MG	–	–	
260hp piston	2	1 x 14in torpedo, 1 x 500lb bomb, 4 x 112lb bombs	1 x .303in MG	–	–	
400hp piston	1	4 x 20lb bombs	2 x .303in MG	–	–	
470hp piston	1	1 x 18in torpedo	–	–	–	
750hp piston	3	1 x 18in torpedo or up to 1,500lb bombs or mines (8 x 3in RP on Mks II/III)	2 x .303in MG	–	–	*Length 40ft 6in with floats; height 14ft 7in with floats
830hp piston	2	1 x 500lb bomb	5 x .303in MG	–	–	
1,260hp piston	3	1 x 18in torpedo or 1 x 1,600lb bomb or 3 x 500lb bombs/mines	2 x .303in MG	500	Radar	
1,750hp piston	3	1 x 22.4in torpedo or 4 x 500lb bombs	3 x .5in, 1 x .3in MG	200 (500 x .3in)	–	
2,480hp piston	1	2 x 1,000lb bombs or 8 x 3in RP or mines etc	4 x 20mm cannon	150	–	
5,200lb thrust jet	1	4 x 500lb bombs or 20 x 3in RP	4 x 20mm cannon	–	–	*Folded
2 x 3,875hp turboprop	3	4 x 1,000lb bombs or 2 homing torpedoes 16 x 3in RP	–	–	ASV radar	
2 x 10,000lb thrust jet	2	4 x Firestreak or Red Top or 4 x 1,000lb bombs or 4 x 2in RP pods	–	–	AI radar	
1,450shp shaft turbine	4	2 homing torpedoes or 2 depth charges, flares	1 x 7.62mm MG	200	Dipping sonar*	*Radar in some
2 x 1,500shp shaft	4	NDB or 3 homing torpedoes or 4 depth charges, flares	1 x 7.62mm MG	200	Dipping sonar, radar	
21,500lb thrust jet	1	4 x AMRAAM or Sidewinder or 2 x Sea Eagle or 5 x 1,000lb bombs, cluster bombs, flares etc	2 x 30mm cannon	100	AI radar	

APPENDIX 7: SAMPLE FLYING PROGRAMMES

Air Office | H.M.S. Glory | 17th March 1952
Sunrise 0649
Sunset 1850

FLYING PROGRAMME

Event	Off	On	A/C	Mission
A.	0630	0815	2 FU	C.A.P.
			2 FU	TARCAP
			4 FU	A.R.
			8 Fi	Strike
			1 Fi	A.S.P.
B.	0800	1000	2 FU	C.A.P.
			4 FU	TARCAP
			4 FU	A.R.
			1 Fi	A.S.P.
C.	0945	1130	2 FU	C.A.P.
			2 FU	TARCAP
			4 FU	A.R.
			8 Fi	Strike
			1 Fi	A.S.P.
D.	1115	1315	2 FU	C.A.P.
			4 FU	TARCAP
			4 FU	A.P.
			1 Fi	A.S.P.
E.	1300	1445	2 FU	C.A.P.
			4 FU	TARCAP
			4 FU	A.R.
			8 Fi	Strike
			1 Fi	A.S.P.
F.	1430	1630	2 FU	C.A.P.
			4 FU	TARCAP
			4 FU	A.R.
			1 Fi	A.S.P.
G.	1615	1815	2 FU	C.A.P.
			2 FU	TARCAP
			4 FU	A.R.
			8 Fi	Strike
			1 Fi	A.S.P.

0539 Flying Stations. 0630 Catapult required.

Briefings as usual. Armament standard. Tarcap land on LAST.

NOTES:

1. Spare Air Group hands clean hangar.
2. Flight Deck Party rig jackstay aft as piped.
3. Royal Marine Band to practise in the forward lift well all day.
4. Q.S. lectures for stand-off pilots (A.E.O. to arrange).
5. Payment, return winter clothing, issue of medals, T.A.B. inoculations as piped (Flight Deck or Hangar).
6. Volley-ball and deck hockey matches as arranged by sports officer.

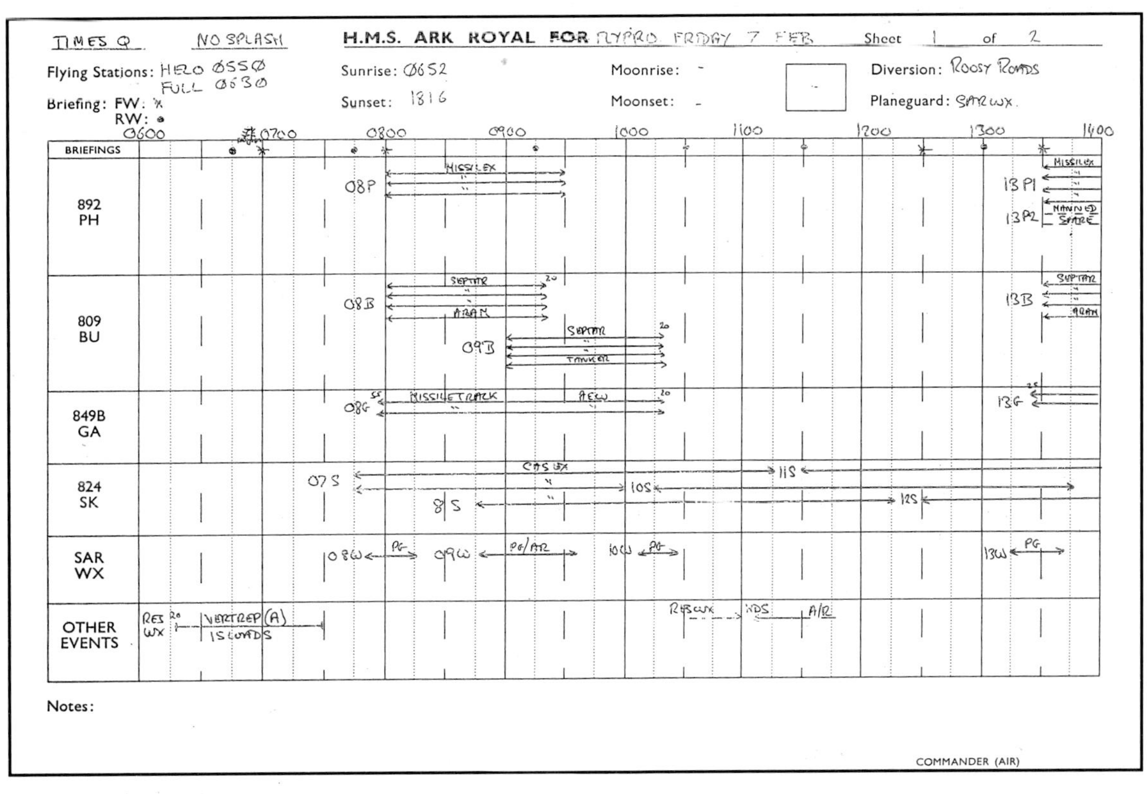

TIMES Q NO SPLASH

H.M.S. ARK ROYAL ~~FOR~~ FLYPRO FRIDAY 7 FEB Sheet 1 of 2

Flying Stations: HELO 0550 FULL 0630

Sunrise: 0652

Sunset: 1816

Moonrise: -

Moonset: -

Diversion: ROOSY ROADS

Planeguard: SAR WX

Briefing: FW: ✱ RW: ●

0600 0700 0800 0900 1000 1100 1200 1300 1400

BRIEFINGS

892 PH: 08P MISSILEX; 13P1 MISSILEX; 13P2 MANNED SPARE

809 BU: 08B SEPTAR, ARAM; 09B SEPTAR, TANKER; 13B SEPTAR, ARAM

849B GA: 08G MISSILE TRACK, AEW; 13G

824 SK: 07S CASEX; 08S; 10S; 11S; 12S

SAR WX: 08W PG; 09W PG/AR; 10W PG; 13W PG

OTHER EVENTS: RES WX; VERTREP (A) 15 LOADS; RESWX; XDS; A/R

Notes:

COMMANDER (AIR)

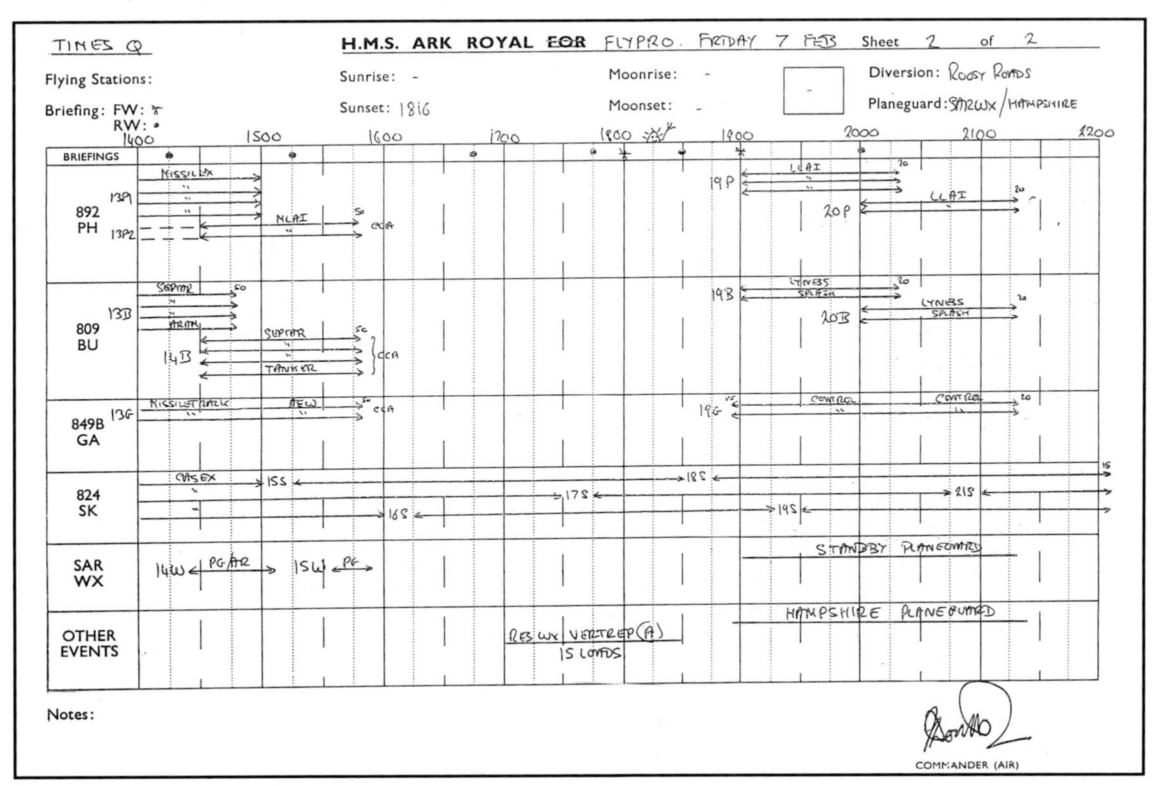

TIMES Q

H.M.S. ARK ROYAL ~~FOR~~ FLYPRO FRIDAY 7 FEB Sheet 2 of 2

Flying Stations:

Sunrise: -

Sunset: 1816

Moonrise: -

Moonset: -

Diversion: ROOSY ROADS

Planeguard: SAR WX / HAMPSHIRE

Briefing: FW: ✱ RW: ●

1400 1500 1600 1700 1800 1900 2000 2100 2200

BRIEFINGS

892 PH: 13P1 MISSILEX; 13P2 NLAI CCA; 19P LLAI; 20P LLAI

809 BU: 13B SEPTAR, ARAM; 14B SEPTAR, TANKER CCA; 19B LYNESS SPLASH; 20B LYNESS SPLASH

849B GA: 13G MISSILE TRACK, AEW CCA; 19G CONTROL, CONTROL

824 SK: CASEX; 15S; 16S; 17S; 18S; 19S; 21S

SAR WX: 14W PG/AR; 15W PG; STANDBY PLANEGUARD

OTHER EVENTS: RES WX; VERTREP (A) 15 LOADS; HAMPSHIRE PLANEGUARD

Notes:

COMMANDER (AIR)

Bibliography

UNPUBLISHED MANUSCRIPTS

Held in the Public Record Office, Kew; the Naval Historical Branch, Great Scotland Yard, London; and the Fleet Air Arm Museum, Yeovilton.

ADM 1/9211: *Hermes* outline design
ADM 1/9259: *Courageous* legend, 1925
ADM 1/9406: *Illustrious*, 1940
ADM 1/9433: *Indomitable* redesign
ADM 1/11845: MAC and CAM ships
ADM 1/12058: Building programme 1942
ADM 1/14798: Post delivery modifications to escort carriers, 1943
ADM 1/14842: Delays in escort carrier completion
ADM 1/15072: Loss of HMS *Dasher*
ADM 1/22421: Angled deck proposal
ADM 1/26842: *Hermes* staff requirement
ADM 116/3871: Air Instructions for the Mediterranean Fleet, 1934–1939
ADM 137/1956: Grand Fleet Advisory Committee on Aviation
ADM 186/173–179: Armament of HM Ships
ADM 199/2063–2072 Reports of war damage, 1939–1945
ADM 234/383: Naval Staff History, 'The Development of British Naval Aviation 1919–1945', vol. 1 (1954)
ADM 234/384: Naval Staff History, 'The Development of British Naval Aviation 1919–1945', vol. 2 (1956)
ADM 239/66–77: Particulars of HM Ships, 1939–1946
CB 04484: Aircraft Carrier and Commando Ship Handbook, 1970 (declassified)
Unpublished notes on Staff History of British Naval Aviation, 1919–1945, vol. 3
BR 1736(43): Naval Staff History, 'Naval Operations off Okinawa, 1945' (1950).
BR 1736(54): British Commonwealth Naval Operations, Korea, 1950–1953 (1967)
BR 1736(55): Naval Staff History, 'Middle East Operations, Kuwait 1961 and Jordan/Lebanon 1958' (1968)
Brown, David. 'Essays on Naval Air Power'. Naval Historical Branch
Naval Staff Historical Branch Monograph: 'The Royal Navy in the Post War Years. Part 1: RN and RM Operational Deployments, 1964–1991'
Naval Historical Branch: 'The Battle of the Atlantic, 1939–1945' (Back Pocket Brief)
Naval Historical Branch: 'Far East Chronology, January 1945–VJ Day
US Office of Naval Intelligence Publication ONI 201: 'Warships of the British Commonwealth'
Flight Deck magazines, 1944–1995
Individual histories, logs and commission books in the possession of the Naval Historical Branch, the Fleet Air Arm Museum and the Author

PRINCIPAL PUBLISHED SOURCES

Apps, Cdr Michael. *Send Her Victorious*. London: William Kimber, 1971
———. *The Four Ark Royals*. London: William Kimber, 1976
Baker, R.; Holt, W. J.; Lenaghan, J.; Sims, A. J.; and Watson, A. W. Selected Papers on British Warship Design in World War 2. London: Conway Maritime Press, 1983; and Annapolis: Naval Institute Press
Barker, Ralph. *The Hurricats*. London: Pelham Books, 1978
Blundell, Walter G. D. *British Aircraft Carriers*. London: Model & Allied Publications, 1969
Brown, David K. 'The Design of Aircraft Carriers prior to World War 2'. *Interdisciplinary Science Review*, vol. 8 no 4. J. W. Arrowsmith, 1983
Brown, J. David. *Aircraft Carriers*. London: Macdonald & Jane's, 1977; and New York: Arco
———. *Carrier Air Groups: HMS Eagle*. Windsor: Hylton Lacy, 1972
———. *Carrier Operations in World War 2. Vol. 1: The Royal Navy*. Shepperton: Ian Allan, 1974
———. *HMS Eagle* (Warship Profile 35). Profile Publications, 1973
———. *The Genesis of Naval Aviation: Les marines de guerre du dreadnought au nucleaire*. Paris: Service Historique de la Marine, 1988
———. *HMS Illustrious* (Warship Profile 10: Technical History). Profile Publications, 1971
———. *HMS Illustrious* (Warship Profile 11: Operational History). Profile Publications, 1971
———. *The Royal Navy and the Falklands War*. London: Leo Cooper, 1987
———. *Warship Losses of World War 2*. London: Arms & Armour Press, 1990; and Annapolis: Naval Institute Press
Burgess, Michael. *Aircraft Carriers and Aircraft Carrying Cruisers*. Dunedin: Burgess Media Services, 1980
Burns, Ken, and Critchley, Mike. *HMS Bulwark*. Liskeard: Maritime Books, 1986
Chesneau, Roger. *Aircraft Carriers of the World, 1914 to the Present*. London: Arms & Armour Press, 1984; and Annapolis: Naval Institute Press
Cronin, Dick C. *Royal Navy Shipboard Aircraft Developments*. Tonbridge: Air Britain (Historians), 1990
Dyson, Lt Cdr Tony. *HMS Hermes*. Liskeard: Maritime Books, 1984

Fleet Air Arm Review, 1960
Frere Cook, Gervis. *The Attacks on the Tirpitz*. Shepperton: Ian Allan, 1973; and Annapolis, Naval Institute Press
Friedman, Norman. *British Carrier Aviation*. London: Conway Maritime Press, 1988; and Annapolis, Naval Institute Press
———. *Carrier Air Power*. London, Conway Maritime Press, 1981; and Annapolis, Naval Institute Press
———. *The Post War Naval Revolution*. London: Conway Maritime Press, 1986
———. *US Aircraft Carriers*. Annapolis: Naval Institute Press, 1983; and London: Arms & Armour Press
Hodges, Peter. *Royal Navy Warship Camouflage 1939–1945*. Almark, 1973
Honnor, A. F., and Andrews, D. J. *HMS Invincible: The First of New Genus of Aircraft Carrying Ships*. Royal Institution of Naval Architects, 1981
Jenkins Cdr C. A. *HMS Furious: Aircraft Carrier 1917–1948* (Warship Profile Nos 23 and 24). Profile Publications, 1972
Kealey, J. D. F., and Russell, E. C. *A History of Canadian Naval Aviation 1918–1962*. Ottawa: Queen's Printer, 1967
Lansdown, Lt Cdr John R. P. *With the Carriers in Korea 1950–1953*. Worcester: Square One Publications, 1992
Layman, R. D. *Before the Aircraft Carrier*. London: Conway Maritime Press, 1989
———. *The Cuxhaven Raid*. London: Conway Maritime Press, 1985
MacIntyre, Capt. Donald. *Aircraft Carriers: The Majestic Weapon*. London: Macdonald, 1968; and New York: Ballantine
———. *Narvik*. London: Evans Bros, 1959
———. *Wings of Neptune: The Story of Naval Aviation*. Kingswood: Peter Davies, 1963
Marriott, Leo. *Royal Navy Aircraft Carriers 1945–1990*. Shepperton: Ian Allan, 1985
Marsh, Maj. A. E. *Flying Marines*. Eastney: Royal Marines Museum, 1980
McCart, Neil. *HMS Albion*. Cheltenham: Fan Publications, 1995
Morgan, Rex. *The Hermes Adventure*. Manley: The Runciman Press, 1985; and London: Robert Hale
Navy Records Society. *The Naval Air Service 1908–1918*, vol. 1 (1969)
Polmar, Norman. *Aircraft Carriers: A Graphic History of Carrier Aviation and its Influence on World Events*. London: Macdonald, 1969; and Garden City: Doubleday
Poolman, Kenneth. *Allied Escort Carriers of World War 2*. London: Blandford Press, 1988; and Annapolis: Naval Institute Press
———. *Ark Royal*. London: William Kimber, 1956
———. *The Catafighters and Merchant Aircraft Carriers*. London: William Kimber, 1970
———. *Escort Carrier: HMS Vindex at War*. London: Leo Cooper, 1983
———. *Escort Carrier 1941–1945*. Shepperton: Ian Allan, 1972
———. *Escort Carriers of World War 2*. London: Arms & Armour Press, 1989
———. *Illustrious*. London: William Kimber, 1955
———. *The Sea Hunters: Escort Carriers v. U Boats 1941–1945*. London: Arms & Armour Press, 1982
Popham, Hugh. *Into Wind: A History of British Naval Flying*. London: Hamish Hamilton, 1969
Reynolds, Clark G. *The Fast Carriers: The Forging of an Air Navy*. New York: McGraw-Hill Book Co., 1968; and (with minor changes) Annapolis: Naval Institute Press, 1992
Schofield, Vice-Admiral Brian B. *Loss of the Bismarck*. Shepperton: Ian Allan, 1972; and Annapolis: Naval Institute Press
———. *The Attack on Taranto*. Shepperton: Ian Allan, 1973; and Annapolis: Naval Institute Press
Silverstone, Paul H. *Directory of the World's Capital Ships*. Shepperton: Ian Allan 1984
Smith, Lt Cdr N. L.; Woodman, D. W. J.; and Gibbings, David. *HMS Tracker and the Attacker Class*. Yeovilton: Society of Friends of the Fleet Air Arm Museum, 1987
Smith, Peter C. *Task Force 57: The British Pacific Fleet 1944–1945*. London: William Kimber, 1969
Snowie, J. Allan. *The Bonnie: HMCS Bonaventure*. Erin: Boston Mills Press, 1987
Steele, John. *The Tragedy of HMS Dasher*. Glendaruel: Argyll Publishing, 1995
Sturtivant, Ray. *Fleet Air Arm 1920–1939*. London: Arms & Armour Press; 1990; New York: Sterling Publishing; and Lane Cove: Capricorn Link (Australia)
Sturtivant, Ray, and Burrow, Mick. *Fleet Air Arm Aircraft 1939–1945*. Tunbridge Wells: Air Britain (Historians), 1995
Sturtivant, R., and Page, Gordon. *Royal Naval Aircraft Serials and Units 1911–1919*. Tonbridge: Air Britain (Historians), 1992
Sturtivant, R., and Ballance, Lt Cdr Theo. *The Squadrons of the Fleet Air Arm*. Tonbridge: Air Britain (Historians), 1994
Till, Geoffrey. *Air Power in the Royal Navy 1914–1945: A Historical Survey*. London: Jane's Publishing, 1979
Waterman, Lt Cdr Jack. *The Fleet Air Arm History*. Old Bond Street Publishing Co., 1970
Watton, Ross. *The Aircraft Carrier Victorious*. London: Conway Maritime Press, 1991; and Annapolis, Naval Institute Press
Wilson, Michael. *Royal Australian Navy Major Warships* (Profile No 1). Marrickville: Topmill
Winton, John. *Carrier Glorious: The Life and Death of an Aircraft Carrier*. London: Leo Cooper, 1986
———. *The Forgotten Fleet*. London: Michael Joseph, 1969
Y'Blood, William T. *Hunter Killer: US Escort Carriers in the Battle of the Atlantic*. Annapolis: Nava Institute Press, 1983

Index

Page references in **bold type** indicate main entries

INDEX OF SHIPS

INDEX OF UNITS